Samuel Hays,

O.B.E. B.COM.(HONS) F.I.S.
Formerly Lecturer in Commercial Subjects
Doncaster Technical College

An Outline of
Statistics

LONGMANS

LONGMANS, GREEN AND CO. LTD
48 Grosvenor Street, London W1
Associated companies, branches and
representatives throughout the world

New Editions © Samuel Hays 1960; 1962; 1966

First published 1937
Second edition 1939
Third edition 1947
New impression 1949
New impression by photolithography 1951
Fourth edition 1953
New impression 1956
New impression 1958
Fifth edition 1960
Sixth edition 1962
New impression 1963
Seventh edition 1966

Set in 10 pt. Monotype Plantin and
Printed in Great Britain by Richard Clay (The Chaucer Press), Ltd
Bungay, Suffolk

Preface to Seventh Edition

SINCE this book first appeared in 1937, the study of statistics has developed along many fresh lines. New and wider applications of its principles have been perfected and popularized. Economists, engineers, scientists, educationalists, accountants, and business efficiency experts now apply its methods in their everyday tasks and problems. Medical science has found statistics a most valuable ally; market research would not have progressed in the way that it has without its help. Varied as its uses have now become, these uses still depend upon a few fundamental principles. Although there may have been changes of emphasis, the approach to the study remains much the same as it did in the middle of the 'thirties. And while there are now very many more students of statistics they begin by treading the same path as did their predecessors, although, let it be said to their credit, most of them go very much further.

It has been the author's privilege in the past to introduce a large body of students to the subject. In his view, there is still ample scope for a simple non-technical introduction to the study. The present edition provides this, as did earlier editions and reprints. Most of the illustrative examples still relate to prewar conditions. Their retention in successive editions and reprints helps to maintain an element of continuity. Moreover, these prewar examples insofar as they relate to economic conditions, are indicative of such conditions in the middle thirties.

So far as the general reader is concerned, statistics makes its greatest impact through its association with economics. Production and export statistics, terms of trade, balance of payments figures, analyses of the national income, of the censuses of population and distribution, all find a prominent place in newspapers and radio and television news bulletins. The Economic Survey and its successor, 'Economic Report', together with the National Income and Expenditure White Papers and Blue Books are tending to become recognized textbooks for elementary courses in Economics. The authors of these publications make great use of statistical analyses in their measurements and comparisons. The statistical tools which they and other economists employ are described in the second part of *An Outline of Statistics*, and the statistics themselves are commented upon. It is thought that this section will have a considerable appeal to the student of economics and the general reader alike. For the student of statistics, it provides many examples of the practical uses of the principles discussed in the first half of the book.

While the subject matter is of the simplest and intended to serve only as an introduction to the study, it still largely covers the requirements of the National Certificate in Business Studies, the G.C.E. Ordinary Level, and those of various professional bodies which set examinations in statistics. At the same time, students who are acquiring specific qualifications as statisticians will find the second part of the book of direct assistance in their papers on statistical sources and published statistics.

The present (seventh) edition includes everything of note which appeared in the sixth. An additional appendix deals with the calculation of rates of growth. The statistics discussed in the second half have, in the main, been brought up to date to the end of 1964. The 1961 Census of Population has been dealt with to a limited extent having regard to the information published by the end of 1964. Material appearing for the first time includes short discussions on the employment of qualified scientists and engineers, national expenditure on research and development, and transport statistics generally, with particular reference to the relation between rail and road transport. A brief reference to Discounted Cash Flows appears as a supplement to the section on Accountancy Ratios.

As in earlier editions, acknowledgement and thanks are due to the following for permission to include copyright material:

The late Sir Arthur L. Bowley, Sc.D., F.S.S.
D. Caradog Jones, Esq., M.A., F.S.S.
The Controller, H.M. Stationery Office.

The actual statistics presented and discussed in the latter half of the book have, in fact, been mainly derived from H.M. Stationery Office publications. The source of these statistics is, for the most part, quoted in the relevant text.

The author wishes to thank the University of London for permission to include a question from their 1938 B.Sc. Economics paper and a number of questions from recent G.C.E. papers on Statistics.

SAMUEL HAYS

Leigh-on-Sea
1965

Acknowledgements

WE are indebted to the Controller of Her Majesty's Stationery Office for permission to reproduce Table 78 from *Monthly Digest of Statistics*, November 1964, Tables 1 and 2 from *Board of Trade Journal*, 8 February 1964, and *Ministry of Labour Form L2* (slightly amended).

Contents

	Preface	v
1	The Meaning and Uses of Statistics	1
2	The Collection of Statistical Data	6
3	Accuracy and Approximation	15
4	Tabulation	22
5	Diagrammatic Representation	31
6	Frequency Distributions	53
7	Statistical Averages	66
8	Dispersion or Variability	82
9	Skewness	92
10	The Analysis of a Time Series	96
11	Correlation	106
12	Index Numbers	119
13	Sources of Statistical Information	129
14	Vital Statistics	141
15	Manpower, Employment, and Related Statistics	154
16	Overseas Trade Statistics	168
17	Statistics of Prices	179
18	Production Statistics	193
19	National Income Statistics	205
20	Statistics of Distribution	220
21	The Application of Statistical Methods to Business Problems	227
	Appendix 1. Sampling	239
	Appendix 2. Quality Control	244

Appendix 3. The Coefficient of Rank Correlation and the Equation of the Regression Line   249

Appendix 4. The Calculation of Rates of Growth   253

General Exercises   255

Supplementary General Exercises   267

Answers to Numerical Examples   270

Index   275

Chapter 1

The Meaning and Uses of Statistics

THE word 'statistics' was first used in the eighteenth century to refer to the collection and arrangement of facts, mainly of a numerical type, relating to the State, and it is said to be derived from the Italian word 'statistica' meaning a statesman. Naturally, such facts had been collected long before this period and indeed, ever since organized government has existed, rulers have found it necessary to obtain numerical facts as an aid to the administration of their domains. The Bible indicates that fairly accurate counts of population were made in Judea, for we read that both Moses and David numbered the people. The Domesday Survey, undertaken by William the Conqueror, is another good example of the collection of statistical data in comparatively early times. As might be expected, the information obtained consisted principally of figures on population and property; the former served as an index of the nation's fighting strength and the latter of the taxable resources of the inhabitants.

These early efforts were very spasmodic and crude; their scope was limited and the methods used unsystematic. Indeed, a government considered itself fortunate in those early days if it had any definite information about its own territory. But, in the seventeenth and eighteenth centuries, the character of the information slowly broadened and the data collected began to include details regarding births, deaths, and marriages. It became possible to make comparisons between nations on the basis of these numerical facts. Writers on economics and sociology began to use numerical facts in their discussions on economic and social conditions. In the nineteenth century the growing complexity of our national and industrial organization gave a great impetus, not only to the compilation of numerical facts concerning this organization, but also to the development of methods of analysing the large masses of figures which were becoming available. The year 1801 saw the first census taken in England. The analysis of available figures became necessary in order that the most important characteristics possessed by these figures could be brought out more clearly. As time went on, statistics came to be regarded as a way of handling numerical facts, rather than as a system of accumulating numerical data, and greater prominence was given to methods of presenting and analysing the facts. Moreover, it was seen that such methods were of general application and a striking development, which belongs to recent times, is the use which is now made of them in the world of both science and business. Thus, the use of methods for dealing with numerical facts is by no means limited to the sphere of government, or to the study of economic problems.

THE MEANING AND SCOPE OF STATISTICS

The term 'statistics' is now commonly used in two senses. First, as a plural noun, it means a collection of numerical facts, such as statistics of population, births, and deaths and the like, and secondly, as a singular noun, it denotes the methods adopted in the collection and analysis of such facts. Whichever meaning is used, it must be emphasized that the subject deals with facts expressed in numerical form. Quantities, and not mere qualitative descriptions, are dealt with. But the subject does not deal with numbers merely as numbers, as is the case in certain branches of mathematics. In statistics the numbers are expressed in units. These units may be feet, inches, etc., if length is being considered; they may be units of time, of weight, or money; or they may combine two or more of the common units, as when we read that the exports from Britain averaged £350 million a month in 1964.

Again, a single figure or an isolated fact does not constitute statistics. A single accident in a road at a place A, however interesting, is not statistics, but the number of road accidents which take place at A during a year, or the number of road accidents which take place in the country on the same day, is statistics. Thus, the study deals with mass phenomena, with the properties of aggregates and the results of collective action.

When statistics are given, care should be taken to see that their meaning is clear; the units in which these figures are expressed should also be clearly stated. Thus, if they refer to a period, the existence of that period should be indicated, or if they refer to one section of the community only, this limitation should be made obvious. Lack of care in explaining the meaning of figures sometimes leads to diametrically opposite conclusions being drawn from the same set of statistics. Figures can only 'prove anything' when their scope or meaning is ill-defined.

Of the two meanings which attach to the word statistics, the public are usually more interested in collections of figures, rather than in the methods necessary to obtain and present such data. There is an increasing tendency to base arguments on numerical facts, but to attempt to handle numerical facts without a knowledge of the right methods of so doing can only lead to confusion and error. One writer on statistics has very ably expressed this point by saying that the public care nothing for the mathematics on which the science of bridge building is founded: they only desire to see the actual bridge.[1] In the same way, they desire to see the results of statistical work rather than interest themselves in the way in which those results have been obtained. Just as the study of mathematics is of extreme importance to the engineer, so a knowledge of the methods of presenting and analysing numerical facts is vital to the statistician.

In this book we are concerned mainly, but not exclusively, with statistics in so far as it deals with the study of the methods of handling numerical facts. We shall first consider how the data for subsequent study are collected and the precautions which must be observed during this process in order that reliance may be placed on the figures so obtained. We shall then proceed to discuss how this material may be classified according to common characteristics and presented in a readily understandable form by means of tables or diagrams. We deal next with the methods of analysing the tabulated data so that the salient characteristics may be brought out in a simple and easily comparable form. We shall then examine, briefly, some of the more important published statistics in the light of the principles we have enunciated and, finally, we shall discuss the application of statistics to business problems.

[1] W. I. King, *Elements of Statistical Method.*

THE OBJECTS OF STATISTICS AND STATISTICAL METHODS

The brief historical review of the development of statistics has already brought out the chief objects of the study. The methods employed were developed to throw light on economic and social problems, but the study is essentially a practical one and its field of usefulness is constantly expanding. In general we may say that its objects are:

1. To present facts in a definite form. Numerical facts give more precise information than facts expressed in general terms. The statement that many people were killed as a result of industrial accidents in August 1952 does not give the same amount of information as the statement that 81 were killed in August 1952 as a result of industrial accidents.

2. To simplify and classify large masses of facts. Thus the population census results in the collection of a large mass of numerical facts which need classifying and analysing before their full significance becomes clear.

3. To furnish methods of comparison. The significance of a series of figures is often better appreciated when these figures are compared with others of the same kind. The development of suitable methods of comparison is essentially a problem of statistics.

4. To settle questions of a general economic or political nature and to enable administrators – governmental, business, or industrial, to determine policy. Our Government requires information regarding the population of this country and the age groups into which that population is divided. This information gives an idea of the possible military strength of the nation; it may also be used to give an idea of what schools are required now and what future requirements will be in this respect. From it, an estimate of the number of new houses which are needed and the amounts needed for old age pensions may be obtained.

5. To indicate trends and tendencies and so help in determining present policy and action, and in the forecasting of future conditions. Our estimates of future happenings are almost entirely based upon our knowledge of the past. If, for example, investigations have shown that the level of business activity follows a definite cycle, periods of good trade or booms being followed by periods of depression. And if it can be decided to what particular stage of the cycle the level of economic activity has reached, the future course of such activity becomes much

more than a matter of mere speculation. Statistical methods are almost the only ones which can be used for such an ascertainment. "The National Plan" for 1970, issued in September 1965, was essentially a statistical appraisal.

STUDENT WORK

Distinguish between the term 'Statistics' used in the singular sense from its use in the plural sense. Into what divisions may the study of statistics be divided?

Chapter 2

The Collection of Statistical Data

THE IMPORTANCE OF THE COLLECTION OF DATA

WE referred in the preceding chapter to two broad divisions of our study, namely (1) the collection of numerical facts, and (2) the analysis of these facts. The numerical facts collected form, as it were, the raw material of our subject; it is from them that our analysis is made, our principles formulated, and conclusions drawn. It will be obvious, therefore, that the value of the analysis and the validity of the conclusions will depend upon the care and accuracy with which the original figures were obtained. Any doubt as to their meaning and scope will tend to vitiate any conclusions which may result from them. With regard to the necessity for care and accuracy, it is shown later that, in general, the final result can be no more accurate than the least accurate of the items which contribute to that result.

THE PRELIMINARY STAGES IN COLLECTING DATA

Before the actual collection is begun, certain preliminary matters must be decided upon. These are mainly in the nature of precautions intended to ensure that the material obtained is reliable. Some of these precautions are of an elementary common-sense type, but even so they are often neglected and as a result the figures obtained may be entirely unreliable.

1. The first step is to determine precisely the nature of the problem for which the data are to be collected. The most comprehensive statistical inquiry yet undertaken is the population census. This is not merely concerned with obtaining the total population, but with the sex, age, nationality, occupation, and place of residence of that population. The method of obtaining the information required will depend upon

6

decisions made as to the nature of that information. Thus the population census inquiry must be so framed as to yield the information wanted, and as this varies slightly from time to time, the nature of the inquiry must also vary slightly.

2. After the nature of the required information has been agreed upon, the units in which that information must be expressed have to be fixed.

The mere act of counting things of the same kind is, of course, a type of measurement, the unit being one thing, one person, one fatal accident, or one emigrant, etc. The census forms require units of a number of kinds. In obtaining the total population the unit is the person. Ages must, however, be stated in years and months. Condition as to marriage has three types of units: 'single, married, or widowed'; but within each type the unit is one person.

At first sight, this insistence on units may appear trivial, but a moment's thought will make it plain that information gathered from various sources may not be comparable or capable of the same type of classification, unless it is given in the same units. Thus, if the Ministry of Agriculture requires information of the amount of wheat under cultivation and, without specifying a unit, asks farmers to make returns relating to their own farms, the information received might be of a very mixed kind. One farmer might reply that he had sown 100 acres with wheat, another that he had sown 180 bushels of wheat, and a third, 80 sacks. Such replies, even though perfectly accurate, are not comparable, nor can their subject matter be grouped together. Unless the unit of measurement is clearly stated and understood, much otherwise valuable information may become useless. The unit is, as it were, the connecting link between information received from many different sources.

3. A further point to be decided upon is the degree of accuracy required in the information. Absolute accuracy in counting rarely exists, and in measurement, never. So far as the latter is concerned, the accuracy of the measurement depends upon the fineness of the measuring implement. It may be necessary to obtain information which contains the highest possible degree of accuracy, or a degree of accuracy less than the best may suffice. The methods adopted and units employed should be such as will give the requisite degree of accuracy. If a ruler is graduated only in tenths of an inch, it is unreasonable to expect to read lengths correct to hundredths of an inch with it. In the same way, in an

inquiry where ages are to be stated in years and months, information as to these ages cannot be obtained therefrom which is correct down to actual days.

So far as the *actual number* of people is concerned, the census requires the greatest possible degree of accuracy. The accuracy in respect of ages need not be so great. There would be no advantage in asking for ages to be expressed in years, months, and days, as it is sufficient for all general purposes if ages are given in years and months.

Again, a little reflection will show that if figures are expressed to a certain degree of accuracy, that degree cannot be exceeded in the results of any mathematical processes to which the figures may afterwards be submitted. An example will make this point clear.

Suppose the ages of six boys were 4 years 7 months, 5 years 2 months, 7 years 8 months, 9 years 9 months, 11 years 10 months, and 13 years 8 months. If the boys are asked to write down their ages in years, they will probably return as answers, 4, 5, 7, 9, 11, and 13. From these figures it would obviously be misleading to say that the average age of the boys is $\frac{49}{6}$, i.e. 8·167 years. The highest degree of accuracy that can be attained in this case is to express the average age in years, i.e. 8. The degree of accuracy imputed by the figures 8·167 years is called 'spurious accuracy', and in expressing numerical facts it is necessary to guard against such fictitious accuracy. In this example, all the actual ages are more than the stated ages. Where the errors are all on one side, i.e. the actual figures are either all greater or all smaller than the recorded figures, the errors are said to be biased. Where the recorded figures are sometimes above and sometimes below the actual figure, the errors are said to be unbiased. An average taken from a set of figures containing unbiased errors will probably contain the same degree of accuracy as do the individual items, but no more.

If various items are added together the degree of accuracy which will be found in the total is no greater than the degree of accuracy shown by the most inaccurate item. If certain employers were asked to make a return of total wages paid and a few firms gave a true total expressed in £ s. d., while other and larger firms gave their figures correct to the nearest hundred £, then the total of all these returns could not be guaranteed beyond the nearest hundred £. It would be another example of spurious accuracy to add up all the returns and express the total, say, as £758,357 17s. 4d. The degree of accuracy to be found in the indi-

vidual items does not warrant the total being expressed in more significant figures than are contained in the amount of £758,400.

4. Still another consideration to be decided upon is the extent of the
field of the inquiry. Must it consist of a complete enumeration of all the
items in the group or will a sufficiently accurate conception be obtained
if only a proportion of the total possible items are examined? This will
depend upon the nature of the inquiry. In the case of the census or the
returns from which the Parliamentary and Local Government electors'
lists are obtained, it is necessary that the field of the inquiry be complete,
i.e. every household must be considered. It is very probable, though,
that if the total population of the country were known, the percentage of
that population and the actual numbers found in each age group – say
0–4 years, 5–14, 15–24, etc. – could be ascertained with sufficient accuracy by examining only a small proportion of households.

A complete enumeration, such as the census, requires a great deal of
preparation and it is extremely costly to conduct. In fact, the Government is probably the only institution which can carry out a complete
inquiry on a wide scale (complete in the sense that every possible item
is enumerated, and on a wide scale, in the sense that there is a very large
number of such items). In a very general way, it may be said that if the
purpose of an inquiry is to obtain the grand total of the subject matter
of the inquiry, whether this be the number of persons in the country, or
the total wages paid, a complete inquiry may be necessary to give
reliable information. If the purpose is to find out the proportion of the
items arranged in different groups, for example, age groups or income
groups, then reliable information may be obtained by examining a
selected proportion of the total possible items. The method of investigation whereby only a proportion of the available subject matter is studied
and the results applied to the whole field of the inquiry, is known as
Sampling. The theoretical basis of sampling is what statisticians call
'The Law of Statistical Regularity'. This principle may be stated as
follows. A small group chosen at random from a larger group will have
much the same composition and characteristics as the larger group.
Thus, if a box contains 400 red balls and 600 white balls, a random
selection of 100 balls would yield about 40 red balls and about 60 white
balls. Conversely, if random selection of 100 balls from a box reveals 40
red and 60 white balls, it is not unreasonable to conclude that, if 1,000
balls are in the box, about 400 will be red and about 600 white.

In the latter case, the results obtained from an examination of a portion only of the field of inquiry are applied to the whole field. This is precisely the method of sampling. But before the results obtained from a sample (as the small group is called) can be applied to the whole, two essential conditions must be fulfilled. In the first place, the sample should be a random one, and secondly, it should be sufficiently representative. A random sample is one in which every item in the whole group has an equally good chance of selection. A representative sample is one in which the proportion of items in the sample to the total of all items is sufficiently large. (A more detailed study of sampling is given in Appendix 1.)

THE METHODS OF COLLECTING DATA

When the preliminary steps relating to an inquiry have been satisfactorily arranged, the next stage is the actual collection of the information. Obviously, it is desirable that the whole process of collection should be under the control of the investigators. It will then be seen that the preliminary steps have been properly carried out and the information received is what it purports to be. Assuming that the collection of information is under the control of the investigators, three methods of obtaining data may be distinguished.

1. *Personal Investigation*

This type is intensive rather than extensive, but the results, though limited in scope, may be very accurate. Past experience has shown that such personal investigations, even though restricted to one town or area, produce much valuable local data and not a little information which is of wider application. In prewar days two investigators studied, by this method of personal investigation, the social conditions existing in Stockton-on-Tees, and their facts and conclusions have attracted very wide attention.

2. *Estimates received from Correspondents*

This method is particularly applicable in the case of crop estimates.

3. *Questionnaire*

By the issue of blank forms of inquiry, to be filled in by individuals or by a few expert officials acting in conjunction with them, the inquiry may be made nationwide. If, in addition, it is possible to provide skilled assistance in the filling in of the forms, and to make their completion obligatory, the resulting information may be both wide and accurate. The population census takes this form. It is obligatory on the part of the head of the household to complete the form, and the enumerators, who distribute and collect them, are bound to see that the forms are filled in according to an agreed plan. This questionnaire method is the most popular and widely used one.

THE ESSENTIALS OF A QUESTIONNAIRE. The inquiry form or questionnaire should be carefully drawn up if it is to act as the basis of a statistical investigation. The foregoing preliminary rules will need to be borne in mind, and, in addition, a number of further points must be considered:

(a) In the first place the questions should be such that the least intelligent and least educated informant can answer them.

(b) If possible, the questions should be capable of a definite answer, either 'Yes' or 'No', a number, a place, or a date, etc.

(c) The questions should be such as will be answered truthfully and willingly. There should be nothing in the questions themselves which might lead the informant to believe that the information he gives will be used to his detriment.

(d) The questions should be so framed that they will elicit the information required, that is, there should be no possibility of ambiguity in the meaning of the questions.

THE CENSUS, 1931. It is interesting to review the Schedule for the 1931 Census in relation to these points. The following questions were asked:

A. Name and surname.
B. Relationship to head of household.
C. Usual residence.
D. Sex.
E. Age.
F. Condition as to marriage.
G. Birthplace.
H. Nationality.
I. Personal occupation.
J. Employer and employer's address.
K. Occupation when not gainfully occupied.

The questions were for the most part simple, the most difficult being questions I and J. Moreover, the schedules gave a number of examples showing how they might be filled in, and the enumerators were instructed to ask for explanations in cases where these answers were given in too vague a form. All the questions were capable of a definite answer and for the most part such as would be answered truthfully. It is, however, well known that women tend to understate their ages and old people to express theirs in round numbers.

QUESTIONNAIRES INVOLVING MORE SKILLED TREATMENT. If the questionnaire is to be filled in solely by people of skill, education, or specialized knowledge, then the questions may be more comprehensive, but they should still be capable of a definite answer. Unless this is so, the results which come from different sources will not be strictly comparable.

Example. For the purpose of obtaining regular information regarding employment, engagements of new labour, short-time, overtime, and employment on defence orders, the Ministry of Labour requires employers to complete, monthly, what is known as an L2 return.

The uses of this return will be dealt with in a later chapter. Briefly, it is the source of the published information on employment in industry and the extent of overtime and short-time working. The numbers on the pay-roll must be given at a specified date in the current month and also at a specified date in the previous month. The estimate of employment on defence orders is called for only twice a year. Elaborate notes and instructions are given on the back of the return. The main sections of the L2 return are illustrated below.

MINISTRY OF LABOUR

Statistics of Trade Act, 1947

NOTICE UNDER SECTION I

To:

Dear Sir/s,

This is to give you notice that the Ministry of Labour requires you to furnish, in respect of the undertaking carried on at the above address, the information asked for below by ....

This information is required for the appreciation of economic trends and the provision of a statistical service for industry.

Section I. Numbers on Pay-Roll and Engagements since ....

M/c Line No.	NUMBERS ON PAY-ROLL (including administrative, technical, and clerical staffs as well as operatives, but excluding outworkers) N.B. Canteen staffs should be included for both dates at .... at						ENGAGEMENTS SINCE .... Total number of individuals on pay-roll at .... who started or re-started work with you after	
(1)	Males (2)	Females (3)	Total (4)	Males (5)	Females (6)	Total (7)	Males (8)	Females (9)
I								

Section II. Percentage of Total Labour Force Employed on Defence Contract Work (direct, indirect, or by sub-contract)

Where defence contract work is being undertaken, state percentage of labour force employed thereon. If an exact figure is not available, an estimate should be given and noted 'est'. If no labour is so employed, enter 'nil'.	M/c Line no.	....
	2	%

Section III. Short-time and Overtime

M/c Line No.	In pay-week covered by Line 1, Cols. (5)–(7), were any operatives:		Time lost and/or overtime worked during pay-week covered by Line 1, Cols. (5)–(7)				
			(a) Number of operatives incl. in Line 1, Cols. (5)–(7) who were stood off for the whole of the week	(b) Short-time		(c) Overtime	
				Number of operatives who were on short-time, but worked part of the week	Approximate total number of man-hours lost by the workers shown in Col. (5) owing to short-time during the week	Number of operatives (excluding maintenance workers) who worked overtime in excess of normal hours during the week	Approximate total number of man-hours of overtime actually worked by these workers
	On short-time	On over-time					
(1)	(2)	(3)	(4)	(5)	(6)	(7)	(8)
3	Please write 'Yes' or 'No' in each of these columns						

Section IV. Principal Products of Factory or Type of Work Being Done

	Description
1. Most important product or activity (according to numbers employed)	
2. Other products or activities	

Signature of Employer or Manager ....
Date ....

PUBLISHED STATISTICS

In many cases the direct method of collecting data is not possible, and use must be made of data gathered by other persons and other agencies. There is a vast amount of published information from which statistical studies may be made and fresh statistics are constantly in a state of production. In a later chapter a list of some of the more important publications containing statistical information is given. Before such material is used for further statistical work, it is essential that the investigator should be satisfied that it is sufficiently accurate for his purpose. This should include a consideration of the methods originally adopted for the collection of the figures, the purpose for which the original investigation was carried out, the units in which the data are expressed, and whether any change has been made in these units during the period of collection. In addition, the degree of accuracy to be found in the figures themselves must be considered.

STUDENT WORK

1. What points must be given particular consideration when a 'questionnaire' is used as the basis of a statistical investigation?
2. How far does the census schedule for 1931 come within the points laid down in Question 1 and how far does it conflict with them?
3. What are the preliminary stages which must be considered when a statistical investigation is being prepared for?

Chapter 3

Accuracy and Approximation

IN Chapter 2 we touched upon a small number of points which arise when the question of the degree of accuracy existing in a set of statistics is being considered. We saw that absolute accuracy in counting rarely exists and that it can never be found in measurement. Knowing this, it is important to be able to measure the margins of error which may be found in any set of figures with which we may be called upon to deal. Further, it is essential to know how these margins of error are affected by the various mathematical processes – addition, multiplication, extraction of square root, etc., to which the original data may be subjected. Used in the foregoing sense the term 'error' does not necessarily involve a mistake. It means rather the difference between the actual figures we are considering and their true value. This difference may be due to the fact that we are working on approximations, either because we cannot arrive at the true value on account of insufficiently sensitive measuring instruments, or because for the particular purpose we are considering greater accuracy is not necessary.

ABSOLUTE AND RELATIVE ERROR

The significance of, and the difference between, these are best illustrated by an example. From figures appearing later in this book it will be seen that the number of males in England and Wales was shown by the Census of 1931 to be 19,133,010. In round figures, which will be sufficiently accurate for many purposes, this number can be stated as 19 million. The *absolute error* in the latter figure is 133,010. Thus, the absolute error is the difference between the true value of any variable[1] and the value obtained or employed in a given circumstance. The magnitude

[1] For a definition of 'variable' see Chapter 4, Tabulation.

of the absolute error is quite independent of the magnitude of the true value. As such, the comparison of absolute errors becomes useless, an error of 133,010 on a true value of 19,133,010 may be of less significance than an error of 1 on a true value of 100. In order that the magnitude of errors may be compared, it is necessary to reduce them to like terms. A convenient way of doing this is by calculating the percentage error. In the foregoing case, the percentage error is

$$\frac{133,010 \times 100}{19,133,010} \text{ or } 0.70\%.$$

The *relative error* relates the magnitude of the error to the magnitude of the true value, i.e. it shows the ratio between the error and the true value. The most convenient way of expressing relative errors is by percentages.

Notice that we attach no sign to the relative error. If we are given a figure of 5,500 and told that this is correct to within $\frac{1}{2}$ per cent, i.e. the relative error is $\frac{1}{2}$ per cent, it is clear that the true value may be either more or less than 5,500. This true value can be expressed as 5,500 $\pm$ 27·5 (27·5 is $\frac{1}{2}$ per cent of 5,500). This value therefore may be anywhere between 5,472·5 and 5,527·5.

COMPENSATING AND CUMULATIVE ERRORS

In the previous chapter we discussed briefly unbiased and biased errors. When the recorded figures are sometimes below and sometimes above the actual figures, the errors are said to be unbiased. Another term for unbiased errors is compensating errors. Clearly when some of the errors are positive and some negative they will tend to compensate or nullify one another. If we require to find the average age of 100 boys we could ask them to state their ages in years and months to the nearest month. On the basis of the figures so obtained we could find their total age and divide by 100 to get their average age. However, we could ask the boys to state their age *correct to the nearest year*, and calculate the average from these. The value of the average so obtained would not greatly differ from the one obtained when ages expressed to the nearest month were used. This is because the errors are unbiased or compensating. However, if the boys gave their ages in terms of the number of complete years, e.g. a boy who is 8 years 9 months returned his age as 8, then all the stated ages will be less than the true value, i.e. the errors will all be on the same side. Such errors are known as biased or cumulative errors. The average age worked out from this latter set of figures would differ appreciably from that obtained by using the ages correct to the nearest month. The absolute, and therefore the relative, error will be greater than when the errors are unbiased. We can state the following rules affecting these two types of errors:

1. In the case of unbiased errors, the relative error will decrease in size as the number of items increases. The absolute error is, however, likely to increase.

2. In the case of biased errors, both the absolute and the relative error will increase in size as the number of items increases.

Some of the foregoing points are illustrated in Table 1

APPROXIMATIONS

When writing down approximated results, the last correct figure should always be stated even though this figure may be zero. The last correct figure always gives an indication of the possible limits between which the true value lies. Thus, if we read that the increase in population of a town in the intercensal period was 3·2 per cent the answer is given to the nearest tenth of 1 per cent. The correct answer lies between 3·15 per cent and 3·25 per cent.

At times it is necessary to carry out arithmetical processes when one or more of the factors concerned is stated as an approximation. In such cases, the degree of accuracy of the final answer needs to be considered. An example should clarify the point.

1. It is known that, in a given year, the number of deaths per 1,000 of a town population was 12·5 ± 0·5. Further, the population of this town (expressed to the nearest thousand) is 129,000. Calculate the number of deaths in the year in question and show the degree of accuracy in the answer obtained.

The death rate may be between 12 and 13; the population of the town between 128,500 and 129,500.

The lowest possible number of deaths is therefore .. .. $12 \times 128·5 = 1542·0$

The highest possible number of deaths is therefore .. .. $13 \times 129·5 = 1683·5$

Table 1. *Ages of twenty young persons*

Individual ages (a)		Age expressed to nearest year (b) (Unbiased errors)	Error (c)	Age expressed in complete years (d) (Biased errors)	Error (e)
Yrs	Mths		Months		Months
15	7	16	+5	15	−7
13	6	14	+6	13	−6
12	4	12	−4	12	−4
7	3	7	−3	7	−3
18	11	19	+1	18	−11
14	2	14	−2	14	−2
15	8	16	+4	15	−8
17	3	17	−3	17	−3
7	6	7	−6	7	−6
4	1	4	−1	4	−1
16	10	17	+2	16	−10
17	5	17	−5	17	−5
12	6	13	+6	12	−6
13	0	13	—	13	—
14	9	15	+3	14	−9
13	6	13	−6	13	−6
13	2	13	−2	13	−2
14	10	15	+2	14	−10
7	8	8	+4	7	−8
6	5	6	−5	6	−5
Totals 256	4	256	−4	247	−112
Average 12	10	$12\frac{10}{12}$		12—	
Absolute error			−4 mths		112 mths
Relative error			$\frac{400}{3076}$ = 0·13%		$\frac{11200}{3076}$ = 3·64%

NOTE. − In those cases in column (a) where the age is so many years 6 months, the age to the nearest year is alternatively increased and decreased by 6 months.

The average of these two quantities is 1,613, which can be taken as the number of deaths. The limits of error are $\pm$ 71. The answer can therefore be stated as 1,613 $\pm$ 71.

2. Find the average of the following quantities (all expressed correct to the first decimal point): 12·8, 18·6, 3·5, 4·0, 12·6:

The highest average is

$$\frac{12·85 + 18·65 + 3·55 + 4·05 + 12·65}{5} = \frac{51·75}{5} = 10·35$$

The lowest average is

$$\frac{12·75 + 18·55 + 3·45 + 3·95 + 12·55}{5} = \frac{51·25}{5} = 10·25$$

The average then can be stated as 10·3 $\pm$ 0·05.

The limits between which the actual error must be are known as the *possible error*. In the foregoing example the possible error is 0·05. In obtaining the upper and lower limits the assumption is made that all the errors are in the same direction. In practice this is not likely to be the case. As the number of items increases the likelihood that all errors are in the same direction will decrease. The *probable error*, i.e. the most likely value of the error to occur when errors are of the compensatory type, is equal to the possible error divided by the square root of the number of items. In example 2 above the *probable error* is $\pm \dfrac{0·05}{\sqrt{5}}$[1]

It is not considered necessary to establish the proof of this expression in the present elementary textbook. It will, however, be readily found in more advanced treatments of the subject.

ESTIMATION OF ERRORS

We must now consider the means adopted for the measurement of errors. These are important because the reliability of any result may be deduced from the possible error to be expected. Again, the reader will be asked to take a little on trust; proof cannot be given at this stage.

[1] This formula applies more closely, the greater the number of items being considered. The chance of an error lying between the limits of the probable error is $\frac{1}{2}$.

Unbiased Errors

The absolute error to be expected in an addition sum is the product of the average probable error and the square root of the number of items. In the example on the age of twenty young persons dealt with earlier in the chapter, the error resulting from the approximation made in column (b) varies from 0 to 6 months with an average probable error of 3 months. The absolute error in the total which could be expected is therefore $3 \times \sqrt{20}$ months, approximately 13 months. This figure is larger than the actual error of 4 months.

Biased Errors

In this case the absolute error to be expected is equal to the average error multiplied by the number of items. In the example we are considering the error in column (d) could vary between 0 and 11 with an average of approximately 5·5. The absolute error in the total which could reasonably be expected is therefore approximately 110 months.

STUDENT WORK

1. Explain what is meant by 'statistical error'. Distinguish between unbiased and biased errors.

2. Distinguish between Possible and Probable Error. How may the latter be obtained in the case of the addition of a large number of items containing unbiased errors?

3. The following table shows the number of Retail Co-operative Societies registered in the years 1922–33:

Year	Number of societies	Year	Number of societies	Year	Number of societies
1922	1,442	1926	1,367	1930	1,279
1923	1,422	1927	1,351	1931	1,266
1924	1,415	1928	1,329	1932	1,253
1925	1,381	1929	1,305	1933	1,238

By expressing the number of societies correct (a) to the nearest hundred; (b) correct to the nearest hundred below, calculate the absolute and relative errors in each case.

4. Obtain the Probable Error for the totals (*a*) and (*b*) of Question 3.
5. Prove that when individual items have been subject to a degree of rounding the accuracy of a total can be no greater than the accuracy of the most inaccurate item.
6. The annual death rate in a certain provincial city is between 20 and 24 per 1,000 and the population is estimated at 800,000 (within 7 per cent). Calculate the number of deaths per annum and show the degree of accuracy for your answer.

Chapter 4

Tabulation

In the last chapter the various methods of collecting statistical data were outlined. All statistical investigations should have a definite purpose and the collection of the data is only one step in the attainment of this purpose. If the investigation is a direct one, e.g. carried out by using a questionnaire, the required information will doubtless be contained in the answers given, but as such it is not in an easily available form. The answers will require some analysis if their salient points are to be brought out. As a rule the first step in the analysis is to classify and tabulate the information collected, or, if published statistics have been employed, rearrange these into new groups and tabulate the new arrangement. In the case of some investigations, the classification and tabulation may give such a clear picture of the significance of the material so arranged that no further analysis is required. In other cases, these processes, although they materially assist the analysis, are not sufficient for a complete presentation of the facts. They are, however, very important whether they complete the analysis or form only part of it. The questionnaire may have been very carefully drawn up and the answers be both complete and accurate, but until these answers are all brought together into the class to which they belong and the whole information displayed in tabular form, no one will be a great deal wiser as to the contents of the replies.

THE MEANING OF CLASSIFICATION

Although the phrase 'classification and tabulation' has been used, classification is, in effect, only the first step in tabulation, for, in general, items having common characteristics must be brought together before the data can be displayed in tabular form. Classification is the process of arranging data according to common characteristics possessed by the items constituting the data. If the reader has ever visited a Post Office sorting-room, he will have seen a large number of pigeon-holes arranged on a geographical basis. The pigeon-holes may be arranged in sections – a section for each county, for example. Each county section may have a separate pigeon-hole for each postal area within that county. Outgoing letters to be sorted are first grouped according to the county to which they are being sent and then placed in the respective pigeon-holes for the separate areas. In this case the common characteristic which forms the basis of the grouping is a place or geographical one. Such a basis is used because it is the one best calculated to expedite the delivery of letters. If the latter were not the aim of letter-sorting, other groupings in accordance with common characteristics might be employed. For example, the letters might be grouped in accordance with their time of posting, or even in accordance with the addressees' names – e.g. all letters for people named Smith being brought together.

Classification of statistical data is a very similar process to the sorting of letters. It consists of providing suitably named compartments in which each item of the data may be included. The names of the compartments will usually be common characteristics possessed by the data, but as in the case of letter-sorting, the ones selected will normally be those which best advance the ultimate purpose of the classification. As an example of such classification, let us consider for a moment the census forms. The total population of the United Kingdom could be obtained by adding together the figures given on each form, which represent the number of persons in each household. The information which can be derived from the census forms is, however, much more complete than this, but this information requires to be classified before its full significance is shown. The common characteristics which could serve as compartment names for an analysis of the census forms might include sex, age, place of residence, occupation, condition as to marriage, nationality, or industry in which the individual is employed. Which of these are chosen will depend upon the purpose of the investigator. If the classification decided upon is merely in relation to sex, then the male population will be grouped together as also will the female. If age is the basis, then persons of the same age will be grouped together.

Naturally, classification may be made in many ways, but in general we may distinguish four distinct types.

B

1. Classification may be on a time basis. For example the percentage attendance in a school could be classified by weeks or months. A single population census could not be classified on this basis, but an analysis of a number of such censuses might.

2. Classification may be on a geographical or place basis. In such a case the population living in one county, city, or town would be grouped together.

3. Classification may be qualitative. In this case, the common characteristic may be a similarity in quality or condition. A grouping together in accordance with sex or nationality or personal occupation would be an example of this type.

4. We may also have classification on a quantitative basis. The distinction between one class and another has, in this case, some reference to a quantitative unit. British imports and exports might be classified quantitatively, i.e. by weight, volume, or value.

TABULATION

The process of tabulation involves the systematic presentation of numerical facts in such a form that the information thus displayed is more readily understood. This presentation usually takes the form of arranging the numerical data in columns and rows. At the head of each column is usually to be found the title of the column. This title forms a part of the general classification adopted for the purpose of sorting out, in accordance with common characteristics, the numerical data in question.

Simple Tabulation

This consists of entering in columns the number or measurement of the items having the characteristics specified at the head of the columns. A simple example of this type of tabulation may be taken from the Census Schedules.

When data are collected over a period of time, as in Table 2, the result is what is called a *Statistical Series*, or a *Time Series*. The population figures themselves are *variables*. A variable is any item which exhibits differences in magnitude at different places, times, or under different conditions. Thus, the figure for fatal road accidents is a variable as is also the value of our exports.

Table 2. *Population of England and Wales (males and females), 1861–1931*

Year	Males	Females
1861	9,776,259	10,289,965
1871	11,058,934	11,653,332
1881	12,639,902	13,334,537
1891	14,052,901	14,949,624
1901	15,728,613	16,799,230
1911	17,445,608	18,624,884
1921	18,075,239	19,811,460
1931	19,133,010	20,819,367

Complex Tabulation

This involves both columns and rows. Each number in the table is the measurement of the item having the characteristic given at the head of the column, and it is also a value of the row to which it belongs. The distribution of males and females into their occupations, at a given census, is an example of tabulation of this type.

Table 3. *Table to illustrate the distribution of population according to industries (1921)*

Great Britain

Industry	Males	Females
1. Fishing	63,289	1,968
2. Agriculture	1,197,795	109,253
3. Mining and quarrying	1,395,716	13,556
	————	————
Totals		

Table 3 is an illustration of a statistical *class*. The items are arranged in industries, and as industries can merely be described but not measured, the grouping belongs to a 'class'. Thus a statistical class is a collection of items arranged in accordance with a non-measurable characteristic.

If, instead of industries, ages, which can be expressed in numbers, were the characteristic composing the rows, then the table would be an example of a statistical *group*. A group is a collection of items arranged in accordance with a measurable characteristic.

Further steps in Tabulation

It may be necessary to subdivide the columns or rows in order that more refined distinctions can be illustrated. This subdivision is the basis of what is sometimes known as treble tabulation. The subdivision of males and females in accordance with their country of residence would change Table 3 into an example of treble tabulation.

Table 4. *Distribution of population into industries*
(from the Census Returns for 1921)

Industries	Great Britain		England and Wales		Scotland	
	Males	Females	Males	Females	Males	Females
1. Fishing	63,289	1,968	38,616	1,630	24,673	338
2. Agriculture	1,197,795	109,253	1,038,490	85,472	159,305	23,781
3. Mining and quarrying	1,395,716	13,556	1,222,933	8,797	172,783	4,975
Totals						

FREQUENCY TABLES

Let us consider again the distribution of population into ages. A table could be drawn up having two columns, one for ages and one for the population at each age, e.g.:

Table 5. *The age distribution of the population of 'X' shire*

Age	Number of persons
1	20,200
2	20,000
3	19,550
4	19,500
5	19,380

Such a table is known as a *frequency table* or *frequency distribution*. The number of persons corresponding to each age is known as the frequency of that particular age; it expresses how frequently that age occurs. It may not be desirable or sometimes even possible to

tabulate a frequency table showing every possible item. If every age
from 1 to 100 were set down and the frequency for each age given, the
table would be extremely long, or if the column headings were repeated
a number of times, very wide. In either case the multiplicity of figures

Table 6. *Age distribution at the 1931 Census*

Age group years	All persons Number	Per- centage	Males Number	Per- centage	Females Number	Per- centage
Under 15	9,520,198	23·8	4,808,480	12·0	4,711,708	11·8
15–19	3,434,501	8·6	1,709,512	4·3	1,724,989	4·3
20–24	3,494,487	8·7	1,699,141	4·3	1,795,346	4·5
25–29	3,357,100	8·4	1,628,993	4·1	1,728,107	4·3
30–34	3,055,286	7·6	1,433,289	3·6	1,621,997	4·1
35–39	2,803,039	7·0	1,283,010	3·2	1,520,029	3·8
40–44	2,663,553	6·7	1,229,346	3·1	1,434,207	3·6
45–49	2,553,939	6·4	1,186,554	3·0	1,367,385	3·4
50–54	2,381,637	6·0	1,116,319	2·8	1,265,318	3·2
55–59	2,068,477	5·2	987,445	2·5	1,081,032	2·7
60–64	1,656,951	4·1	778,064	1·9	878,887	2·2
65–69	1,270,670	3·2	577,970	1·4	692,700	1·7
70–74	870,751	2·2	376,480	0·9	494,271	1·2
75 and over	821,788	2·1	318,397	0·8	503,391	1·3
Totals	39,952,377	100	19,133,010	47·9	20,819,367	52·1

NOTE. – The above table really shows three frequency distributions, one for
all persons, one for males, and one for females.

would prove very confusing and for most purposes such a fine division
of ages is not required. A useful device in tabulation to avoid such confusion is to group the items. In the case we are considering, if ages were
grouped as follows: under 6 years, 6–10 years, 11–15 years, and so on,
the size of the table would be very considerably reduced and the information obtained hardly less valuable.

Again, where figures are large, the percentage of each frequency to
the total of the items is more readily appreciated than the figures themselves and, if set down alongside the corresponding frequency, makes a
useful addition to the table. (See Table 6.)

SOME GENERAL RULES FOR TABULATION

The ability to draw up a neat, well-balanced, and informative table
is of great use in every study. The mass of information required by

persons in administrative positions is often more readily conveyed by suitable tabulation than by description. There is no one best method of tabulating and any rules given must be general. Much more can be learned of tabulation by actually displaying figures in tabular form, or by studying the composition of well-drawn-up tables, than by learning rules. Nevertheless, certain general principles can be applied to most forms of tabulation, since whatever be the matter to be tabulated the aim is to arrive at a more striking and informative method of presentation.

1. Classification is a first step in the process of tabulation. It is important therefore to decide upon the classification to be adopted as this will provide the compartments into which the material is entered.

2. When the compartments have been decided upon, make out a rough draft of the table. This will give an idea of the width required for each column and also of the general appearance of the table.

3. The title should be clear and it should convey, in as few words as possible, the contents of the table. The column headings should also be definite and comprehensive.

4. Units of measurement must be clearly stated and any figures derived from the tabulated items, e.g. percentages, should be as close to their originals as possible.

5. A variation in the type used attracts attention. Totals might be given in thicker type than individual items.

6. The table should be well balanced, i.e. its length and breadth in keeping with each other. If the table shows signs of undue length, try grouping the items. If this is not desirable because of some loss in the informative value of the table accruing thereby, leave a break every few lines. The breaks should be at equal distances. By these means the table will become less confusing.

7. Light rulings may be used to separate sub-columns, while heavier rulings normally distinguish main columns. An alternative to a thick ruling is a double line.

8. Notes may be added at the foot of the table to clear up any doubts which exist in the table itself.

Some of the foregoing points may be illustrated by reference to Table 7. It is taken from the *Report on the Census of Production*, 1930. It is a well-balanced table, i.e. its width and depth are in keeping with each other. Notice that unnecessary width in the 'Total production' columns is avoided by omitting ooo's and heading the columns by them. The division between main columns and sub-columns is shown by a single line. The title and column headings are sufficiently definite, and at the same time, sufficiently comprehensive.

Table 7. *Production and employment in the textile trades in 1924 and 1930*

Trade	Total production			Persons employed in 1930 as a percentage of 1924	Value of production (at 1930 average values) per person employed	
	1930	1924 at 1930 average values	1930 as a percentage of 1924		1930	1924
	£'ooo	£'ooo	Per cent	Per cent	£	£
Cotton spinning	78,624	103,920	75·7	75·5	412	411
Cotton weaving	79,631	118,120	67·4	72·2	401	429
Woollen and worsted	114,833	147,890	77·6	83·9	499	539
Silk and artificial silk	23,012	13,510	170·3	149·9	384	338
Linen and hemp	22,981	28,270	81·3	73·2	316	285
Jute	9,605	11,700	82·1	83·5	334	340
Hosiery	39,444	37,870	107·0	110·3	374	386
Textile finishing	30,379	38,940	78·0	91·7	289	339
Leather (tanning and dressing)	27,792	30,140	92·2	93·7	975	991
Tailoring, dressmaking and millinery	112,408	101,500	110·8	108·9	348	342
Boot and shoe	46,982	44,220	106·3	93·2	386	339
Hat and cap	12,291	10,750	114·3	102·3	401	359

The reader will see later that some of the mathematical work in statistics calls for fairly elaborate tables. In working such exercises, care should be taken in their arrangement. In fact, unless such tables are carefully drawn up and properly headed, it will be easy for errors to creep into the mathematical work.

STUDENT WORK

1. Define carefully, the following terms: (*a*) statistical classes; (*b*) statistical groups; (*c*) time series; (*d*) frequency distribution.
2. Draw up a classification which will show the types of programme broadcast on the Light Programme wavelength, and construct a blank table which could be used to show the time devoted to each class of programme during a given week.

3. Draw up a scheme, including a classification and a blank table, which could be used for taking a census of road traffic at a very busy point when the number of each type of vehicle passing per hour, from 6 a.m. to 6 a.m. the following morning, is required.

4. A certain steel tube firm classifies its output into the following sections: (1) cold-drawn boiler tubes; (2) steam pipes; (3) other cold-drawn tubes; (4) hot-drawn tubes; (5) air vessels; (6) gas bottles. At the directors' monthly meeting a statement is presented showing: (a) the value of orders received during the previous month; (b) the value of deliveries made, and (c) the value of orders on hand at the end of the month. Draw up a ruling for such a statement, classified in accordance with the above type of output and make specimen entries for each class.

5. Draw up a table to show the number of wholly unemployed, temporarily stopped, and the total unemployed, each class being divided into males and females, for the following industries: fishing, coal-mining, iron-ore mining, cotton manufacture, wool and worsted, engineering, and shipbuilding.

Chapter 5

Diagrammatic Representation

IN the four preceding chapters we have discussed how the raw material for statistical study is collected, and how, as the first step in its analysis, this material has to be classified and tabulated. Tabulation brings together related items and suggests further analysis. While tabulation is an essential step in the working up of statistical data, it is sometimes difficult to hold in mind the great mass of figures which may be contained in the tables and any relations which may exist are often obscured in the effort to grasp the quantities themselves. The degrees of difference between items are not always easily grasped when the data are expressed in quantities. It is to overcome these difficulties, and to throw into high relief related items, that pictorial representation is used. In order to assist the working of the mind, the power of visualization is introduced: the mind through the eye can more readily appreciate the significance of figures presented in the form of a picture than it can follow the figures themselves. Pictorial representation is particularly valuable in administration and in business, for it enables the important parts of the information to be displayed in a form which makes a quick and lasting impression and saves the necessity of a detailed examination of a formidable mass of figures in order to obtain the significant facts.

The number and types of pictorial representation of statistical data are very great and new ones are constantly being added. It would be outside the scope of this book to deal exhaustively with the subject, but the following examples will serve to show the value and limitations of this method of presenting statistical facts.

PICTUREGRAMS

Within recent years picturegrams have become a popular method of exhibiting the size-relationships between a series of related statistics.

These picturegrams are simple diagrams in which the subject-matter to be represented is shown by figures, sketches, or designs which can readily be associated with the subject-matter in question. For example, if we wished to give a pictorial representation of the sizes of the armies of the United Nations and Axis Powers in, say 1943, the basis might be little figures representing soldiers carrying the national flag or emblem of the country whose army they are illustrating. The size of the British Army would be indicated by a number of men carrying a Union Jack; that of Russia by a larger number of men bearing the hammer-and-sickle device; that of Germany by an intermediate number of men with the swastika badge. The important thing to note, however, is that the number of men in each case would be directly proportionate to the size of the armies of each country. Naturally, this type of pictorial representation provides a very wide scope for the ingenious artist. It is very easy to understand and is particularly useful in conveying information to persons who have not the skill or training necessary to appreciate other forms of diagrammatic representation.

In 1944 the Government produced a White Paper entitled *Statistics Relating to the War Effort of the United Kingdom*. This contained a mass of statistical information showing the extent of Britain's man-power and industrial mobilization for war purposes in the period September 1939 to June 1944. In order to increase the popular appeal of the main facts contained in the White Paper, a pamphlet which contained many picturegrams was issued at the same time. This procedure was also adopted when the White Paper on the Government's Social Insurance Scheme was issued in the same year. The picturegrams on page 33 are taken from the leaflet which accompanied this particular White Paper. Many modern examples will occur to the reader.

BAR AND CIRCLE DIAGRAMS

Statistical *classes*, i.e. data grouped according to some non-measurable characteristic, are often conveniently and satisfactorily represented by bar or circle diagrams, particularly if the items in the class represent component parts of a whole.

Table 8 can be illustrated by what is called a *percentage bar chart* (Fig. 2). A bar is divided into sections, each section corresponding in size to the size of the item it represents and the full length of the bar

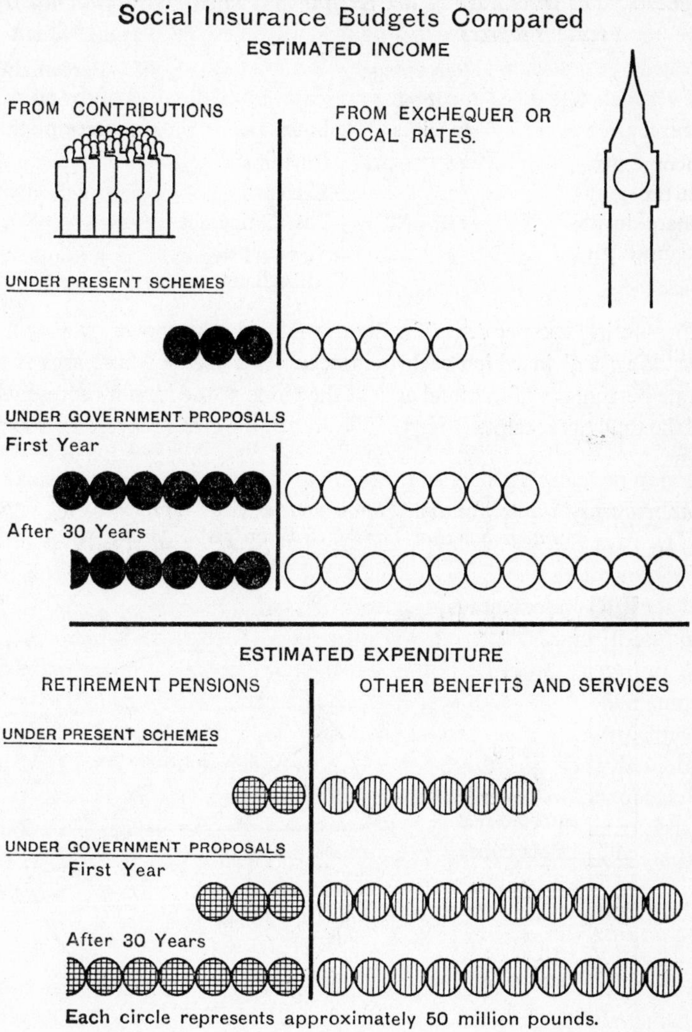

Social Insurance Budgets Compared
ESTIMATED INCOME

FROM CONTRIBUTIONS

FROM EXCHEQUER OR
LOCAL RATES.

UNDER PRESENT SCHEMES

UNDER GOVERNMENT PROPOSALS

First Year

After 30 Years

ESTIMATED EXPENDITURE

RETIREMENT PENSIONS   OTHER BENEFITS AND SERVICES

UNDER PRESENT SCHEMES

UNDER GOVERNMENT PROPOSALS

First Year

After 30 Years

Each circle represents approximately 50 million pounds.

Fig. 1

NOTE. – The above proposals are those made by the Coalition Government in 1944.

Table 8. *The percentage of tax receipts in a prewar year obtained from various sources*

Source	Percentage of total receipts	Source	Percentage of total receipts
Income tax	32	Customs	26
Surtax	7	Excise	14
Estate duties	11	Post Office net (receipts)	$1\frac{3}{4}$
Stamp duties	$3\frac{1}{2}$	Miscellaneous	$4\frac{3}{4}$

representing 100 per cent. The figures may also be shown by a *circle* or *'pie' diagram*,[1] in which each item occupies a sector whose area is the same percentage of the total area of the circle as the item it represents is of the total tax receipts (Fig. 3). The area of the circle represents 100 per cent.

The sources of the tax revenue (for a prewar year) represented by a 'percentage bar chart' and a circle or 'pie' diagram

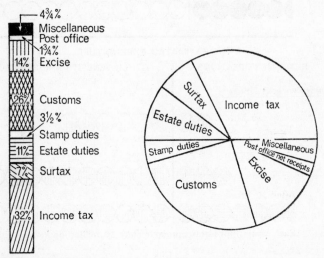

Fig. 2. *Percentage bar chart*

Fig. 3. *Circle or 'pie' diagram*

[1] The term 'pie' diagram is given to this type because of its resemblance to a pie.

If the items of a statistical class are not component parts of a whole, but related to each other by their possession of a common characteristic, then simple bar charts provide a suitable method of diagrammatic representation. In this case, bars having equal widths, but with lengths proportional to the values they represent, are erected from a base line. Sometimes the bars touch each other like organ-pipes, in other cases

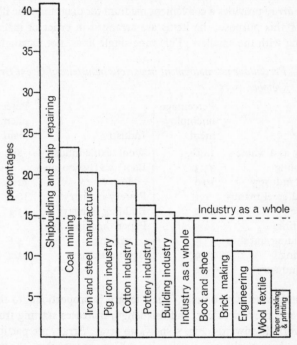

Fig. 4. *Diagram illustrating the percentage unemployment in various industries (the figures relate to October 1935)*

they may be spaced at equal intervals. There is no definite ruling on this point, but if the latter method is used the bars may need some distinctive shading in order to give a more striking effect.

Table 9 gives the percentage unemployment in various industries in Great Britain for October 1935. Fig. 4 shows the diagrammatic representation by a simple bar diagram. The percentages are arranged in descending order of magnitude, and if the bars touch each other, this order is probably better than having the values displayed in a haphazard manner.

THE ARRAY

A variation of the bar diagram becomes necessary when a comparatively large number of items is to be illustrated diagrammatically. In such a case the *array* provides a convenient medium for diagrammatic illustration. For this purpose, the items are arranged in order of magnitude beginning with the smallest. This time single lines, not rectangles, are

Table 9. *Percentage unemployment in various industries of Great Britain – October 1935*

Industry	Percentage unemployment	Industry	Percentage unemployment
Industry as a whole	14·6	Wool textile industry	8·2
Coal mining	23·3	Boot and shoe industry	12·4
Pig iron industry	19·0		
Iron and steel manufacture	20·1	Pottery industry	16·2
Engineering	10·5	Building industry	15·1
Shipbuilding and ship repairing	40·9	Paper making and printing	5·6
Cotton industry	19·2	Brick making	12·2

drawn and these, horizontally. Their length is proportional to the size of the items they represent, and this length increases starting from the top to work downwards. Fig. 5 shows an array. Arrays are particularly useful in showing the value of 'positional' averages such as the median which are dealt with in Chapter 7.

Bar diagrams are usually easier to draw than circle diagrams. The latter, too, are not susceptible to such great accuracy as bar diagrams. For in order to ensure that the sectors of the circle have an area proportional to the item they represent, the angle they subtend at the centre must be proportional to this item. As a result circle diagrams are not greatly to be relied on in statistical work. Again, the actual values represented by bar diagrams may be read off from the scale of values (see Fig. 4), but unless the values of the items are given for circle diagrams, it is much more inconvenient to obtain them. Both serve to assist in the understanding of statistical data because their significance is more easily grasped than is the significance of the figures they represent.

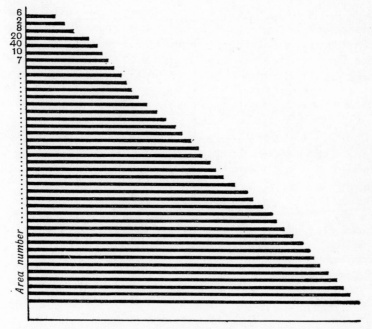

Fig. 5. *Number of flying bombs*

GRAPHS

The most widely used forms of diagram consist of line charts or graphs.[1] Such diagrams not only illustrate figures, they may in addition suggest relationships between sets of figures which are not obvious from the data themselves.

Figures represented by graphs may relate to a state of affairs existing at a given period of time or they may be successive values of a given variable taken over a period of time. In other words, graphs may be used to represent statistical groups or statistical time series. Since a graph

[1] For a note on the construction of simple graphs, see p. 47.

cannot be drawn unless there are two measurable variables, statistical classes cannot be shown by this means, but may be illustrated by the types of diagram already described, i.e. bar, circle, or pie diagram. The graphical representation of a statistical series is known as a Historigram.

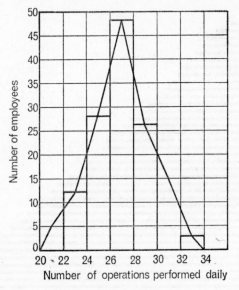

Fig. 6. *Two methods of representing a frequency distribution diagrammatically*

USES OF GRAPHS

The diagrammatic representation of Frequency Distributions

Frequency distributions may be illustrated either by bar diagrams or by graphs.

Both the pictorial and graphical representation of the above table are shown in Fig. 6. Rectangles proportional in height to the number of employees for each group are erected for the diagram. Such a diagram is known as a *histogram*. (Carefully distinguish this from a historigram which is the graphical representation of a time series.) If now the middle points of the tops of the rectangles are joined, then a graph, known as the *frequency polygon*, results.

If the full frequency distribution, i.e. the frequency for every individual item and not groups of items, is given, the frequency curve may

Table 10. *Operations performed daily by employees in a machine shop*

Number of operations performed daily	Number of employees performing these
20–22	5
22–24	12
24–26	28
26–28	48
28–30	26
30–32	15
32–34	3

still be plotted. The abscissae will then be the actual items given, e.g. an extract from the complete figures for Table 10 is as follows:

Number of operations performed daily	Number of employees performing these
20	2
21	3
22	5
23	7
24	11
25	17

In plotting the above, the abscissae would be the values in the first column.

FREQUENCY CURVES. By 'smoothing' a frequency polygon, a frequency curve is obtained. More will be said, however, about this type of graphical representation in Chapter 6, which deals specifically with frequency distributions.

The Recognition of Correlation by Graphical Methods

The figures in Table 11 relate to the yield of corn per acre and the rainfall in July for a period of twenty successive years and are quoted by D. C. Jones in his book *A First Course in Statistics*. A number of interesting points are brought out by the graphs of these figures (Fig. 7).

1. Fig. 7 shows how the values of two different variables may be illustrated on one graph. The values of the two are for the same period, and therefore the horizontal scale is common to both. Two scales must,

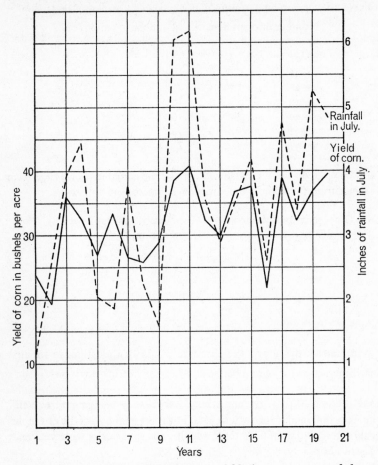

Fig. 7. *Graph showing relation between yield of corn per acre and the July rainfall*

however, be used for the dependent variables, as the values of the two are widely different. Thus, the two scales are marked down either side, but, naturally, the values are plotted from left to right. By a judicious choice of scales, two or more graphs may be plotted on a single sheet.

In this way the relationship between two or more sets of figures may be more clearly brought out.

2. The relationship between the values of the two dependent variables, in the case we are considering, is a special one. The figures themselves show that some connexion exists between the two series, but the graphical representation brings out this connexion in a very striking fashion. The graphs tend to move up and down in unison. In statistical

Table 11. *Rainfall and yield of corn per acre in bushels*

Year	Yield per acre of corn in bushels	Rainfall in July in inches	Year	Yield per acre of corn in bushels	Rainfall in July in inches
1	24·5	1·15	11	40·5	6·16
2	19·2	2·40	12	32·5	3·59
3	35·7	3·83	13	30·0	2·84
4	32·3	4·45	14	36·0	3·42
5	26·2	2·03	15	37·0	4·15
6	33·5	1·88	16	21·4	2·63
7	26·2	3·71	17	38·7	4·78
8	25·7	2·20	18	32·2	3·41
9	28·8	1·58	19	36·5	5·23
10	37·4	6·01	20	39·8	4·78

language, this tendency is known as *correlation*. If two or more quantities vary in unison, so that a movement in one is accompanied by a movement in the other, then they are said to be correlated, and the mathematical value of the connexion between them, their correlation. The existence of correlation and the extent of this correlation are usually more obvious from the graphical representation of the figures than from the figures themselves. The question of correlation is discussed at greater length in Chapter 11, and we will content ourselves here with one further example of its recognition by graphical methods.

The figures given in Table 12 are records of the price of gold per ounce, and the franc–sterling rate of exchange on twenty successive days when France was on the gold standard some time during the 1930s.

The general tendency in this particular case is for one set of figures to go up while the other goes down. This is quite well shown in Fig. 8

Table 12. *The price of gold per oz. and the franc–sterling rate*

Day	Price of gold per oz. s.	d.	No. of francs to £ sterling	Day	Price of gold per oz. s.	d.	No. of francs to £ sterling
1	141	0	74·78	11	141	1	74·50
2	141	1	74·82	12	141	1	74·50
3	140	11½	74·91	13	141	1½	74·51
4	140	11½	74·94	14	141	1½	74·50
5	141	0	74·56	15	141	3	74·34
6	141	1½	74·54	16	141	1	74·78
7	141	0½	74·72	17	141	1½	74·81
8	141	0	74·72	18	141	1	74·78
9	141	2½	74·62	19	141	1	74·81
10	141	2	74·48	20	141	0	74·87

which is a graphical illustration of the figures. The graph indicates that there is a definite connexion or correlation between the two, but that the correlation is inverse. Thus, an increase in the price of gold is accompanied by a decrease in the franc rate; as the price of gold increases,

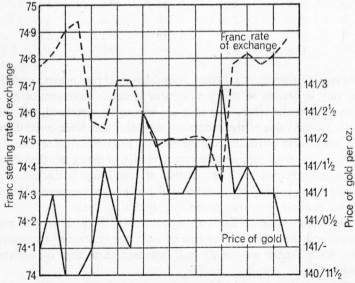

Fig. 8. *Graph showing connexion between franc rate of exchange and price of gold per oz.*

the franc rate falls, and vice versa. The mathematical value of the correlation existing between the yield of corn per acre and the July rainfall as given in Table 11, will later be found to be positive, that which exists between the two variables given in Table 12, negative (Chapter 11).

INTERPOLATION BY GRAPHICAL METHODS

In certain cases, as, for example, the census, it is impracticable to conduct a statistical investigation, except at comparatively rare intervals. Thus, it may be that the value of the variable which is being considered may only be known with accuracy at periods at some distance from each other. The population of the country is known with great accuracy at the time of each successive census, but the population at any time during an inter-censal period can only be estimated. The population was known in 1861, for example, and also in 1871, but what of the population in the intervening years? This can be worked out roughly by the arithmetical process known as *interpolation*. Graphical methods may also be used for the determination of intermediate values by the process of interpolation, and they have one great advantage over the corresponding arithmetical process. If the latter is used, a separate calculation must be made for each value of the variable required. When graphical methods are used, all the intermediate values may be read from one suitably drawn graph.

Table 13. *Population of England and Wales from 1831 to 1931*

Year	Population	Year	Population
1831	13,896,797	1891	29,002,525
1841	15,914,148	1901	32,527,843
1851	17,927,609	1911	36,070,492
1861	20,066,224	1921	37,886,699
1871	22,712,266	1931	39,952,377
1881	25,974,439		

Fig. 9 shows the graphical representation of the population of England and Wales from 1831 to 1931. If now the population in 1855 is required, this may be read from the graph. The point C represents the year 1855, and B, the point vertically above it, gives the population in this year, which may be read off by reference to the point A: 19 million. Similarly, if the year in which the population reached 30 million is required, this may also be read off, i.e. 1893. Naturally, the results obtained will only be approximately correct and should not be given the appearance of a greater degree of accuracy than the circumstances really warrant.

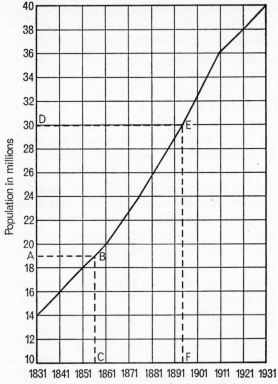

Fig. 9. *Graph showing population of England and Wales, 1831–1931*

CONTINUOUS AND DISCRETE SERIES

When the temperature of a body rises from 0° C. to 50° C., it must pass through every temperature reading between the two values. When the price of any shares rises from £5 to £8 10s. 0d., it does so in a series of jumps and there is a definite break between one value and the next. Temperature records, because they pass from one value to another by immeasurably small gradations, form what is known as a *continuous series*. The prices of shares form a *discontinuous* or *discrete series*, because the successive values are capable of exact measurement and there are breaks between each one. A discrete series whose discontinuities are relatively small may be considered as a continuous series. Theoretically, the population of England and Wales is a discrete series, but as variations are really in single units, and each unit is only a small proportion of the total, the discontinuity is of no importance.

The distinction between the two series is important from the point of view of graphical representation. A continuous series, or a series which is treated as continuous, should be represented by a smooth curve, i.e. there should be no breaks or sudden jumps in the graph. A discrete series may be properly represented by a series of straight lines joining the points which have been plotted. Thus the population figures in Table 13 were represented by a smooth curve, but the price of gold per ounce by a succession of straight lines.

RATIO SCALES

So far, we have considered line charts or graphs drawn on absolute scales, i.e. one inch represents the same number of units at any part of the scale. In the case of Fig. 9 one inch represents 2 million on the vertical scale and an increase in the population from 14 million to 16 million takes up 0·1 inch just as does an increase from 36 million to 38 million. Thus, absolute scales show the actual change only. If we were more concerned with plotting the relative change, then it would follow that an increase in population from 14 million to 16 million would require more space than an increase from 36 million to 38 million since the former is the greater relative change.

Ratio or logarithmic scales have the vertical scale proportional to the logarithms of numbers, not to the numbers themselves. Thus, graphs plotted on ratio scales show relative change, not absolute change. Fig. 10 gives an example of ratio scales. Note how the proportion of the scale taken up by one unit gets less and less as the units increase. If ratio scales are not available, the same result may be obtained by plotting on the ordinary or absolute scale, not the values of the variable, but the logarithms of these values.

It should be clear from the foregoing that graphs plotted on natural scales have a somewhat limited field as regards the range of magnitudes which can be represented. For example, it would be difficult to show conveniently on such scales magnitudes varying from 20,000 to 20 million. The scale adopted would be such that small changes would not be apparent. In such cases we are compelled to use either ratio scales or logarithmic computation and plotting. By these means we reduce the apparent range between the two extreme items. But it must be clear, however, that by using ratio scales or by plotting the logarithms of

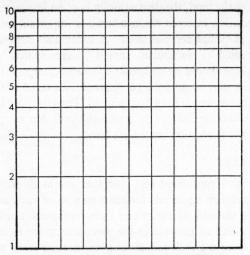

Fig. 10. *The Logarithmic Scale*

variables we are showing the rate of change, not the absolute change. A rate of change of, say 10 per cent, would be shown by equal distances on ratio scales or logarithmic graphs, but this of course is not so when natural scales are used.

GENERAL RULES FOR GRAPHICAL REPRESENTATION

In view of the value and widespread use of graphs in statistical work, it is important that they should be drawn with care so as to exhibit the data clearly. Some of the precautions to be taken in preparing graphs have already been referred to in the course of this chapter; they are here repeated and amplified.

1. The title of a graph (or diagram) should be made as complete and clear as possible.

2. The variables represented by each axis should be clearly indicated on the graph and sufficient values should be written along both scales to enable any value of the variable to be read off easily.

3. The horizontal scale for graphs should read from left to right and the vertical scale from bottom to top. If two vertical scales are used, it will be convenient in most cases to set down the scales on the left-hand and right-hand sides of the paper respectively, but both must be read from left to right.

4. Continuous series or series which are taken to be continuous should be represented by a curve. Discrete series should be represented by straight lines joining the successive points plotted.

CONSTRUCTION OF SIMPLE GRAPHS

The text assumes that the reader is familiar with the construction of a simple graph. The following description is intended for those readers who may find a little difficulty in understanding their preparation. Assume that the following figures for monthly sales are to be represented graphically:

Month	Value of sales	Month	Value of sales
January	£2,300	July	£3,100
February	£1,000	August	£3,200
March	£2,500	September	£3,000
April	£2,400	October	£2,700
May	£2,800	November	£2,500
June	£2,800	December	£3,200

Both the month and the value of the sales are variables. The months are, however, independent variables while the sales figures are dependent variables. Once the independent variable is chosen, the value of the other variable depends upon that choice.

The essential feature of graphs is that the value of each corresponding pair of variables is represented by a point, the distance of the point from two lines (known as axes) being proportional to the value of each variable. These axes are at right angles to each other as in the accompanying diagram. In the case of the horizontal axis XOX', distances to the left of O, the origin and point of intersection of the axis, are taken as negative, while those to the right of the origin are positive. In the same way, vertical distances below the origin are negative and those above, positive. Measurements along the horizontal axis are called abscissae, those along the vertical, ordinates. The axes divide the plane into four quadrants, but for most statistical work quadrant (1) is sufficient. If the dependent variable becomes less than zero, quadrant (4) will then usually be employed. In the example given above, all the values for the dependent variable are positive. If profits were being illustrated graphically, losses could be considered as negative profits, in which case, quadrant (4) would be employed.

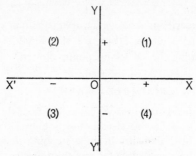

Fig. 11. *The four quadrants*

To facilitate the location of any point squared paper is used. It is customary to measure values of the independent variable in a horizontal direction from the origin, i.e. along OX: values of the dependent variable are measured along OY or OY'. The question of scales must next be considered. These may be varied to suit the particular case and should be chosen so as to fill the available space to the greatest possible extent, and at the same time lend themselves to easy computation. Refer now to Figure 12. There are twelve values of the independent variable to be illustrated. If the origin is taken as the first value, i.e. January, and the other values at distances of half an inch from each other, most of the available space along the horizontal axis will be used. The values of the dependent variable vary from £1,000 to £3,200, but in order to keep the value of the sales in true relation to each other, the scale should preferably start at zero. (This is not essential, however.) If now every half-inch is taken as representing £200, the vertical scale will be as shown. In the vertical direction each one-tenth of an inch now represents £40.

The fixing or locating of points which represent the values of the two variables is known as plotting, and is carried out as follows. For January the sales figure is £2,300. The reading on the horizontal scale corresponding with January is found, and then the vertical distance corresponding with £2,300 from the first reading is located. This gives point A, and this is the first point on the graph. Next, the point for February, £1,000, is decided upon. This will be vertically above the point representing February on the horizontal scale and at a distance representing £1,000 from it, i.e. point B. Point C represents the March reading £2,500, and so on. The points are then joined giving the line chart which represents the variation in the value of the monthly sales.

NOTE.—I. Only one quadrant, the first, is required for this graph; there is, therefore, no object in showing the other three.

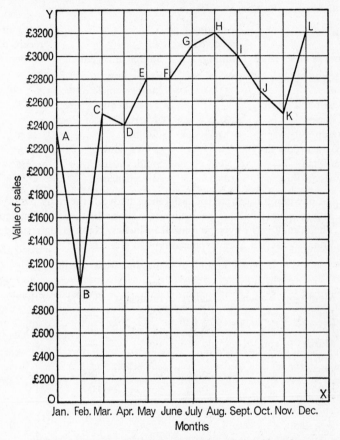

Fig. 12. *Graph representing the value of monthly sales*

Reference to the text shows that each of the above squares is taken as representing a $\frac{1}{2}''$ square.

2. Along the horizontal scale months are shown as the independent variable. The independent variable might, however, be capable of expression in actual figures, e.g. ages might be plotted along the horizontal scale, and the number of persons of these ages along the vertical.

STUDENT WORK

1. Draw a diagram to show the relative amounts of revenue obtained from various sources for the financial year 1934–35, from the following figures:

Source of revenue	Amount received in million £'s	Source of revenue	Amount received in million £'s
Income tax	228·9	Excise duty	104·6
Surtax	51·2	Motor vehicle duty (Exchequer share)	5·1
Death and estate duties	81·4	Net receipts of Post Office	12·3
Stamp duty	24·1	Crown lands	1·3
Excess profits duty	2·3	Sundry loans	4·4
Land tax	0·8	Miscellaneous	15·1
Customs duty	185·1		

2. On one graph illustrate the differences between the rainy period in a Monsoon and Mediterranean climate as shown by the following figures. The rainfall is the average rainfall in inches. Naples, Algiers and San Francisco have a Mediterranean type of climate.

Average rainfall in inches in various towns

Month	Naples	Algiers	San Francisco	Bombay	Lake Tsana Ethiopia
Jan.	3·5	4·0	5·0	—	0·5
Feb.	3·8	4·0	4·0	—	0·5
March	3·0	4·0	3·0	—	0·5
April	2·5	2·0	2·0	—	1·0
May	1·5	2·0	1·0	0·5	2·0
June	1·5	1·0	—	21·0	4·0
July	0·5	—	—	25·0	8·0
Aug.	1·5	—	—	15·0	12·0
Sept.	2·5	1·0	—	11·0	4·0
Oct.	4·5	3·0	1·0	2·0	2·0
Nov.	5·0	4·0	3·0	0·5	0·5
Dec.	4·5	5·0	5·0	—	0·5

3. The amount of a sum of money left at Compound Interest is given by the formula $A = P(1 + \frac{r}{100})^n$ where A is the amount, P the principal, r the rate per cent, and n the number of years. Calculate the respective

figures to which £100 would amount in 5, 10, 15, 20, and 25 years at 3 per cent per annum. Plot a graph to illustrate these results and then obtain by interpolation the amounts of £100 at the end of 7, 14, and 21 years.

4. Plot a graph to illustrate the variations in the value of British imports and exports from the following figures:

Year and quarter		Imports	Exports	Year and quarter		Imports	Exports
1927	1st	289·5	170·5	1931	3rd	191·0	93·2
	2nd	261·5	171·9		4th	224·3	98·2
	3rd	258·1	176·2	1932	1st	177·3	92·3
	4th	286·3	190·6		2nd	154·2	94·7
1928	1st	276·5	181·9		3rd	149·7	84·1
	2nd	261·3	173·3		4th	169·5	93·9
	3rd	256·7	179·7	1933	1st	146·5	89·7
	4th	280·8	188·6		2nd	148·6	56·6
1929	1st	275·9	181·2		3rd	155·6	93·1
	2nd	268·3	177·6		4th	175·2	99·5
	3rd	268·6	184·7	1934	1st	168·8	94·7
	4th	298·3	185·9		2nd	164·3	95·0
1930	1st	259·0	164·1		3rd	164·1	99·3
	2nd	233·4	140·7		4th	182·9	106·9
	3rd	224·9	136·3	1935	1st	164·4	105·5
	4th	239·8	129·7		2nd	166·1	101·0
1931	1st	192·5	103·3		3rd	168·4	105·3
	2nd	189·6	95·8		4th	202·7	114·1

5. Draw a diagram to illustrate the percentage unemployment among insured workpeople aged 16–64 in the various Administrative Districts for October 1935:

District	% Unemployment
Country as a whole	14·6
London	7·7
South-Eastern	7·6
South-Western	11·0
Midlands	9·8
North-Eastern	19·1
North-Western	19·0
Scotland	20·1
Wales	30·9
North Ireland	23·4

6. The following statistics show the relative value of Railway Traffic
Receipts for Goods Traffic and the Board of Trade Index Number of
Industrial Production. In each case the figures for 1924 are taken as

Year and quarter	Railway traffic goods 1924 = 100	Industrial production 1924 = 100	Year and quarter	Railway traffic goods 1924 = 100	Industrial production 1924 = 100
1928 1st	101·1	109·3	1932 1st	80·3	95·0
2nd	92·8	103·6	2nd	74·2	94·3
3rd	93·4	100·2	3rd	69·4	87·4
4th	97·2	108·4	4th	77·0	95·0
1929 1st	100·3	110·6	1933 1st	75·5	94·8
2nd	97·6	112·0	2nd	70·3	96·7
3rd	97·2	110·7	3rd	72·2	96·8
4th	100·2	114·0	4th	82·4	105·0
1930 1st	99·6	111·0	1934 1st	83·0	105·7
2nd	90·0	103·1	2nd	75·9	104·6
3rd	86·9	99·5	3rd	75·6	103·2
4th	92·5	99·0	4th	82·3	111·9
1931 1st	87·5	94·6	1935 1st	81·7	113·0
2nd	82·4	92·1	2nd	75·9	111·5
3rd	80·9	89·3	3rd	75·1	110·8
4th	85·0	97·3	4th	85·4	120·7

100. Plot the figures on one graph. Do the graphs show any degree of
correlation? If so to what do you ascribe the correlation? (From the
Ministry of Labour Gazette, February 1936.)

Chapter 6

Frequency Distributions

IN the course of our discussion on tabulation, we saw that the special name of *frequency table* was given to a type of table which showed how frequently a particular item in a group occurred, and in our last chapter we indicated certain ways in which these frequency distributions, as they are called, can be illustrated graphically. Although frequency distributions really form part of the statistical methods discussed under the headings of tabulation and diagrammatic representation, they form so important a section of statistical work that it is desirable to develop this section a little further.

For the purpose of reviewing what has already been said about frequency tables and for the purpose of adding to our knowledge of the problem, let us assume that a certain business wishes to analyse its sales. The firm in question manufactures various kinds of steel tubes and the invoice copies contain a record of the weight of the tubes sold, as well as their value and price per ton. The first step in the analysis will be to set down the amount sold at the various prices obtained for it. We can imagine two employees working on the task, the first reading through the invoice copies and calling out the price per ton and the weight sold at that price, and the other writing down the information he hears. The latter will probably find it most convenient to write down, in order, every possible price per ton, from the lowest which occurs to the highest, and then as the items are called out, write down the output alongside the corresponding price. If this is done, a table somewhat as overleaf will be the first result.

The foregoing method of arranging the items is known as *arraying*. Without any totals being inserted it would appear that the most usual price per ton is £36, as at this price the row of figures is the widest. It is fairly clear from this arrangement that the number of times each item

53

Price per ton £	Amounts sold (in tons)
20	1, 3, 2
21	2, 3, 2, 1
22	2, 5, 3, 2, 5
23	1, 2, 3, 2, 7
24	2, 5, 3, 2, 7
25	1, 12, 3, 1, 1, 2, 1
26	2, 5, 7, 2, 1, 8
27	2, 1, 6, 5, 5, 2, 6
28	1, 6, 10, 5, 1, 1, 2, 3, 2
29	2, 5, 7, 4, 3, 2, 2, 5, 3, 2
30	2, 3, 6, 4, 3, 2, 3, 5, 3, 2, 3, 2
31	6, 1, 3, 4, 2, 7, 6, 5, 3, 3, 2, 2, 2, 4
32	2, 7, 7, 3, 2, 5, 4, 3, 3, 2, 5, 5, 2, 3, 4
33	3, 3, 7, 8, 8, 2, 5, 4, 2, 2, 3, 2, 2, 2, 2, 4, 1
34	3, 3, 5, 6, 6, 6, 2, 4, 3, 5, 2, 3, 4, 2, 2, 4, 2
35	5, 5, 2, 1, 3, 8, 7, 1, 3, 3, 10, 3, 10, 3, 7, 5, 3, 1
36	6, 7, 2, 1, 3, 5, 2, 2, 1, 4, 3, 2, 2, 10, 3, 3, 2, 7, 5, 5
37	3, 2, 6, 10, 2, 1, 7, 2, 2, 3, 5, 2, 2, 3, 5, 5, 3, 2, 6
38	2, 4, 3, 3, 3, 5, 5, 4, 3, 2, 1, 7, 2, 3, 10, 5, 3
39	3, 5, 3, 4, 3, 2, 1, 5, 5, 3, 5, 2, 3, 7, 7
40	2, 3, 5, 7, 3, 2, 1, 3, 5, 6, 2, 7, 3, 7
41	2, 1, 1, 10, 7, 3, 5, 3, 2, 5, 2, 3, 7, 1
42	3, 1, 2, 6, 5, 5, 2, 2, 3, 7, 5, 3, 4
43	1, 2, 7, 7, 3, 3, 5, 6, 3, 3, 3, 3, 3
44	5, 2, 1, 3, 1, 2, 5, 7, 5, 3, 3, 9, 2, 1
45	2, 5, 5, 3, 3, 5, 2, 3, 7, 6, 5, 2, 2, 2
46	5, 2, 1, 3, 5, 2, 7, 3, 1, 7, 3, 5, 3, 3
47	1, 3, 7, 6, 3, 5, 2, 3, 7, 3, 3, 4
48	2, 5, 3, 3, 5, 2, 3, 10, 5, 2
49	1, 5, 6, 2, 5, 2, 5, 6, 6
50	3, 2, 3, 10, 5, 3, 7
51	2, 2, 5, 3, 5, 3, 10
52	2, 3, 2, 5, 5, 5, 5
53	5, 1, 3, 2, 7, 7
54	7, 2, 3, 4, 4
55	3, 5, 5, 4
56	2, 2, 3, 3
57	3, 2, 3
58	2, 2
59	1, 1

occurs tends to increase with the price until the most usual price is reached, after which the number of occurrences tends to fall off again.

However, the analysis would not stop at that point. The totals for each price per ton would be found and the result set down in tabular form as follows:

Table 14. *Frequency table showing output of steel tubes*

Total output – 1,474 tons

Price per ton (Variable) £	Output in tons (Frequency)	Price per ton (Variable) £	Output in tons (Frequency)
20	6	40	56
21	8	41	52
22	17	42	48
23	15	43	49
24	19	44	49
25	21	45	52
26	25	46	50
27	27	47	47
28	31	48	40
29	35	49	38
30	38	50	33
31	50	51	30
32	57	52	27
33	60	53	25
34	62	54	20
35	80	55	17
36	75	56	10
37	71	57	8
38	62	58	4
39	58	59	2

The above table is another example of a *frequency distribution*, i.e. it is a *table showing successive values or sizes of a variable and the number of times each value or size occurs*. The number of times each value or size occurs is called the frequency of that value or size.

The frequency distribution given above has certainly helped forward the analysis, but the table is still too big for its significance to be very

C

clear. The eye cannot quickly look over the forty sets of figures nor can the mind grasp what they have to show. The next step in the analysis is a fairly obvious one. The table could be condensed by grouping the figures. It would probably occur to the two employees to make one group of each successive five items. The total output for the first five is 65 tons and the price varies from £20 to £24 per ton, for the next five the total is 139 tons and the price varies from £25 to £29, and so on.

Regrouped in this way, the following table would result:

Table 15. *Frequency table showing output of steel tubes*

Price per ton £	Output in tons
20–24 inclusive	65
25–29	139
30–34	267
35–39	346
40–44	254
45–49	227
50–54	135
55–59	41
	1,474 tons

The groups are equal in size and the group interval £5. As before, the number of items within each group is called the frequency of that group.

The above arrangement is by no means the only one which might be drawn up. For example, the groups might have been £20–25, £25–30, etc. One difficulty might arise here: the assistants might not know what to do with the items on the margin of the group, i.e. outputs at £25, £30, £35, etc., per ton. One way of getting over this difficulty would be to divide the output at these marginal figures between the two groups which contain them. For example, the output at a price of £25 per ton would be divided between the groups £20–25 and £25–30, giving 10 to the first and 11 to the second. The output at £30 per ton would be divided between the two groups £25–30, and £30–35, giving 19 tons to each. It is true that there will be some little loss of accuracy in so apportioning the items, but it will not be serious for all practical purposes.

When this has been completely carried out, the frequency distribution would be as follows:

Table 16. *Output of steel tubes*

Price per ton £	Output in tons
20–25	75
25–30	148
30–35	288
35–40	334
40–45	252
45–50	217
50–55	127
55–60	33
	1,474 tons

On the whole, the arrangement in Table 16 will be found to be rather more suitable for further analysis than the one given in Table 15. From it, still another arrangement is possible. Instead of stating the output at a price £20–25 per ton, the output could be stated at £22½ (i.e. the middle point of the interval) per ton. Again, since it is likely there will be just about as many items above £22½ as below it, in the group £20–25, the new arrangement concedes little in the way of accuracy. The frequency table would then be:

Table 16A

Price per ton £	Output in tons
22½	75
27½	148
32½	288
etc., etc.	

DIAGRAMMATIC ILLUSTRATION OF THE FOREGOING FREQUENCY DISTRIBUTIONS

We have already seen how a frequency distribution may be represented by a histogram, and also by a frequency curve or frequency polygon. Fig. 13 shows the histogram and frequency polygon for the distribution we have been considering. The latter is obtained by plotting the mid-interval figures. The frequency polygon has an advantage over the histogram in that, for the purpose of comparison, two frequency polygons can be plotted on one sheet, whereas it would be difficult to do this with histograms for the simple reason that they would overlap a great

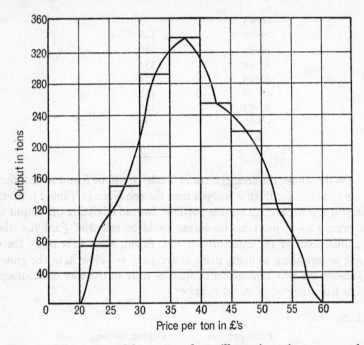

Fig. 13. *Histogram and frequency polygon illustrating price per ton and output of steel tubes for Tables 16 and 16A*

deal. Again, frequency polygons may be smoothed, i.e. the curve made more regular in shape, by smoothing out irregular fluctuations. Smoothing brings out tendencies at the expense of actual occurrences. If the data shown by a frequency polygon consist of economic facts, as in the case we are considering, it is only permissible to eliminate minor irregularities. If the data consist of natural or chance phenomena, which, if sufficient observations were taken, would give a symmetrical curve, a greater degree of smoothing may be undertaken (see later in this chapter).

Fig. 14 shows a smoothed frequency curve for the foregoing frequency distribution, and also a smoothed curve which can be taken to represent the corresponding distribution in the output of steel tubes for the previous year.

The practical value of frequency curves becomes immediately ob-

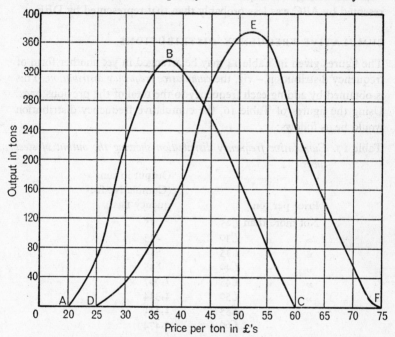

Fig. 14. *Frequency curves showing output and prices of steel tubes in two successive years*

Curve ABC: Smooth curve for distribution given in Table 16.

vious from Fig. 14. The following points may be gathered from this diagram:

1. Since the area enclosed by curve DEF is greater than that enclosed by ABC, the output represented by the first curve is greater than that represented by the second.

2. The lowest price per ton received in the case of the year's output represented by curve ABC was about £20, in the case of the previous year, it was about £25. The highest prices per ton were about £60 and £75 respectively.

3. The price at which most tubes were sold was about £37½ in the case of the figures represented by curve ABC. In the other case it was about £52. (These two figures represent the highest points attained by the curves.)

4. The average price per ton received for the year's output represented by ABC was less probably than that represented by DEF.

CUMULATIVE FREQUENCY DISTRIBUTIONS

The figures given in Table 14 may be arranged in yet another form of frequency distribution – viz. the *cumulative frequency distribution*. This is obtained by adding each frequency to the total of the previous ones. Using the figures of Table 16, the cumulative frequency distribution would be as follows:

Table 17. *Cumulative frequency distribution showing the output of steel tubes*

Price per ton			Output in tons (Cumulative frequency figs.)
Not more than		£25	75
,,	,,	£30	223
,,	,,	£35	511
,,	,,	£40	845
,,	,,	£45	1,097
,,	,,	£50	1,314
,,	,,	£55	1,441
,,	,,	£60	1,474

The cumulative frequency of 'Not more than £30' is obtained by adding the output at £20–25 per ton to the output at £25–30 per ton; and the figure for not more than £35, by adding the output at £30–35 per ton to the total of the other two, and so on.

Just as the frequency distribution may be illustrated graphically, so may the cumulative distribution. The curve for the latter is known as an 'Ogive' or Cumulative Frequency Curve. Fig. 15 shows the ogive for the figures given in Table 17.

Originally the term 'ogive' was restricted to the symmetrical S-shaped curve illustrated in Fig. 18 at the end of this chapter. But it has long been generally used to describe any cumulative frequency curve.

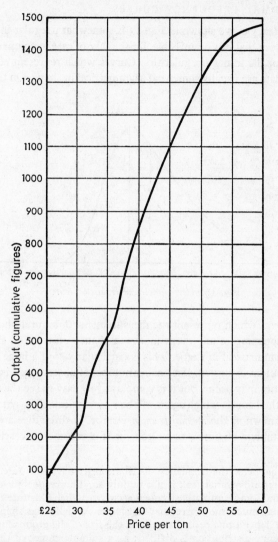

Fig. 15. *Ogive or Cumulative Frequency Curve for Table 17*

THE NORMAL FREQUENCY CURVES

The frequency curve shown in Fig. 13 is somewhat irregular in shape.[1] We have seen that it is permissible, for the sake of ease in comparison, to smooth out the minor irregularities. Curves which represent economic or social data are usually somewhat asymmetrical in shape. On the other

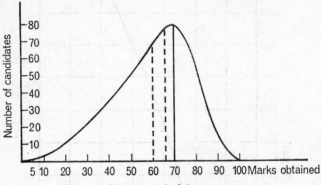

Fig. 16. *Unsymmetrical frequency curve*

hand, curves which represent the measurements of natural phenomena or the happening of any event in which chance plays a full share are usually symmetrical in shape. This is particularly so if a large number of observations is plotted. If a smaller number of observations is plotted, irregularities may occur, but it is comparatively easy to see the shape of the smoothed curve, which again will be symmetrical. This symmetrical curve is known as the *normal frequency curve*. If three dice are shaken a large number of times, say 1,000, or if 1,000 men are selected at

---

[1] As it happens, the frequency distribution we have illustrated in Fig. 13, although unsymmetrical, is not unduly so. The reader must be prepared to find some cumulative frequency curves, which illustrate economic phenomena, much more irregular in shape. Actually the shape of the curve will depend to a certain extent on the size of the groups into which the frequency distribution is divided; by a suitable choice of the size of the groups, certain irregularities may be hidden. Fig. 16 illustrates a frequency curve of a slightly more unsymmetrical type; in this case we have the diagrammatic representation of marks obtained in an examination.

random and their heights and weights taken or their intelligence measured, the results obtained will give normal frequency curves.

Fig. 17 represents the results obtained by shaking three dice a large number of times and the curve is an example of a normal frequency curve. Note that the curve is symmetrical about the vertical line from the base to the highest point of the curve.

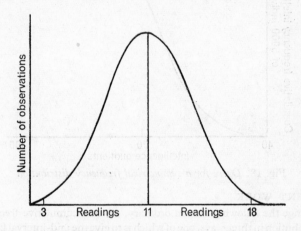

Fig. 17. *Frequency curve obtained by throwing three dice 1,000 times*

Along the vertical scale is the number of times each reading, 3, 4 ... 18, etc., occurs, and along the horizontal the readings 3–18. If the experiment is performed, 11 will probably occur most often and the diagram is symmetrical about a vertical line drawn from 11 on the horizontal scale to the curve.

The normal frequency curve is sometimes called the *probability curve* because it is the one which is obtained when the frequency distribution of a variable, the value of which depends upon the combination of independent chances, is plotted.

THE NORMAL OGIVE

The ogive which is obtained from a symmetrical frequency distribution is illustrated below (Fig. 18).

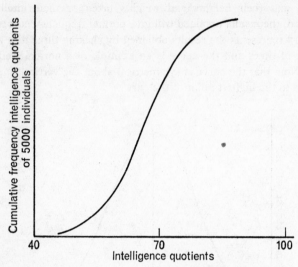

Fig. 18. *Ogive for a symmetrical frequency distribution*

STUDENT WORK

1. Arrange the following into an ordinary, i.e. non-cumulative frequency distribution in three ways, one of which is to give the mid-interval figures:

Marks obtained by 470 Candidates in an Examination

Marks obtained	No. of candidates obtaining these marks	Marks obtained	No. of candidates obtaining these marks
0	2	38	40
3	1	40	35
4	5	42	30
9	6	45	22
10	9	48	20
14	10	50	17
18	12	52	12
20	14	55	8
22	18	56	7
25	20	58	4
27	24	61	3
31	30	62	2
32	35	64	1
34	40	65	1
36	42		

2. Using one of your frequency distributions from Question 1 draw up a cumulative frequency distribution.

3. Draw the frequency polygon, the histogram and the ogive which represent the frequency distributions you have drawn up (for Questions 1 and 2).

4. What do you understand by the following terms: (a) continuous and discrete frequencies; (b) the normal frequency curve?

Chapter 7

Statistical Averages

AFTER drawing up the frequency tables showing output and price per ton of steel tubes, the next step in our analysis of the figures is a fairly obvious one – viz. the calculation of the average price per ton received for the tubes. While tabulation and graphical representation have considerably advanced our knowledge of the real significance of the statistical data we have been considering, they have by no means completed it. Tabulation arranges facts in logical order and helps their understanding and comparison, but often the groups tabulated are still too large for their characteristics to be readily grasped. Moreover, any comparisons which may be made from tabulated results are merely verbal. What is desired is a numerical expression which summarizes the characteristics of the group. Averages serve this purpose. An *average* then is a single figure which sums up the characteristics of a whole group of figures. A statistical average is sometimes called a 'type', partly to avoid confusion between the various uses of the word and also to emphasize that in some ways it is typical of a group or series.

In ordinary language, the word average may mean normal. We speak of 'the average student', with no idea of expressing his characteristics in a numerical way; we merely mean the typical or normal student. In statistics, types or averages are numerical expressions. They give precise information, not information of a vague general kind. They are exceedingly useful in statistical analysis, so much so that statistics has been called the 'science of averages' – an indication of their importance in our study.

THE ARITHMETIC AVERAGE OR ARITHMETIC MEAN (A.M.)
The Simple Arithmetic Mean

There are several kinds of averages or types used in statistical work, but we shall consider first the familiar simple arithmetic mean, obtained by adding up all the items and dividing the result by the number of items. Thus the mean of 3, 5, 7, 9 is $\frac{24}{4}$ or 6; the mean wage for the following wages, 35s., 50s., 55s., and 65s. is 51s. 3d.

This is the average of everyday life and is the one most commonly used. When the average and the number of items is known, the total can be calculated.

$$\text{Thus the Arithmetic Mean} = \frac{\text{The total of the items}}{\text{The number of the items}}$$

The total of the items = the arithmetic mean of the items × the number of the items. For example, if the mean of 4 numbers is 17, then the total of the numbers = 17 × 4 = 68.

The Weighted Arithmetic Mean

The simple arithmetic mean is really an example of a wider kind of average which we now proceed to describe. Suppose that in the foregoing example, there had been not just one person receiving each of the wages, 35s., 50s., 55s. and 65s., but a different number, thus:

> 3 men receive a wage of 35s.
> 5   „   „   „   50s.
> 4   „   „   „   55s.
> 2   „   „   „   65s.

Clearly in this case a true mean can only be obtained by making due allowance for the varying number of persons receiving the wages.

> The total wages paid are: 3 × 35s. = £5   5   0
> 5 × 50s. = 12 10   0
> 4 × 55s. = 11   0   0
> 2 × 65s. =   6 10   0
> _____
> £35   5   0

and the number of men 3 + 5 + 4 + 2 = 14.

$$\text{The A.M. then is } \frac{£35 \ 5s. \ 0d.}{14} = £2 \ 10s. \ 4d. \text{ approx.}$$

The arithmetic mean obtained in this way is called a *weighted mean* (or average), because each item has been given its proper importance or weight in its calculation. We can illustrate the calculation of the weighted average by one or two further examples.

A firm in the Steel Tube Trade divides its output into four classes – Steam pipes, Boiler tubes, Locomotive boiler tubes, and Other cold drawn tubes. The price per ton obtained for each class is given in column ii of the following table.

Table 18

(i) Class	(ii) Price per ton £	(iii) Output in tons	(iv) Relative proportions	(v) Product of ii and iv
Steam pipes	52	165	5½	286
Boiler tubes	38	30	1	38
Loco. boiler tubes	30	150	5	150
Other cold drawn tubes	45	210	7	315
Total			18½	789

In calculating an average price it would, as we have shown, be incorrect to add the four prices and divide by 4. We must multiply each price by a figure – called the weight – which represents its importance or its contribution to the total effectiveness. This weight may be absolute or relative, that is, we may use the actual output in tons or simpler figures (percentages would do) which show the relative proportions of output. In this example we divide each output by the lowest (30 tons) and thus obtain the relative proportions shown in column iv.

The weighted average or mean

$$= \frac{\text{Total of prods. of cols. ii and iv}}{\text{Total of col. iv}} = \frac{789}{18\frac{1}{2}} = £42 \text{ } 11s. \text{ } 0d.$$

In this example, the exact weights can be determined, since the actual production is known. Such precision is not always possible, but relative importance can usually be estimated and weights assigned. Thus in the calculation of the cost-of-living figure of the urban working classes carried out by the Ministry of Labour, where a weighted average was used to determine the percentage increase in the cost as compared with 1914, both the percentage increase and weights are estimated. (We shall deal with this case in detail in a later chapter.)

In a Commercial School with which the writer was connected, the marks awarded in each subject are stated as a percentage, but the subjects are weighted in order to obtain the final percentage mark. The weights assigned are directly related to the amount of time spent in their study. Thus, shorthand, typewriting, and arithmetic each have a weight of 4, book-keeping has 3, history 1, and so on. The percentage marks in each subject are multiplied by the weight assigned and the result divided by the total of the weights to give the final percentage mark.

The Calculation of the Arithmetic Mean from a Frequency Distribution

We shall now return to our analysis of the price and output of steel tubes and proceed to calculate the average price per ton obtained for the tubes. For the purpose of this calculation, we assume that the output in each class is sold at the central or mid-interval price for that class – an assumption which introduces only a slight error where the numbers in each class are large. The figures are given in Table 16A; we repeat them here in columns i and ii of Table 19.

Table 19. *Calculation of the arithmetic mean of the selling price of steel tubes*

(i) Price per ton (central prices) £	(ii) Output in tons	(iii) Deviations from assumed mean	(iv) Products of columns ii and iii
22½	75	−3	−225 ⎫
27½	148	−2	−296 ⎬ −809
32½	288	−1	−288 ⎭
37½	334	0	
42½	252	+1	+252 ⎫
47½	217	+2	+434 ⎪
52½	127	+3	+381 ⎬ +1,199
57½	33	+4	+132 ⎭
	1,474		

The arithmetic mean can be found by multiplying columns i and ii together, finding the total, and dividing this by the total output, i.e. 1,474 tons. This would be a long and tedious process, particularly with a large number of items, and we can shorten the work considerably by making use of the fact that the algebraic sum of the deviations from the arithmetic mean is zero. For example, the arithmetic mean of 5, 7, 8, and 12 is $\frac{32}{4} = 8$, and the deviations are -3, -1, 0, and $+4 = 0$.

The procedure is as follows: (1) Assume any convenient figure as the arithmetic mean; (2) Calculate the average of the deviations from the assumed mean; (3) Add or deduct this average from the assumed mean.

Applying this method to the figures given in Table 19, we assume the arithmetic mean to be £37½, for although any level might be chosen, it is convenient to use one near the true arithmetic mean, which is likely to be somewhere near the most common group.

Thus the average deviations from £37½

$$= \frac{-809 + 1,199}{1,474} \text{ units of £5 (the group interval)}$$

$$= + \frac{£390 \times 5}{1,474}$$

$$= + £1 \cdot 323$$

$$\therefore \text{ Arithmetic Mean} = £37\tfrac{1}{2} + £1 \cdot 323$$

$$= £38 \cdot 823$$

$$= £38 \text{ 16s. 0d. roughly.}$$

Had the average deviation been a minus quantity, it would have been deducted from the assumed arithmetic mean.

This short-cut method can also be used where the group intervals are unequal, but it is necessary in this case to express the deviations in terms of the actual units employed. Table 20 shows the calculation of the arithmetic mean in an example where the group intervals are unequal.

Advantages and Limitations of the Arithmetic Mean

The arithmetic mean is, as we have said, the most familiar kind of average. It is easy to understand and fairly easy to calculate. It can also be utilized for further calculation, since the arithmetic mean multiplied by the number of items gives the aggregate. It is not, however, equally useful in every circumstance and in certain circumstances it may be somewhat misleading. A retailer of boots and shoes is not particularly interested in the mean size of men's feet; if this were known, it might not represent any stock size in boots and shoes at all, but be some point

Table 20. *Distribution of dividends paid by 400 companies*

Dividend (%) (mid-interval fig.)	No. of companies	Deviation from assumed mean	Total deviation	
0	28	$-4\frac{1}{4}$	-119	
$1\frac{1}{2}$	6	$-2\frac{3}{4}$	$-16\frac{1}{2}$	$\left.\right\}\,-208$
$3\frac{1}{4}$	37	-1	-37	
$3\frac{3}{4}$	71	$-\frac{1}{2}$	$-35\frac{1}{2}$	
$4\frac{1}{4}$	64	0		
$4\frac{3}{4}$	53	$+\frac{1}{2}$	$+26\frac{1}{2}$	
$5\frac{1}{2}$	60	$+1\frac{1}{4}$	$+75$	$\left.\right\}\,+412\frac{3}{4}$
7	48	$+2\frac{3}{4}$	132	
$9\frac{1}{2}$	29	$+5\frac{1}{4}$	$152\frac{1}{4}$	
11	4	$+6\frac{3}{4}$	27	

$$\text{Arithmetic Mean is then } 4\tfrac{1}{4}\% + \frac{204\tfrac{3}{4}}{400}\%$$
$$= 4\tfrac{1}{4}\% + \tfrac{1}{2}\% \text{ approx.}$$
$$= 4\tfrac{3}{4} \text{ approx.}$$

between two stock sizes. Again the average size of families, if worked out as an arithmetic mean, might give a result of 3·4 children per family. Here the arithmetic mean, although a useful piece of information, does not represent an actual item at all. But the greatest disadvantage of the arithmetic mean is that it is unduly affected by extreme items. To quote a possible example. Suppose the treasurer of a village church is giving his annual report on the collections during the year. He reports that the total collections received were £780 and therefore the average weekly collections amounted to £15. If, however, on one particular Sunday a rich man who was staying in the village had attended church and placed £200 in the box, this single item would have raised the average by nearly £4 a week. But to say that the average collections were £15 a week would be misleading. If, therefore, extreme items do occur, it is better to look elsewhere for an average, and we now proceed to consider the other averages in detail.

THE MEDIAN

In any distribution in which all the items are arranged in ascending or descending order of magnitude, the median is the one which is half-way

along the series, and in general there will be an equal number of items
both below and above the median. Thus, if there are twenty-one pupils
in a class and we wish to know the median height, the heights must be
arranged either in ascending or descending order of magnitude and then
the eleventh reading will be the median height.

Arranged in order of magnitude the heights, in inches, might be:
$55\frac{1}{2}$, 57, $57\frac{1}{2}$, 58, $58\frac{1}{2}$, 59, $59\frac{1}{2}$, 60, $60\frac{1}{2}$, 61, $61\frac{1}{2}$, 62, 63, $64\frac{1}{2}$, $64\frac{1}{2}$, 65, $65\frac{1}{2}$,
66, 66, 67, 69, and the median height is $61\frac{1}{2}$, i.e. the eleventh item. If
there is an even number of items, then the median is half-way between
the two middle ones and it is found by taking the average of these two
items.

Calculation of the Median in the case of a Frequency Distribution

Since we require the middle item, or the two middle items, to calculate
the median, we must use the cumulative figures, i.e. arrange the figures
in the form of a cumulative frequency distribution. We will find the
median for the prices of steel tubes and use the figures given in Table 17,
Chapter 6.

Table 21. *Calculation of the median value of the price per ton of steel*
tubes

Price per ton	Output in tons (cumulative figs.)	
Not more than £25	75	
,, ,, 30	223	$226\frac{1}{2}$
,, ,, 35	511	
	Median corresponds with	$737\frac{1}{2}$ item
,, ,, 40	845	
,, ,, 45	1,097	$107\frac{1}{2}$
,, ,, 50	1,314	
,, ,, 55	1,441	
,, ,, 60	1,474	

Since the total output is 1,474, the median price per ton will correspond to the average of items 737 and 738, i.e. $737\frac{1}{2}$. A glance at the
frequency distribution shows that the median price per ton must be
between £35 and £40. Its actual value can be obtained by interpolation.
Since $737\frac{1}{2}$ is nearer to 845 than it is to 511, the median will be nearer
£40 than £35. If we divide the difference between £35 and 40, i.e. £5,

in the ratio of $226\frac{1}{2}$ to $107\frac{1}{2}$, we shall arrive at the figure to be added to £35 to give the median. We take the ratios $226\frac{1}{2}$ and $107\frac{1}{2}$ because they represent the differences between the frequencies at the above prices, and the median price. In the same way, if we divide £5 in the ratio of $107\frac{1}{2}$ to $226\frac{1}{2}$, and take the result from £40, we shall arrive at the same figure for the median.

$$\text{The Median price is then } £35 + £\frac{5 \times 226\frac{1}{2}}{226\frac{1}{2} + 107\frac{1}{2}}$$

$$= £35 + £\frac{1132\frac{1}{2}}{334} = £35 + £3\cdot393$$

$$= £38\cdot393 = £38 \; 8s. \; 0d. \text{ roughly};$$

$$\text{or Median price} \quad = £40 - £\frac{5 \times 107\frac{1}{2}}{226\frac{1}{2} + 107\frac{1}{2}}$$

$$= £40 - £1\cdot607$$

$$= £38\cdot393 = £38 \; 8s. \; 0d. \text{ roughly.}$$

Computation of the Median by Graphical Methods

The median can be obtained graphically from the ogive, or cumulative frequency curve. When this curve is plotted, the reading which corresponds with the middle items gives the value of the median. The larger the scale of the graph, the more accurate will be the result. See Fig. 19.

THE QUARTILES

The median is an average or type which depends for its value on its position. Other positions in the group may be taken as types, the most common being the quartiles. These divide the group into four equal parts; half the items, or half the extent of the values, lie between the quartiles. The item which corresponds with a position one-quarter the way along the distribution, is known as the *lower quartile* (Q_1), the item corresponding to the three-quarters position, as the *upper quartile* (Q_3). The quartiles may also be calculated or obtained graphically in the same way as the median.

Other position types are the deciles and percentiles, the former dividing the group into 10 equal parts, the latter into 100 equal parts. The method of finding these types is the same as for the quartiles and median.

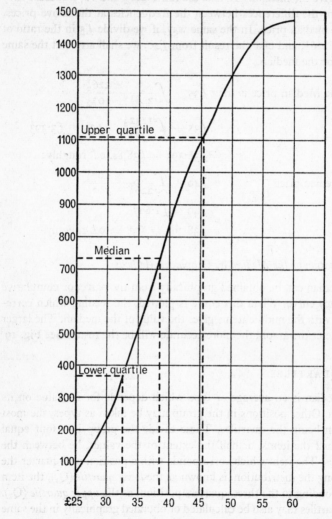

Fig. 19. *Cumulative frequency curve for Table 21*

THE MODE (OR NORM)

In estimating his requirements for the next year, the retailer of boots and shoes may not find the mean or median size of great use to him. He will find most useful the size which is most usually purchased, e.g. size 8. Naturally he will then stock more of that size than any other. The item which occurs most frequently in any distribution is called the *mode*; it is the most fashionable item in the series or group. When we consider what is normally meant by the term 'the average man', it is reasonable to suggest that it is the idea of the mode, or most usual type of man, which is implied.

The mode, being the typical item, may sum up the characteristics of the group more satisfactorily than either the arithmetic mean or median. Had the church treasurer of our example on page 71 given the mode, or the most usual collection, a clearer picture of the state of affairs would have been given than that implied by the arithmetic mean.

Calculation of the Mode

When the frequency distribution is given in the form that it occurs in Table 14, i.e. each measurement or value is stated separately, and the frequency distribution for each measurement is given, then the value of the mode is obvious. It is the measurement which occurs most often; in the case of Table 14 its value is £35. If, however, the exact measurements or readings are not given, the mode is more difficult to locate. Let us repeat once more the frequency distribution for the price and output of steel tubes.

Selling price per ton £	Mid-interval price per ton £	Output in tons
20–25	22½	75
25–30	27½	148
30–35	32½	288
35–40	37½	334
40–45	42½	252
45–50	47½	217
50–55	52½	127
55–60	57½	33

The most usual selling price is £35–40 per ton, with a mid-interval of £37½. Should this be taken as the mode? Actually we have seen that the mode is £35 and if the grouping were arranged so that the limits were finer, e.g. £20-22, £22-24, etc., we might find that the most common group would be £34-36. It will be seen that in such cases it may be difficult to locate the mode with precision but an idea of its value may be obtained by considering the groups on either side of the modal one.

Price	Output	
£		
30-35	288	46
35-40	334	334
40-45	252	82

Since the frequency in the group below the modal one is greater than that above it, it would suggest that the mode is less than £37½. If we divide £5 (the frequency interval) in the ratio of the differences between the modal frequency and the two adjoining frequencies, we shall get an idea of the extent to which it is less than £40.

$$\text{The mode is then } £40 - £\frac{82 \times 5}{82 + 46} = £40 - £\frac{410}{128}$$
$$= £40 - £3 \cdot 2$$
$$= £36 \text{ 16s. od.}$$

It will readily be seen that if the frequencies on either side of the modal group are equal, then the mode will probably be near the middle point of the modal group.

Location of the Mode by Graphical Methods

If the frequency distribution is plotted, the modal value is the abscissa of the highest point of the graph. In the last chapter, Fig. 17 shows the graphical representation of the results obtained by throwing three dice. The highest point of the frequency curve corresponds with a reading of 11, thus 11 is then the modal value. If the frequency curve represents economic statistics, e.g. wage rates, two modes may be indicated. The existence of the second modal value shows that the frequencies decline after the first modal point has been reached and then increase for a time until the second modal point has been attained.

In certain circumstances the mode is the most useful of all averages, especially when it is important to ascertain the most typical item of the group. The mode is easily understood, and like the median, it is entirely unaffected by extremes, and only the items in the centre of the frequency need be known for its calculation. On the other hand, the mode is often ill defined and its position difficult to ascertain with mathematical precision. Like the median, too, it is unsuitable for arithmetic or algebraic manipulation.

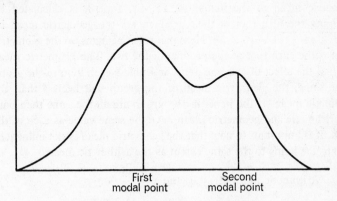

Fig. 20. *Curve with two modal points*

The Differences between the Arithmetic Mean, Median, and Mode

These three averages are those in most general use, but the particular one to be used will obviously depend on the objects of the inquiry. In the example of the steel tubes, the arithmetic mean would probably give the best idea of the value of the output for purposes of comparison with other years. Had there been an exceptional item having a considerable influence on the arithmetic mean, then the median would have been a more suitable type. And, as we have already seen (p. 75), if the typical or most common item is being sought, the mode will be used. Actually in this example the arithmetic mean and the median have nearly the same value and there is a small difference between these two and the mode. This is so because the frequency distribution is fairly symmetrical, i.e. it falls away evenly on either side of the highest point. Where the frequency distribution is perfectly symmetrical as in the example given in Chapter 6, the arithmetic mean, median, and mode have the same value. Where the curve is unsymmetrical or 'skewed', then the three values are different and the more pronounced the skewness, the greater the differences. In fact, we shall see later (Chapter 9) that these differences are used as the basis of measures of skewness.

THE GEOMETRIC MEAN (G.M.)

A further average used in statistical work is the *geometric mean*. This is the *n*th root of the product of the *n* items in the group. Thus the geometric mean of the items, 10, 12, 14, 16, 18, is calculated by obtaining the fifth root of their product, i.e. the geometric mean is: $\sqrt[5]{10 \times 12 \times 14 \times 16 \times 18}$. Here there are five items, so the geometric mean is the fifth root of the product of the five. The geometric mean modifies the effect of extreme items and unless each item in the group is the same, the geometric mean of the group will be less than the arithmetic mean. If the items in the group are all the same then both the arithmetic and geometric mean have the same value as each of the items. It is important to note that the geometric mean is not influenced by extreme items to the same extent as the arithmetic mean.

$$\text{Arithmetic mean of 15, 4, and 3} = \frac{22}{3} = 7 \cdot 3$$
$$\text{Geometric mean of 15, 4, and 3} = \sqrt[3]{15 \times 4 \times 3} = 5 \cdot 6.$$

This average is not widely used because of its difficulty of calculation. Its most important application is in the preparation of index numbers and we shall refer to it again in the chapter devoted to this topic. But even here we shall find that it is employed much less frequently than in prewar days.

STUDENT WORK

1. The following table shows the wages earned by males in a certain industry:

Weekly wage	Number of wage earners	Weekly wage	Number of wage earners
15s.–17s.	600	29s.–31s.	600
17s.–19s.	200	31s.–33s.	800
19s.–21s.	400	33s.–35s.	1,000
21s.–23s.	600	35s.–37s.	1,000
23s.–25s.	1,400	37s.–39s.	1,800
25s.–27s.	2,000	39s.–41s.	100
27s.–29s.	1,200		

Calculate the average wage (arithmetic mean) earned, the median wage, and the modal wage.

2. A firm wishes to fix a piece-work rate for its employees and to do this wishes to know the average number of operations performed per person per day. Observations are taken over a period with the following results:

Work-man	No. of operations performed on fourteen successive days													
A	85	87	86	92	93	90	82	98	96	82	82	70	98	90
B	90	85	80	79	92	90	87	86	93	92	95	90	93	95
C	87	86	86	87	85	90	93	92	90	89	88	88	90	91
D	100	97	97	95	95	93	98	100	98	97	95	93	92	94
E	87	86	91	98	95	94	89	88	87	94	95	91	90	88
F	93	92	92	90	95	94	90	97	95	95	94	94	94	93
G	88	100	97	84	88	90	92	97	85	87	87	90	92	95
H	100	100	88	89	97	97	98	89	92	93	97	97	96	94

(a) Arrange the above results as a frequency distribution having the following particulars:

Number of processes; number of observations.

(b) Calculate the average number of processes performed daily, i.e. the arithmetic mean, the median, and the mode.

(c) If the workmen had previously been paid a flat rate of 19s. 6d. a day, suggest a reasonable piece-rate price bearing in mind the results obtained in (b).

(d) Calculate the average number of daily processes performed by *each* workman; then find the average for the whole group and compare your answer with that obtained in (b).

3. The holdings of shares (nominal value, £1) in a certain company are as follows:

No. of shares held	No. of persons with these shares	No. of shares held	No. of persons with these shares
Under 50	80	300–350	28
50–100	142	350–400	15
100–150	110	400–450	9
150–200	75	450–500	7
200–250	52	500–550	3
250–300	38	550–600	2

Calculate the average holding of shares (i.e. arithmetic mean), the median holding and the modal holding. Which of these averages best sums up the position? Give your reasons.

4. In a certain examination the percentage marks obtained were as follows:

Percentages	No. of students obtaining these percentages	Percentages	No. of students obtaining these percentages
Under 5	—	50–55	332
5–10	3	55–60	275
10–15	37	60–65	112
15–20	45	65–70	75
20–25	87	70–75	37
25–30	137	75–80	20
30–35	177	80–85	12
35–40	212	85–90	4
40–45	270	90–95	1
45–50	337	95–100	1

Calculate the mean, median, mode, and both quartiles.

5. By using the figures in Table 20 (distribution of dividends paid by 400 companies) calculate the arithmetic mean, taking as your guess any other dividend than $4\frac{1}{4}$ per cent. Calculate also the median.

6. Calculate the average weight, the median weight, and the modal weight of 3,404 boys whose weight distribution is as follows (from Professor Bowley):

Weight in lb.	No. of boys	Weight in lb.	No. of boys
65–70	3	125–130	131
70–75	9	130–135	76
75–80	142	135–140	52
80–85	301	140–145	20
85–90	289	145–150	29
90–95	380	150–155	14
95–100	416	155–160	10
100–105	404	160–165	2
105–110	315	165–170	2
110–115	320	170–175	5
115–120	262	175–180	1
120–125	221		

7. In the particular school mentioned in Chapter 7, the 'weights' assigned to each subject taken are as follows: English 4, History 1, Geography 2, Commercial Arithmetic 4, Shorthand 4, Typing 4, Book-keeping 3, Commerce 2, Science 2, French 3, respectively.

Calculate the weighted average percentages for the following students:

Subject (initial only)	E.	H.	G.	A.	S.	T.	B.	C.	S.	F.
Student										
A percentages	76	73	81	80	75	74	80	79	56	54
B „	47	52	54	63	62	68	53	67	58	47
C „	35	39	53	48	47	40	51	50	49	53

8. Distinguish between the arithmetic mean, the median and the mode and give examples to show in which cases each is the most suitable.

9. The following table is given in Mr D. C. Jones's book on Statistics. It shows the wages earned by certain women tailors:

Wages	No. of women earning them	Wages	No. of women earning them
5s.–6s.	180	16s.–17s.	642
6s.–7s.	384	17s.–18s.	453
7s.–8s.	553	18s.–19s.	401
8s.–9s.	690	19s.–20s.	272
9s.–10s.	900	20s.–21s.	251
10s.–11s.	1,145	21s.–22s.	138
11s.–12s.	1,201	22s.–23s.	124
12s.–13s.	1,138	23s.–24s.	64
13s.–14s.	930	24s.–25s.	54
14s.–15s.	885	25s.–30s.	122
15s.–16s.	790		Note the last item

Calculate the mean, median, mode, and quartiles.

10. The buying costs (or expenses) of a large number of firms were found and expressed as a percentage of the gross profit. The costs were then weighted in proportion to the amount of sales made by each shop and the following arithmetic mean, median, and quartiles found for the group. What conclusions do you draw from the figures?

Arithmetic mean	Lower quartile	Median	Upper quartile
1·89%	1·92%	2·34%	2·86%

11. (a) Define the term 'the geometric mean' and state its characteristics.

(b) Calculate the geometric mean of the following items: 7·8, 5·6, 6·3, 5·7, 8·2, 20·8, 25·6.

Chapter 8

Dispersion or Variability

THE various kinds of averages considered in the last chapter sum up certain characteristics of a group: they may be typical items in the group, and as such, facilitate comparison between two groups. But before we can give a complete description of a group, we must know at least two other factors. We must know first, how the items in the group differ in size from each other and from the average, and second, how they are distributed about the average, i.e. whether there are more items above the average than below it, or vice versa. An actual example will make these points clearer. We take the case of two firms whose profits during ten consecutive years have been as follows:

Table 22. *Profits earned by two firms, A and B*

Year	Profits earned by Firm A	Profits earned by Firm B
	£	£
1925	24,000	40,000
1926	20,000	5,000
1927	23,500	22,500
1928	26,200	38,000
1929	27,000	45,000
1930	27,000	30,000
1931	24,000	15,000
1932	24,000	Loss 2,000
1933	26,000	10,000
1934	28,300	46,000
Total profits	£250,000	£250,000
(Average profit) A.M.	£25,000	£25,000

A cursory inspection of the table shows that, although the average profit is the same in each case, there is a wide difference in the extent to which the individual items vary from the average and in the way the items are grouped around the average.

The variation in size of the items of a group from each other and from the average is called 'dispersion or variability', and we deal in this chapter with the various ways in which dispersion may be measured, leaving to the next chapter the discussion on the form of the distribution of the items.

THE RANGE

One very obvious method of measuring dispersion is to obtain the difference between the two extreme items and this is called the *range*. Thus in the foregoing example we have these results:

	Greatest profit	Least profit	Range
	£	£	£
Firm A	28,300	20,000	8,300
Firm B	46,000	—2,000	48,000

Although the highest profit earned by firm B was £46,000 and the lowest a loss of £2,000, the remaining profits might still have been packed round the average and differ little from it. The range gives no information on this point. And since the range is calculated from extreme items which may have been caused by abnormal circumstances, it is not in many cases a sound basis of comparison.

THE QUARTILE DEVIATION

We saw in the last chapter that the items in a distribution which correspond with positions one-quarter and three-quarters the way along the distribution are known as quartiles. They are obtained by arranging the items in order of size or in the form of a cumulative frequency distribution and calculating the values corresponding to the quarter and three-quarters positions. They may also be obtained graphically.

The quartiles may be employed to arrive at a measure of dispersion. This latter is known as the *quartile deviation* and is obtained by halving the inter-quartile range, i.e. the difference between the upper and lower quartile.

$$\text{Thus the quartile deviation} = \frac{Q_3 - Q_1}{2}$$

Firm A		Firm B	
£		£	
20,000		−2,000	
23,500		5,000	
24,000 ⎱ Lower quartile		10,000 ⎱ Lower quartile	
24,000 ⎰ £24,000		15,000 ⎰ £12,500	
24,000 ⎱ Median		22,500 ⎱ Median	
26,000 ⎰ £25,000		30,000 ⎰ £26,250	
26,200 ⎱ Upper quartile		38,000 ⎱ Upper quartile	
27,000 ⎰ £26,600		40,000 ⎰ £39,000	
27,000		45,500	
28,300		46,000	

In the above table, the items have been arranged in ascending order of magnitude, and the quartile deviations work out as follows:

$$\text{Firm A } \frac{£26,600 - £24,000}{2} = £1,300$$

$$\text{Firm B } \frac{£39,000 - £12,500}{2} = £13,250$$

The quartile deviation is free from the objection attaching to the range, i.e. it is not calculated from extreme items. Notice that the quartile deviation obtained in this way is expressed in absolute units – £s, feet, tons, etc. – and that the value of this deviation will, to a certain extent, be affected by the size of the items in the group. Other things being equal, the larger the items in the group, the larger will be the variation or dispersion they show. For purposes of comparison it is desirable to reduce the absolute dispersion to relative or proportional dispersion, in which case it is necessary to use some figure as a standard or denominator. Although the average, mode or median, may be used as a standard, the method most commonly employed for determining relative quartile deviation is to use the average of the two quartiles and to express the quartile deviation as a fraction. This fraction is known as the *quartile coefficient of dispersion or deviation.*

$$\text{Quartile coefficient of dispersion} = \frac{Q_3 - Q_1}{2} \div \frac{Q_3 + Q_1}{2}$$

$$\text{Firm A. Quartile coeff. of dispersion} = \frac{£1,300}{£25,300} = 0.052$$

$$\text{Firm B. Quartile coeff. of dispersion} = \frac{£13,250}{£25,750} = 0.51$$

THE AVERAGE OR MEAN DEVIATION

The quartile method of measuring dispersion is convenient and the deviation is easy to calculate. It does not use extreme items like the range and it is satisfactory where the distribution is fairly uniform. But it confines itself to considering only two items and where important items lie beyond the quartiles, or it is important to know the variation of all the items, this method is unsatisfactory and other methods are therefore used, of which the simplest is the determination of the average or mean deviation. As its name implies, it is the sum of all the deviations, all taken as positive from one of the averages – arithmetic mean, mode or median – divided by the number of deviations. The following shows the calculation of the mean deviation using the median as the average and arranging the profits of firm A in the form of a frequency distribution.

(i) Profit £	(ii) No. of times this profit occurs	(iii) Deviation from median (£25,000) £	(iv) Product of columns (ii) and (iii) £
20,000	1	5,000	5,000
23,500	1	1,500	1,500
24,000	3	1,000	3,000
26,000	1	1,000	1,000
26,200	1	1,200	1,200
27,000	2	2,000	4,000
28,300	1	3,300	3,300
	10		£19,000

Total deviation from median = £19,000
No. of deviations = 10

$$\text{Mean deviation} = \frac{£19,000}{10} = £1,900$$

To obtain a relative measure of dispersion using the mean deviation, we divide the mean deviation by the average used in calculating the individual deviations, in our case, the median. This gives the *coefficient of mean dispersion*.

$$\text{Coefficient of mean dispersion} = \frac{\text{Mean deviation from median}}{\text{Median}}$$

$$= \frac{£1,900}{£25,000} = 0 \cdot 076$$

For many purposes, the mean deviation method is a satisfactory way of measuring dispersion, but it is not greatly used in statistical work. This is partly because the fact that the deviations are all taken as positive makes it rather artificial to the logical mind, and partly because it is desirable to emphasize the larger deviations by giving them more weight than the smaller ones. The next method, that of standard deviation, takes note of the sign of the deviations and at the same time emphasizes the larger deviations. It is thus the one most commonly used in statistical work.

THE STANDARD DEVIATION (S.D.)

The standard deviation method is really a modification of the mean deviation method and we again take into account the deviations of each item from the average, which in this case is usually the arithmetic mean. Instead of ignoring the signs of the individual deviations, each of the latter is squared, the mean of the squares found, and the square root of the result taken.

Thus the standard deviation

$$= \sqrt{\frac{\text{Sum of squares of individual deviations from A.M.}}{\text{Number of items}}}$$

To take a simple example, the mean of the five numbers, 4, 7, 8, 12, 14 is 9, the deviations from the mean -5, -2, -1, $+3$, $+5$. The squares of these deviations: 25, 4, 1, 9, 25, with a total of 64.

[1]The mean square deviation $= \dfrac{64}{5} = 12 \cdot 8$ and the

Standard deviation $\sqrt{12 \cdot 8} = 3 \cdot 58$

[1] This is also called the 'variance'.

In determining the standard deviation in the case of a grouped frequency distribution, the arithmetical labour involved may be considerable, particularly if the deviations are not whole numbers. A short-cut method, similar to that used for the calculation of the arithmetic mean, may be adopted. In principle this method consists of assuming a convenient arithmetic mean, finding the sum of the squares of the deviations from this mean, adjusting these deviations to the true mean, dividing the adjusted deviations by the number of items, and then finding the square root.

Thus, using our former example of the price and output of steel tubes, and adding further columns for the squares of the deviations from the assumed mean, we get the following. (The mean is again assumed to be £37½.)

Table 23. *Calculation of the standard deviation of the price per ton of steel tubes*

(i) Selling price per ton mid-interval figs. £	(ii) Output in tons	(iii) Deviations from assumed mean	(iv) Square of this deviation	(v) Product of cols. ii and iii	(vi) Product of cols. ii and iv
22½	75	−3	9	−225	675
27½	148	−2	4	−296	592
32½	288	−1	1	−288	288
37½	334	0			
42½	252	+1	1	252	252
47½	217	+2	4	434	868
52½	127	+3	9	381	1,143
57½	33	+4	16	132	528
	1,474			+390	+4,346

The mean of the total squares of the deviations from the assumed arithmetic mean is $\frac{4346}{1474}$. Let this total be represented by x. Before taking the square root of this result, a correction has to be made to allow for the difference between the assumed mean and the true

D

arithmetic mean. This difference is represented in terms of the deviations from the assumed mean by $\frac{390}{1474}$. For the standard deviation, this amount is squared and subtracted from x.

$$\text{The standard deviation} = \sqrt{\frac{4,346}{1,474} - \left(\frac{390}{1,474}\right)^2} \text{ units}$$

$$= \sqrt{\frac{6,406,004 - 152,100 \text{ units}}{1,474^2}}$$

$$= 1 \cdot 70 \text{ units}$$

$$= 1 \cdot 70 \times £5 \text{ since each unit} = £5$$

$$= £8 \text{ 10s. 0d.}$$

Expressed in words, the short-cut method of calculating the standard deviation in the case of a frequency distribution is:

Standard deviation =

$$\sqrt{\frac{\text{Sum of sq. of individual items from the assumed mean}}{\text{Number of items}} - \left(\frac{\text{algebraic sum of deviations of items from assumed mean}}{\text{Number of items}}\right)^2}$$

The relative standard deviation, or as it is called, the coefficient of dispersion, is the standard deviation divided by the arithmetic mean. In this case its value is:

$$\text{Coefficient of Dispersion} = \frac{\text{Std. dev.}}{\text{A.M.}} = \frac{£8 \text{ 10s. 0d.}}{£38 \cdot 825}$$

$$= 0 \cdot 22$$

As with all the coefficients of dispersion, the smaller the coefficient, the less the dispersion of the items from which it is calculated. In the case of a normal frequency distribution, the coefficient of dispersion is under 0·1; Professor Pearson has shown that for stature in man it varies around 0·04, and for the length of long bones (human) around 0·06. It will be recalled that the coefficient of dispersion for the profits made by firm A (Table 22) was less than 0·1.

THE RELATION OF THE QUARTILE DEVIATION, MEAN DEVIATION, AND STANDARD DEVIATION TO EACH OTHER

It has been found that in a fairly symmetrical distribution the following approximate relationships exist:

1. The quartile deviation = $\frac{2}{3}$ standard deviation.
2. The mean deviation from the arithmetic mean = $\frac{4}{5}$ standard deviation.

These differences in the various measures of dispersion are to be expected from the nature of the methods used in obtaining them. Thus, the quartile deviation ignores the extreme items and will be less than either the mean or standard deviation, which take all the items into account. By squaring the deviations the standard method gives more emphasis to the extreme items than does the mean deviation and is therefore greater.

Before leaving the subject of averages and measures of dispersion, it will be useful to illustrate their application to a simple example.

The wages paid in two factories in the same line of business are to be compared. This can be done by considering the averages and measures of dispersion. Suppose the following are the results:

		Firm A	Firm B
Number of wage earners		586	602
	Arithmetic mean	52s. 6d.	47s. 6d.
Average wages	Median	51s.	46s. 6d.
	Mode	50s.	46s.
Quartiles		42s., 55s.	38s. 6d., 52s. 6d.
Standard deviation		10s.	11s.
Coefficient of dispersion (Standard deviation method)		0·19	0·23

From the foregoing figures, the total wages paid to the firms' employees may be calculated by multiplying the mean wage by the total number of wage earners. It is obvious that the wages paid by firm A are higher than those paid by firm B. The most usual wage in firm A is 50s., in firm B, 46s., i.e. more persons receive these wages than any other. Further, half the employees in A receive between 42s. and 55s. a week, half of those in B, 38s. 6d. to 52s. 6d. Since the standard deviation for firm B is slightly greater than that for firm A, and since the coefficient of dispersion for firm B is appreciably greater than that for firm A, there is a greater variation from the average wage in the case of B than in the case of A. And, since the averages are generally less for B, it is probable that the range of wages in B goes down to a lower level than that of firm A.

STUDENT WORK

1. Calculate the standard and quartile deviations for Exercise 1 of Chapter 7.
2. Calculate the quartiles, the quartile deviation and the standard deviation for Exercise 3 of Chapter 7.
3. Draw up a comparison between the following firms, so far as the wages they pay is concerned. The comparison should show: the total wages paid by each firm, the average wage, the median wage, the modal wage, the standard deviation, and the quartiles.

Firm A Number of men – 850		Firm B Number of men – 630	
Wages	No. of men	Wages	No. of men
25s.–30s.	70	25s.–30s.	50
30s.–35s.	130	30s.–35s.	80
35s.–40s.	200	35s.–40s.	120
40s.–45s.	280	40s.–45s.	160
45s.–50s.	150	45s.–50s.	110
50s.–55s.	15	50s.–55s.	70
55s.–60s.	5	55s.–60s.	40

Explain fully what your results mean.
4. Calculate the mean deviation from the median, the quartile deviation, and the standard deviation in Exercise 4 of Chapter 7.
5. Calculate the standard deviation and the corresponding coefficient of dispersion for the following values of the £1 in francs on twenty successive days:

74·94	74·62	74·50	74·81
74·56	74·48	74·34	74·87
74·54	74·50	74·78	74·94
74·72	74·50	74·81	74·57
74·72	74·51	74·78	74·56

6. Compare the variability in the price of Courtauld's shares and United Steel Co.'s shares (nominal value £1) on twenty successive days by calculating the standard deviation and the corresponding coefficient of dispersion.

Courtauld's		U.S. Co. Ltd.		Courtauld's		U.S. Co. Ltd.	
s.	d.	s.	d.	s.	d.	s.	d.
56	$1\frac{1}{2}$	32	$4\frac{1}{2}$	56	$4\frac{1}{2}$	32	$7\frac{1}{2}$
55	9	32	3	56	3	32	9
55	$10\frac{1}{2}$	32	$1\frac{1}{2}$	56	$1\frac{1}{2}$	32	$7\frac{1}{2}$
56	$1\frac{1}{2}$	32	$4\frac{1}{2}$	56	0	32	$4\frac{1}{2}$
56	9	32	$4\frac{1}{2}$	56	$1\frac{1}{2}$	32	$4\frac{1}{2}$
55	9	32	0	55	$10\frac{1}{2}$	32	0
55	6	31	9	56	6	31	9
56	$4\frac{1}{2}$	32	$1\frac{1}{2}$	56	$7\frac{1}{2}$	31	$10\frac{1}{2}$
56	$10\frac{1}{2}$	32	$1\frac{1}{2}$	56	9	32	3
56	9	32	6	57	0	31	6

Chapter 9

Skewness

WE have already seen that a knowledge of the values of the averages and measures of dispersion is of very considerable help in assessing the properties of a group. The averages are typical items in the group or are typical of the group, and the measures of dispersion give an indication as to how the items in the group differ in size from each other and from the averages. There is, however, still another factor to be considered before our analysis of the group is complete. This further factor considers how the items are distributed about the average, whether there are more items below the average than above it, or if the reverse is true. In other words, it concerns itself with the question whether the items are arranged in a symmetrical fashion about the averages. This new factor is known as *skewness*; it really means lopsidedness and the presence of skewness indicates that the distribution is not symmetrical. The existence of skewness may perhaps be more easily explained by a reference to the following diagrams.

Figure 21 shows the frequency curve illustrating the results of throwing three dice a large number of times. The curve falls evenly on both sides of the highest point, showing that not only is there an equal number of items on either side of the highest point, i.e. there are as many items below the mode as above it, but also that these items are symmetrically arranged about the mode. If the arithmetic mean and median are calculated for this and for all symmetrical distributions, they will be found to be the same. In this case, skewness, which is the opposite of symmetry, is not present.

Fig. 22 is a graphical representation of a frequency distribution showing the marks obtained in an examination. Notice that both the marks obtained and the number of candidates receiving these marks increase until a mark of 70 is reached. After this, the number of candidates receiving individual marks above 70 rapidly falls off. There is a considerably greater number of students obtaining less than 70 marks than more than 70, although there are more students obtaining 70 marks than any

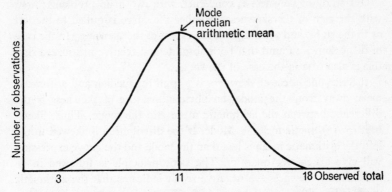

Fig. 21. *Symmetrical frequency curve, showing results of throwing three dice a large number of times*

other mark. The modal mark is therefore 70, but the median and arithmetic mean are both less than this. In the case of a skewed distribution, the arithmetic mean and the median are pulled away from the

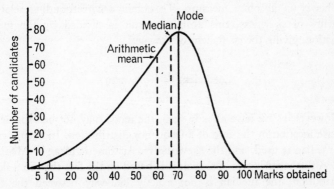

Fig. 22. *Frequency curve for a 'skewed' distribution; in this case, marks obtained at an examination*

mode by a preponderance of items on one side. The median is pulled towards the skewed side by an amount depending merely upon the excess number of items on that side. The arithmetic mean, however, is influenced both by the excess number of items and the size of these items, and is thus pulled farther away from the mode than is the median.

Our study of skewness is concerned with two main problems; first, with the sign of the skewness (whether the curve is pulled to the left or to the right) and second, with the extent of the skewness. In the case of dispersion we found that both absolute and relative measures exist; this is also true in the case of skewness.

1. Since one effect of skewness is to pull the median and arithmetic mean away from the mode, an obvious measure of skewness is the difference between the arithmetic mean and the mode. Thus, Skewness = Arithmetic mean — Mode. If the distribution is skewed to the left, the arithmetic mean is less than the mode and the above expression will give a negative quantity. The same principle is followed in all measures of skewness – a negative result indicates that the arithmetic mean is less than the mode; a positive, that it is greater.

Using once more the price and output of steel tubes problem, the measure of skewness, using this method, is

$$\text{Arithmetic mean} - \text{mode} = \pounds 38 \cdot 8 - \pounds 36 \cdot 8 = \pounds 2$$

This is an absolute measure. To obtain a corresponding relative measure of skewness, this absolute result is divided by the mean deviation, giving the coefficient of skewness.

$$\text{Coefficient} = \frac{\pounds 2}{\pounds 7} = 0 \cdot 29$$

However, as we have already seen, the mode may not be capable of precise location in the case of a frequency distribution. In such a case the median is used, and the skewness is: Arithmetic mean — Median.

2. A further measure of skewness is based on the fact that, in a skew distribution, the median is not exactly half-way between the two quartiles. The quartile on the skew side is pulled more in that direction than the other quartile in its direction. This measure of skewness, known as the *quartile measure* of skewness, is given by the expression:

Skewness = sum of quartiles — twice the median.

The amount of skewness registered in the case of the price and output of steel tubes and calculated by this method:

$$= £32 \ 10s. \ 0d. + £45 \ 5s. \ 0d. - 2 \ (£38 \ 10s. \ 0d.)$$
$$= £77 \ 15s. \ 0d. - £77 = 15s.$$

The coefficient of skewness in this case is obtained by dividing the amount of skewness by the quartile deviation, i.e. $\dfrac{15s.}{£6 \cdot 8s.} = 0 \cdot 12$. The amounts and coefficient of skewness as calculated by these two methods may be somewhat different. This is so because the two methods are based on different principles.

3. A third measure of skewness is obtained by cubing the deviations from the arithmetic mean, dividing by the number of deviations and then finding the cube root of the result. This method is sometimes known as the *Third Moment* method.[1]

$$\text{Skewness} = \sqrt[3]{\frac{(\text{Deviations from A.M.})^3}{\text{Number of deviations}}}$$

The difficulty of calculation limits the use of this measure to more advanced work. If a relative measure of skewness is required, it is obtained by dividing this measure of skewness by the standard deviation of the frequency.

STUDENT WORK

1. What do you understand by 'skewness'? Illustrate your answer diagrammatically.
2. Explain carefully what are meant by the first, second, and third 'moments'.
3. Using the figures given in Exercise 1, Chapter 7, calculate the median and quartile coefficients of skewness.

---

[1] The first moment is the mean deviation; the second the standard deviation.

Chapter 10

The Analysis of a Time Series

UP to the present we have confined our analysis mainly to statistical groups, i.e. to a state of affairs existing at a certain time. Although the methods we have described apply equally well to time series, these have certain peculiarities which call for special treatment and it is our purpose in this chapter to deal with these peculiarities.

Suppose, for example, a manufacturer is considering the purchase of one of two firms, A and B. The statement that the average annual profits over the last ten years have been the same for A and B is not a sufficient indication of the value of the goodwill of the two firms. Even if the measures of dispersion give the same result, it can by no means be said that the value of the goodwill of the two firms is identical. Suppose the actual profits of the two firms A and B are as follows:

	Firm A	Firm B
	£	£
Annual profits	1,750	2,450
	1,850	2,450
	2,050	2,300
	2,000	2,100
	2,100	2,000
	2,300	1,950
	2,350	1,950
	2,300	1,800
	2,400	1,850
	2,500	1,750
Total profits	£21,600	£21,700
Average profits (A.M.)	£2,160 p.a.	£2,170 p.a.

It will be seen that what little difference there is in the average profits favours firm B, but the prospective purchaser will be ready to pay more for the goodwill of firm A than for firm B. This is because the profits of firm A show a steady upward trend or tendency while those of firm B show a steady downward tendency. The example shows that some knowledge of the existence of trend is necessary for the fuller understanding of the significance of a time series. (The reader will recall that we have previously defined a series as the successive measurements of the size or value of a variable over a period of time.) In the case of a series, it may be necessary not only to know the averages and measures of dispersion, but also to know how each individual item is related to those which have gone before, and to those which follow.

TREND AND VARIATIONS

The Trend or general tendency is, however, not the only characteristic which affects a time series. In general such series may be made up of several component parts, the chief of which are the following:

1. General trend or secular variation.
2. Seasonal variation.
3. Cyclical variation.
4. Special variations due to accidental or occasional happenings.

Our task in this chapter is to show how each of these may be recognized and, in certain cases, its value calculated. Before this is attempted a short description of each type of variation is desirable. We will base our explanation on the figures for the number of insured persons in employment in Great Britain in the period before the war.

Trend or Secular Variation

In the first quarter of 1926 it was estimated that there were 9·8 million people in employment; in November 1936 the number had grown to 11·1 million. This growth has not been uniform by any means. The figures for some months have been lower than those for the previous month and this monthly decrease has persisted, at times, over a period of several months. But in spite of setbacks, the number of persons in employment has tended to rise and has, in fact, shown a very appreciable increase in the eleven years from 1926 to 1936. This long-term tendency in a time series is known as *trend* or *secular variation*.

Seasonal Variation

Each year there is a tendency for the number of persons unemployed to increase in winter and particularly so in January, with the result that the number of persons employed may show a decline from November to December and from December to January. This increase in unemployment in winter is due to seasonal causes. The building industry, for example, is usually slack in the winter months. This variation in the number of persons employed is repeated year after year and is known as seasonal variation.

Cyclical Variation

The upward trend in the number of persons in employment has been affected not only by seasonal variations, but by a variation which takes a number of years to work itself out completely. Booms, i.e. periods of good trade with consequent good employment figures, are followed by depressions, or periods of bad trade with high average unemployment. These booms and depressions follow each other with steady regularity and the full cycle, from the height of one boom to the height of the next, may take 8–10 years. 1929 was a boom year. In that year the average number of persons in employment was 10·2 million. From 1929 to 1932, the number in employment tended to fall and at the worst of the depression in 1932, the number had fallen to 9·2 million. In 1933 the movement out of the depression began to take shape and from 1933 to 1936 the number of persons in employment tended to rise continuously, apart, that is, from seasonal influences. This variation over the period of the trade cycle is known as cyclical variation.

Special Variations

The number of persons in employment may be affected by such happenings as strikes, or political crises, which occur at irregular intervals. The great coal strike of 1926 was a case in point, and in this year the number of persons employed fell from 9·8 million to 8·4 million. On the other hand, the employment figures rose to a very high level owing to the special conditions existing during the war.

Fig. 23 is a historigram representing the course of employment from 1926 to 1936. Any point on this graph may be affected by each of the four types of variation discussed. The seasonal and cyclical variations may act in the same way as the trend, as at the point A, in which case the effect of the trend seems to be enhanced, or they may act in the opposite way to the trend, as at B, when they appear to lessen the effect of the trend. Again, the cyclical variation may be positive with regard to the trend and the seasonal variation negative, as at C. Special variations may act in the same way as the trend or in opposition to it; the effect of the strike of 1926 was to reduce the level of employment to the point D.

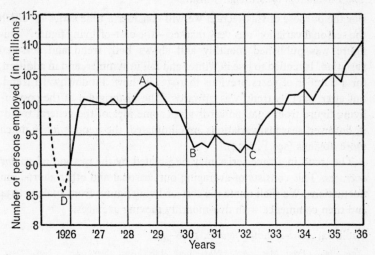

Fig. 23. *Variation in the number of persons employed, 1926–36*

The war brought about a complete break in the operation of the variations with which we had become familiar prior to 1939. For some years after 1945, employment was at a high level owing to the great leeway which had to be made up in the production of most consumer goods and capital equipment to which little attention could be paid in the period 1939–45. The Government, too, was pledged to follow a 'full employment' policy designed to maintain employment at a high level, i.e. to eliminate cyclical variations and to keep the general trend steadily upwards. It is too early yet to assess how long the present high level of employment can be maintained without any special measures being taken by the Government. And, as yet, we have no experience in the effectiveness of the proposed plans for maintaining 'full employment'. But we cannot ignore the possibility of the resumption of the once familiar economic phenomena of boom and depression although we must hark back to prewar days to find examples of it.[1]

DETECTION AND ESTIMATION OF GENERAL TREND WHEN OTHER FACTORS EXIST

The Elimination of Seasonal Variation

For the purpose of this section we will consider a time series in which the seasonal variation was very marked – the cost-of-living figure.[2] This figure was published monthly and shows both trend and seasonal variation. It tended to rise in winter and fall in summer, and in addition, for a number of years previous to 1933, it showed a downward trend, but after 1933 its trend was upwards. The historigram of the cost-of-living figure from 1928 onwards gives some idea of the general trend; if, however, seasonal variations are eliminated, the trend is made much more obvious (see Fig. 24).

The trend in a time series may be isolated by the method of *moving averages*. This consists of averaging out seasonal and other short-term fluctuations. We shall quote the cost-of-living figures from 1928 to 1934 and then commence with five-monthly moving averages.

Table 24. *Cost-of-living figures, 1928–34*

Year	Jan.	Feb.	Mar.	Apl.	May	June	July	Aug.	Sept.	Oct.	Nov.	Dec.
1928	68	66	64	64	64	65	65	65	65	66	67	68
1929	67	65	66	62	61	60	61	63	64	65	67	67
1930	66	64	61	57	55	54	55	57	57	56	57	55
1931	53	52	50	47	47	47	45	47	45	45	46	48
1932	47	47	46	44	43	42	43	41	41	43	43	43
1933	42	41	39	37	36	36	38	39	41	41	43	43
1934	42	41	40	39	37	38	41	42	43	43	44	44

The Calculation of the 5-monthly Average

The average of the first five items – 68, 66, 64, 64, 64, is obtained, i.e. 65·2. Then the first item is dropped out and the average for the next five

---

[1] This is no longer true. Unemployment exceeded half a million at the end of 1958 (and again at the end of 1962). Incentives were given to private consumption, and public investment was encouraged to meet the situation. These measures resulted in an increase in economic activity and a fall in unemployment.

[2] See Chapter 17, p. 183.

taken, i.e. the average of 66, 64, 64, 64, 65, giving 64·6. Then the first of these five items is omitted and the next one included and the average of these found, i.e. the average of 64, 64, 64, 65, 65, or 64·4. This process is continued throughout the set of figures. In actual practice, a quicker way of calculating moving averages than by adding up each set of items, is to increase or diminish the cumulative total of the set by an amount made necessary by the dropping out of one item, and the inclusion of another. For example, the total of the first five items is 326; if now 68 is dropped out and 65 put in its place, the total will be 323 and so on. It is comparatively easy then to divide these totals by 5 and so obtain the average. When this has been done the following results are obtained. Note that the first average is in the position occupied by the fifth item.[1]

Table 25. *Five-monthly moving averages*

Year	Jan.	Feb.	Mar.	Apl.	May	June	July	Aug.	Sept.	Oct.	Nov.	Dec.
1928					65·2	64·6	64·4	64·6	64·8	65·2	65·6	66·2
1929	66·6	66·6	66·6	65·6	64·2	62·8	62·0	61·4	61·8	62·6	64·0	65·2
1930	65·8	65·8	65·0	63·0	60·6	58·2	56·4	55·6	55·6	55·8	56·4	56·4
1931	55·6	54·6	53·4	51·4	49·8	48·6	47·2	46·6	46·2	45·8	45·6	46·2
1932	46·2	46·6	46·8	46·4	45·4	44·4	43·6	42·6	42·0	42·0	42·2	42·2
1933	42·4	42·4	41·6	40·4	39·0	37·8	37·2	37·2	38·0	39·0	40·4	41·4
1934	42·0	42·0	41·8	41·0	39·8	39·0	39·0	39·4	40·2	41·4	42·6	43·2

When these figures are examined or illustrated graphically, it will be seen that evidences of seasonal variations still exist. These variations are not so pronounced as in the original figures, but by taking the process a little further and working out the ten-monthly moving averages these variations are reduced much further. The results are plotted in Fig. 24.

Table 26. *Ten-monthly moving averages*

Year	Jan.	Feb.	Mar.	Apl.	May	June	July	Aug.	Sept.	Oct.	Nov.	Dec.
1928										65·2	65·1	65·3
1929	65·6	65·7	65·9	65·6	65·2	64·7	64·3	64·0	63·7	63·4	63·4	63·6
1930	63·6	63·8	63·8	63·5	62·9	62·0	61·1	60·3	59·3	58·2	57·3	56·4
1931	55·6	55·1	54·6	53·9	53·1	51·9	50·9	49·8	48·6	47·6	46·9	46·5
1932	46·2	46·2	46·1	46·0	45·6	45·3	45·1	44·2	44·7	43·7	43·3	42·9
1933	42·5	42·2	41·8	41·3	40·6	40·1	39·8	39·4	39·2	39·0	39·1	39·3
1934	39·6	40·0	40·4	40·7	40·6	40·5	40·5	40·6	40·6	40·6	40·8	41·1

[1] It might be more correct, however, to begin with the third or middle item.

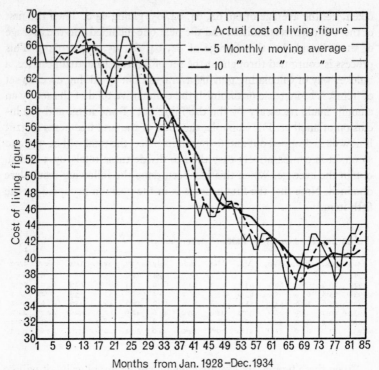

Fig. 24. *Cost-of-living figure, 1928–34*

When using the method of *moving averages*,[1] the question naturally arises, how far must the process of calculating moving averages be taken? The answer will depend upon the type of variation which is to be eliminated and how often this variation repeats itself. In the case of the cost-of-living figure, a five-monthly moving average was insufficient to remove the effect of seasonal variations entirely. The ten-monthly moving average did not give an entirely smooth curve but was much

[1] Moving averages must not be confused with progressive averages. In this case, the number of items on which the average is based continuously increases, but the average is always taken from a fixed point. For example, in Table 26, beginning with the first item, the progressive averages would be: 65·2;

$$\left(\frac{65·2 + 65·1}{2}\right); \left(\frac{65·2 + 65·1 + 65·3}{3}\right); \left(\frac{65·2 + 65·1 + 65·3 + 65·6}{4}\right)$$

more satisfactory in this respect than the five-monthly one. It would require a twelve-monthly average to eliminate completely the effect of seasonal variations, as the full period of such variations is twelve months, i.e. the tendency repeats itself every year.

Another question which arises is, what significance may be attached to the results obtained by these moving averages? Assuming that the seasonal variation is eliminated entirely, then the general trend may be expressed both qualitatively and quantitatively. Let us refer again to Table 26 and Fig. 24. From these two, we see that the trend in the cost-of-living figure was downwards from the beginning of 1928 to the middle of 1933, after which an upward trend is apparent. Expressed in figures, the ten-monthly moving average shows that from October 1928 to October 1933, the average cost-of-living figure fell from 65·2 to 39·0, i.e. 26·2 points, over a period of five years. This works out at 5·2 points per year on an average. The period during which the cost-of-living figure is shown to be rising is too short for any mathematical deductions to be drawn.

THE CALCULATION OF SEASONAL VARIATION

In many cases, it is desirable to know not only the amount of general trend but also the size of the seasonal variation. Thus, to a business man, a knowledge of the existence and amount of seasonal variation is of great importance. As an example of the calculation of seasonal variation we shall again use the cost-of-living figures, but we shall use figures for 1928, 1929, 1930, 1931, and 1932, which are here repeated.

Year	Jan.	Feb.	Mar.	Apl.	May	June	July	Aug.	Sept.	Oct.	Nov.	Dec.	Ave.
1928	68	66	64	64	64	65	65	65	65	66	67	68	65·6
1929	67	65	66	62	61	60	61	63	64	65	67	67	64·0
1930	66	64	61	57	55	54	55	57	57	56	57	55	58·0
1931	53	52	50	47	47	47	45	47	45	45	46	48	47·9
1932	47	47	46	44	43	42	43	41	41	43	43	43	43·5
Total	301	294	287	274	270	268	269	273	272	275	280	281	
Average	60·2	58·8	57·4	54·8	54·0	53·6	53·8	54·6	54·4	55·0	56·0	56·2	

Average for whole of period   55·7

Seasonal variation } +4·5 +3·1 +1·7 −0·9 −1·7 −2·1 −1·9 −1·1 −1·3 −0·7 +0·3 +0·5

From the above we see that from 1928 to 1932 the average cost-of-living figure was 55·7. The average for January was 60·2, which is 4·5 above this, the February average is 3·1 above the average, and so on. However, before we apply these seasonal variations to future figures we must remember the trend of the cost-of-living figure, which is downward at the end of 1932. If we assume that the same trend will continue during 1933, the average cost-of-living figure for that year should be about 39, in which case it would be reasonable to expect the January 1933 figure to be about 43·5, the February figure 42, the July 37, and so on. A glance at the actual figures for 1933 will show that these bear some relation to actual fact.

CYCLICAL VARIATIONS

When the general trend is partially obscured by cyclical variations, the latter may be removed by the method of moving averages. In this case, the average period employed should be the length of time taken by the trade cycle to run a complete course. As this is normally eight to ten years,[1] a ten-year moving average will eliminate the cyclical variations and reveal the general trend. Exports are, of course, affected by this cyclical variation, and if the general trend of yearly exports is required, the cyclical fluctuation must be eliminated. In the exercises on Chapter 10 (p. 105), the annual values of British exports from 1870 to 1913 are given. The historigram for these figures reveals this cyclical variation, but a ten-year moving average shows the general trend quite clearly.

A FURTHER APPLICATION OF THE USE OF MOVING AVERAGES

The following example, although it has no direct connexion with the idea of general trends, illustrates how the method of moving averages may be used for a purpose other than that of isolating the general trend.

The firm to which the writer once belonged calculated that the cost of making successive thicknesses of tubes of a given outside diameter warranted the following charges per foot for the tubes.

Table 27. *Price per foot for successive thicknesses of tubes (in pence)*

10	9	$8\frac{1}{4}$	$6\frac{1}{4}$	$3\frac{1}{2}$
$9\frac{1}{2}$	$9\frac{1}{4}$	8	$6\frac{1}{2}$	$3\frac{3}{4}$
$9\frac{1}{2}$	9	$8\frac{1}{2}$	6	3
$9\frac{1}{4}$	$9\frac{1}{2}$	$7\frac{3}{4}$	$5\frac{1}{4}$	
$9\frac{3}{4}$	$8\frac{3}{4}$	$7\frac{1}{2}$	4	
$9\frac{1}{2}$	$8\frac{1}{2}$	7	$4\frac{1}{4}$	

[1] This was largely true of the period 1870–1939, but has not been so since.

From the general sales point of view, a price list which showed a continuous decrease from the first size to the last was preferred. Assuming that equal quantities of tubes of all sizes were sold, a revised price list which yielded the same monetary return but which showed the required price gradation was obtained by taking a moving average of four sizes. This practically eliminated all items not in accordance with the plan for a steady decrease, but it took out the first three items. These were calculated by extrapolation, but they could have been obtained by graphing the new results and producing the graph backwards until the three missing items were read off.

STUDENT WORK

1. Draw a graph of British Exports from 1870 to 1913 from the following figures (which are due to Professor Bowley). Calculate five-year moving averages and ten-year moving averages and illustrate graphically in order to bring out the general trend of British exports in this period.

Value of British exports in million £'s

Year	Value of exports	Year	Value of exports	Year	Value of exports
1870	199·6	1885	213·1	1900	283·6
1871	223·1	1886	212·7	1901	270·9
1872	256·3	1887	221·9	1902	277·7
1873	255·2	1888	234·5	1903	286·5
1874	239·6	1889	248·9	1904	296·3
1875	223·5	1890	263·5	1905	324·4
1876	200·6	1891	247·2	1906	367·0
1877	198·9	1892	227·1	1907	416·0
1878	192·8	1893	218·1	1908	366·5
1879	191·5	1894	215·8	1909	372·3
1880	223·1	1895	225·9	1910	421·6
1881	234·0	1896	240·1	1911	448·5
1882	241·5	1897	234·3	1912	480·2
1883	239·8	1898	233·4	1913	514·2
1884	233·0	1899	255·3		

2. From Table 27, page 104, draw up a new price list based on a moving average of four items and obtain a price for the three missing sizes at the beginning.

Chapter 11

Correlation

WE saw in Chapter 5 (Diagrammatic Representation) that when two sets of statistics are plotted on the same graph, any connexion which might exist between the two is brought out more clearly. Thus, in the examples discussed in that chapter, we saw that as the franc rate of exchange moved up, the price of gold fell, and vice versa; when the July rainfall was high, the yield of corn was also high. The determination of the existence and extent of the relationship between two phenomena of this type is one of the most important problems in statistics, and the answers to many practical questions turn on the real or apparent connexion between two economic or social factors. Among the questions which are still receiving attention, the following may be quoted. Is there a connexion between smoking and the incidence of lung cancer? Does a high infant mortality rate coincide with a high degree of overcrowding? Has any particular accident rate fallen since the introduction of safety devices? and so on. The graphical representation of two factors may establish the fact that some definite relationship exists, but it can give little indication of the amount of the relationship. Again, unless the factors considered are time series, their graphical representation may not be of the type which lends itself to comparison. If therefore some definite idea of the amount of the connexion which exists between two or more factors is required, more precise methods than those which are possible in graphical representation are necessary. It is the purpose of this chapter to deal with such methods.

The relationship between two factors is called in statistics, *correlation*, which may be defined as the tendency of two or more groups or series of items to vary together, directly or inversely; and the mathematical value of this connexion is given by the corresponding coefficient correlation.

MEASUREMENT OF CORRELATION

A number of methods of measuring the extent of correlation have been developed, of which the one most widely used is the expression given on page 108, prepared by Karl Pearson. Although a full description of the mathematical processes used in obtaining the expression would be outside the scope of this book, we can give a brief account of the principles on which it is based. For this purpose we give the marks obtained in an examination in English and in French by twenty pupils. (Table 28.)

Table 28. *Calculation of correlation between English marks and French marks*

(i) Percentage marks in English	(ii) Deviation from mean	(iii) Percentage marks in French	(iv) Deviation from mean
87	+33	68	+22
77	23	55	9
70	16	58	12
68	14	62	16
63	9	50	8
58	4	48	2
55	1	53	7
54	0	50	4
53	− 1	38	− 8
52	− 2	43	− 3
51	− 3	53	7
50	− 4	45	− 1
48	− 6	43	− 3
48	− 6	45	− 1
47	− 7	40	− 6
46	− 8	35	−11
46	− 8	33	−13
43	−11	38	− 8
40	−14	32	−14
24	−30	31	−15

1,080		920	
A.M.			
54		46	

Let us consider for a moment the deviations from the mean. If there is any direct correlation between the two sets of marks, then there will be a tendency for positive deviations in the English marks to occur along with positive deviations in the French marks. Further, the higher the degree of correlation the greater will be the tendency for large positive deviations in both to occur together and the same will also apply in the case of negative deviations. If there is any inverse correlation, then the positive deviations in the English marks will tend to occur along with negative deviations in the French marks, and vice versa. If the marks are absolutely independent, positive and negative deviations will occur indiscriminately. If now we find the mean algebraic sum of the products of the deviations, the greater this mean product the greater will be the amount of correlation. If there is little or no correlation, the algebraic sum of the product of these deviations will not be great because positive deviations will be connected indiscriminately with both positive and negative deviations. (The reader will remember that the product of two negative items gives a positive answer, while the product of positive and negative items gives a negative answer.)

Thus, the mean product of the deviations, i.e. the algebraic sum of the products of the deviations divided by their number, gives a sensitive measure of correlation. This product is, however, in one respect, similar to the standard deviation, in that it is expressed in absolute units, and therefore its value could vary within very wide limits depending upon the nature of the original items. In the case of correlation, the relative measure known as the coefficient of correlation, is obtained by dividing the mean product of the deviations by the product of the standard deviations of the two sets of figures under consideration.

The coefficient of correlation

$$= \frac{\text{The mean product of the deviations from the mean}}{\text{The std. dev. of the 1st} \times \text{the std. dev. of the 2nd}}$$

If the correlation between two sets of figures is perfect and also direct, the mean product of the deviations will exactly equal the product of the two standard deviations and hence the coefficient will be $+1$. Where the correlation is perfect but inverse, the coefficient will be -1.

The extent of the correlation between two statistical groups or between two statistical series may be obtained by the use of the above expression. The case of the English and French marks is one of statistical groups; we give later an example involving statistical series.

Let us now calculate the value of the coefficient of correlation in the case of English and French marks for these twenty pupils.

Table 29. *Calculation of coefficient of correlation*

(i) English marks	(ii) Deviation from mean	(iii) Square of deviation	(iv) French marks	(v) Deviation from mean	(vi) Square of deviation	(vii) Product of columns ii and v +	−
87	+33	1,089	68	+22	484	726	
77	23	529	55	9	81	207	
70	16	256	58	12	144	192	
68	14	196	62	16	256	224	
63	9	81	50	4	16	36	
58	4	16	48	2	4	8	
55	1	1	53	7	49	7	
54	0	0	50	4	16		
53	− 1	1	38	− 8	64	8	
52	− 2	4	43	− 3	9	6	
51	− 3	9	53	7	49		21
50	− 4	16	45	− 1	1	4	
48	− 6	36	43	− 3	9	18	
48	− 6	36	45	− 1	1	6	
47	− 7	49	40	− 6	36	42	
46	− 8	64	35	−11	121	88	
46	− 8	64	33	−13	169	104	
43	−11	121	38	− 8	64	88	
40	−14	196	32	−14	196	196	
24	−30	900	31	−15	225	450	
1,080		3,664	920		1,994	2,410	21

Standard deviation of English marks $= \sqrt{\dfrac{3,664}{20}} = \sqrt{183 \cdot 2} = 13 \cdot 54$

Standard deviation of French marks $= \sqrt{\dfrac{1,994}{20}} = \sqrt{99 \cdot 7} = 9 \cdot 98$

Algebraic sum of product of deviations $= 2,410 - 21 = 2,389$

Mean product of deviations $= \dfrac{2,389}{20} = 119 \cdot 45$

Coefficient of correlation $= \dfrac{119 \cdot 45}{9 \cdot 98 \times 13 \cdot 54}$

$= 0 \cdot 90$

SUBJECT AND RELATIVE

The two sets of figures which are considered when the coefficient of correlation is calculated, are known as 'subject' and 'relative'. In general, the more important set, i.e. the one which is being used as the standard, is the subject and the one of less importance, the relative. The first set, i.e. the English marks, is the subject in our last example.

THE PROBABLE ERROR IN THE COEFFICIENT OF CORRELATION AND THE INTERPRETATION OF THE COEFFICIENT

We have already seen that in the majority of statistical investigations, it is not possible to examine all the items and that conclusions must be based on a sample. If the sample is small, then the averages, measures of dispersion, etc., may differ appreciably from the true values. Even with a large sample, there will probably be a slight difference. If, therefore, in the calculation of the coefficient of correlation, only a few items are used, the results will not be sufficiently reliable for the purpose of basing comparisons. If the coefficient is very small, it may be due purely to chance. In order, therefore, to guard against false conclusions, it is usual to calculate the probable error in the coefficient of correlation. For this purpose, a formula, embodying the number of items and the coefficient of correlation, is used.

$$\text{Probable error} = \frac{0 \cdot 67\{1 - (\text{coeff. of correl.})^2\}}{\sqrt{\text{Number of items}}}$$

1. If now, the coefficient of correlation is less than the probable error, there is no evidence of correlation.

2. If the coefficient is more than six times the size of the probable error, the existence of correlation is practically certain.

If the probable error is relatively small, then:

3. If the coefficient of correlation is less than 0·30, the correlation is not appreciable.

4. If the coefficient is above 0·50, there is a definite degree of correlation.

Applying the formula for the probable error to the coefficient we have just calculated, we get:

$$\text{Probable error} = \frac{0 \cdot 67\{1 - (0 \cdot 897)^2\}}{\sqrt{20}}$$

$$= \frac{0 \cdot 67 \times 0 \cdot 196}{4 \cdot 47} = 0 \cdot 029$$

and the coefficient should be stated as $0 \cdot 90 \pm 0 \cdot 029$.

The coefficient is greater than six times the probable error, and much above $0 \cdot 50$. It can therefore be concluded that, in the case of the twenty observations given, there is a very noteworthy tendency for high marks in English to be accompanied by high marks in French; those who did well in English did well in both, those who did badly, did so in both.

Let us now take an example where the coefficient of correlation is negative.

Table 30. *Exports of coal and unemployment percentages in the coal mining industry*

		Coal exports per quarter 1924 = 100	% of unemployment in coal mining in the same quarter			Coal exports per quarter 1924 = 100	% of unemployment in coal mining in the same quarter
1930	1	97·4	13·5	1932	3	60·6	40·6
	2	87·8	20·8		4	63·2	32·5
	3	85·8	24·9	1933	1	61·2	29·4
	4	85·1	22·4		2	61·8	36·1
1931	1	67·6	23·1		3	64·2	36·7
	2	70·5	29·8		4	66·3	29·4
	3	67·1	33·0	1934	1	60·4	25·7
	4	72·2	26·9		2	65·7	30·6
1932	1	61·4	27·6		3	66·1	30·5
	2	67·2	35·3		4	65·0	25·8

Arithmetic mean of exports = 69·83
Arithmetic mean of unemployment = 28·73 %
Standard deviation of exports = 10·3
Standard deviation of unemployment = 6·11 %
Algebraic sum of products of deviations = − 954·0

$$\text{Mean product of deviations} = -\frac{954 \cdot 0}{20} = -47 \cdot 7$$

$$\text{Coefficient of correlation} = -\frac{47 \cdot 7}{10 \cdot 3 \times 6 \cdot 11}$$

$$= -0 \cdot 76 \pm \text{Probable error}$$

Probable error = 0·060

Again, this figure shows a fairly high degree of correlation, but as it is negative the correlation is inverse. Generally speaking, as the value of coal exports fell over this period, unemployment rose. This rise in unemployment was partly due to the fall in exports and a fall in unemployment was due partly to a rise in exports. It would, however, be too sweeping a generalization to say that the rise in unemployment was wholly caused by the fall in exports, as unemployment also depends upon the extent of the home consumption of coal of which no figures are here given.

SPECIAL POINTS TO BE CONSIDERED IN THE CASE OF TIME SERIES

Trend and Short-term Variation

When the coefficient of correlation between two time series is to be calculated, the effect of trend and short-term (seasonal or cyclical) variation may need to be considered. It may happen that the trends of two series are directly correlated while the short-term variations are inversely correlated. If the coefficient of correlation for the long-term tendency is required, then the short-term fluctuations must be eliminated and the trend figures used for the purpose of calculating this coefficient. If the value of the coefficient for the short-term period is required, then the effect of trend must be eliminated before the calculation is made.

Lag and Lead

The comparison of two historigrams may reveal the existence of an appreciable degree of correlation, but the crests and troughs of the waves may not occur at the same time. The relative may be affected by the subject, but an interval may elapse before this effect makes itself felt. Thus it is natural to expect that wholesale and retail prices should be directly correlated, but movements in wholesale prices will usually precede movements in retail prices.

An increase in unemployment will probably cause an increase in the number of persons in receipt of National Assistance but an interval will elapse between the happening of the two events. The increase in retail prices is said to lag behind the increase in wholesale prices, just as an increase in the number of persons in receipt of National Assistance lags behind an increase in unemployment. The increase in wholesale prices is said to lead the increase in retail prices. Fig. 25 shows two histori-grams in which both correlation and lag are present. Note that curve *b* lags behind curve *a*, the crests in the latter curve being reached three months earlier than those in curve *b*.

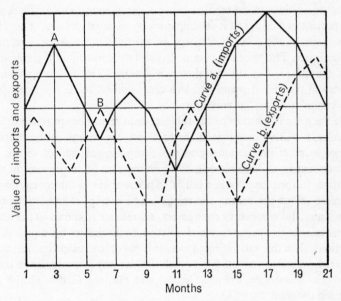

Fig. 25. *Example of lag. Curve* b *lags behind Curve* a

When the degree of correlation between the items in curves *a* and *b* is to be calculated, allowance must be made for lag, for without this allowance it is probable that a high degree of inverse correlation would be indicated. In the above case, if curve *a* is lagged by three months, i.e. brought into line with curve *b* by arranging point A vertically above point B and so on, the direct correlation will be more obvious and its value can be calculated. When lagging takes place, it is important to recognize clearly which historigram lags behind the other and by what period.

THE RATIO OF VARIATION

In one respect, the information conveyed by the coefficient of correlation is rather deficient. If the correlation is direct and perfect, we know that the subject and relative always move up and down in unison. If the correlation is not perfect but still direct, we know that the subject and relative *tend* to move up and down in unison. In neither case, however, have we any idea of the relative *extent* of the movements, i.e. whether a movement in the subject is accompanied by an equal, greater, or smaller movement in the relative. Perhaps an example will make this point a little clearer. The price of a commodity and the demand for it are doubtless correlated, but the correlation is inverse. The following figures represent possible demands for two commodities, the first a necessity, the second a luxury, at varying prices.

If the price is taken to be the subject, and the number purchased, the relative, it will be seen that in the first case, the change in the relative is not so great proportionally as the change in the subject. A fall of 50 per cent in the subject calls forth an increase of 40 per cent in the relative. In the second case, a fall of 50 per cent in the subject causes an increase of 700 per cent in the relative. The average ratio between the proportional deviations of the subject and relative is known as the *ratio of variation*. If the subject and relative both change by equal proportions, then this ratio is equal to 1. It is possible to calculate this ratio by arithmetical processes, but a much simpler way is to use the method first put forward by Francis Galton, and plot the Galton Graph or Scatter Diagram.

Table 31

1.		2.	
Price	Number purchased	Price	Number purchased
6d.	22,000,000	£6 0s. 0d.	500,000
5½d.	25,000,000	£5 10s. 0d.	800,000
5d.	27,000,000	£5 0s. 0d.	1,200,000
4½d.	28,500,000	£4 10s. 0d.	2,000,000
4d.	30,000,000	£4 0s. 0d.	2,900,000
3d.	31,000,000	£3 0s. 0d.	4,000,000

THE SCATTER DIAGRAM

If the subject is plotted on the vertical scale and the relative on the horizontal, a number of points, rather widely scattered, but tending to form a definite band, is obtained. If the line which most nearly indicates the trend of the points is then drawn, we have what is known as the *regression line*. The whole diagram is called a *scatter diagram*. The slope of the regression line gives the ratio of variation. Where the ratio of variation is unity, the regression line will slope at an angle of 45°. If the slope of this line is more than 45° to the horizontal, there is a greater proportionate change in the subject than in the relative. When the slope of the line is less than 45° to the horizontal, the relative shows the greater proportionate change.

Fig. 26 shows the scatter diagram for the example we have used earlier in the chapter for the correlation of English and French marks (Table 29). The points are plotted as follows. The first point corresponds with 87 on the vertical scale and 68 on the horizontal, the second, with 77 on the vertical and 55 on the horizontal, and so on.

The actual ratio of variation is the tangent of the angle which the regression line makes with the vertical, i.e. tan. α. This ratio may be obtained by dividing the horizontal distance of any point B from this line by its vertical distance, i.e. $\frac{BC}{BA}$. In this case, the ratio is $\frac{21\frac{1}{2}}{22\frac{1}{2}}$, i.e. 0·96. This means that on the average, for every change of 1 per cent in the subject, there is a tendency for the relative to change in the same direction by 0·96 of 1 per cent. In this case the changes are nearly in the same proportion and the angle which the regression line makes with the vertical is just over 45°. A simple method of calculating the algebraic equation of the regression line is explained in Appendix 3 (page 250).

THE APPLICATION OF THE COEFFICIENT OF CORRELATION AND ITS LIMITATIONS

The reader must be warned against attaching too much importance to coefficients of correlation calculated from a few items. The two examples chosen for the calculation of the coefficient illustrate the method of calculation, but the actual results can only be applied to the items concerned and then with reservations. When an amount of correlation

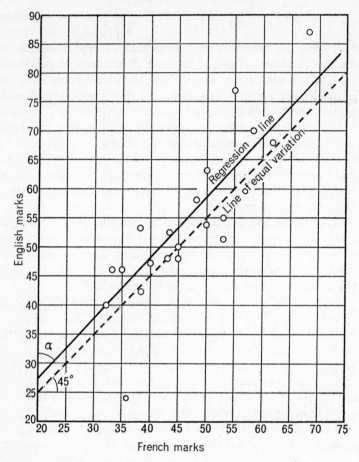

Fig. 26. *Scatter diagram to show ratio of variation between English and French marks*

is used as a basis of argument, it should be calculated from a sufficient number of items to make its general application possible.

Again, because two groups can be shown to have a fairly high degree of correlation, this must not be taken as evidence that one is the cause of the other. Consider the first example we dealt with in this chapter. There is a high degree of correlation between the English marks and the French marks. But it is not therefore necessarily true that a person is good in French because he is good in English, or poor in French because he is poor in English. It is true that a good knowledge of English is a great asset in learning French, but a capacity to do well in both is probably due to the student's inherent capabilities.

On the other hand, a high degree of correlation between the extent of overcrowding and infant mortality might well be used as an argument that one cause of high infant mortality is overcrowding. Before assuming cause and effect for correlated groups, it is desirable to see if both sets of figures may not be the result of some third factor.

RANK CORRELATION

For a discussion on this subject see Appendix 3, page 249.

STUDENT WORK

1. Calculate the coefficient of correlation between the following readings of the price of gold per ounce and the corresponding franc rate of exchange.

Price of gold		Franc rate	Price of gold		Franc rate	Price of gold		Franc rate
s.	d.		s.	d.		s.	d.	
141	0	74·56	141	1	74·50	141	0	74·87
141	1½	74·54	141	1½	74·51	140	11	74·94
141	0½	74·72	141	1½	74·50	141	3	74·57
141	0	74·72	141	3	74·34	141	2	74·67
141	2½	74·62	141	1	74·78	141	1½	74·81
141	2	74·48	141	2½	74·81	141	2	74·47
141	1	74·50	141	1	74·78			

2. Using the figures quoted in Chapter 5, Table 11, calculate the coefficient of correlation between the July rainfall and the yield of corn per acre.

3. Calculate the coefficient of correlation between the following figures giving the value of exports per head of the population of the United Kingdom, and the index of unemployment (1884–1913).

Exports per head	Unemployment index	Exports per head	Unemployment index	Exports per head	Unemployment index
£		£		£	
6·5	8·1	5·6	6·9	7·1	6·0
5·9	9·3	5·8	5·8	7·7	5·0
5·9	10·2	6·1	3·4	8·7	3·6
6·1	7·6	5·9	3·5	9·7	3·7
6·4	4·6	5·8	2·9	8·5	7·8
6·7	2·1	6·5	2·2	8·5	7·7
7·0	2·1	7·1	2·5	9·6	4·7
6·5	3·5	6·7	3·3	10·0	3·0
6·0	6·3	6·8	4·0	10·7	3·2
5·7	7·5	6·9	4·7	11·4	2·1

4. The following figures are taken from a volume of London statistics published by the London County Council. They refer to 1911. Calculate the coefficient of correlation between the percentage of population overcrowded and the infant mortality rate.

% Overcrowded	Infant mortality	% Overcrowded	Infant mortality
13·3	124	12·4	119
23·4	156	14·2	146
33·2	151	7·1	78
13·5	109	25·6	115
14·9	109	20·0	127
12·3	124	17·1	133
12·2	142	13·6	123
39·8	156	3·9	104
14·6	125	16·2	127
12·1	128	20·6	157
20·7	108	36·6	170
25·5	112	25·8	144

5. What is meant by 'ratio of variation'? Explain how it is obtained.

6. Obtain the ratio of variation for the figures given in Chapter 5, Table 11.

7. Interpret briefly the expression $\dfrac{0·67(1 - r^2)}{\sqrt{n}}$ and state its purpose.

8. What do you understand by 'lag' in the case of time series? How may its effect be eliminated for the purpose of calculating the coefficient of correlation?

Chapter 12

Index Numbers

IN Chapter 10, The Analysis of a Time Series, we saw that many sets of statistics collected over a period of time revealed a definite tendency which we called *general trend*. In that chapter, also, we saw how the amount of the general trend might be estimated. The consideration of this trend was, however, limited to individual series; there was no attempt to combine a number of related series and to obtain an expression which would sum up the variations in all the constituent items. The purpose of this chapter is to show how the movements in a large number of related items may be shown by the use of a single expression which typifies, in its calculation and changes, the variations of the items to which it refers. Let us first consider a simple illustration.

Table 32. *Variations in the price of steel and lead*

(i)	(ii)	(iii)	(iv)	(v)	(vi)
	Price per ton	Index	Price per ton	Index	Composite index
Year	of steel	number	of lead	number	number
	£		£		
1926	12	100	45	100	100
1927	10	83·3	40½	90	86·7
1928	9	75·0	40½	90	82·5
1929	8	66·7	36	80	73·4

A convenient way of showing the price movements of both steel and lead is to call the 1926 price of each 100 and then calculate the other prices by the method of proportion. Columns iii and v, in which this has been done, show the extent and direction of these price movements. The figures in these columns are, in effect, simple index numbers; they show the comparative movements of single variables over a period of time. Is it possible to obtain index numbers which show the movements in the prices of both steel and lead? Column vi gives composite index numbers which are the averages of the other two. On the assumption that steel and lead are of equal importance in calculating these index numbers, the variations in the figures in this column indicate the movements in the price of both steel and lead. In the above example only two prices have been considered, but the method is capable of great extension, and we might construct a table of index numbers which would show the variation in the prices of all metals. Composite index numbers, or as they are usually called, index numbers, enable the comparative movements of a group of related variables for a period of time to be followed.

Index numbers, which are really nothing but combined percentages, have been widely employed and their use is extending. They are particularly valuable where it is desired to compare quantities which cannot be directly measured owing to the complicated nature of the data or the imperfection of the knowledge concerning it. The method of index numbers was first employed for the measurement of changes in general prices, or in other words, the purchasing power of money. Unable to collect the prices of all relevant commodities, a number of commodities was selected which was thought to be sufficiently representative of the whole. The price of each in a standard year was called 100; its price in each succeeding year expressed as a percentage of this and the percentages of all the commodities in such a year added together and the sum expressed as a percentage of the whole, formed the index number for that year. Originally used for prices, the method of index numbers is now applied to ascertain the variations in wage levels, rents, cost of living, the level of business activity, and many other forms of economic activity.

THE CONSTRUCTION OF AN INDEX NUMBER

Let us assume that we have to construct an index number which is to show the variations in the wholesale price of metals. In so doing we shall meet four problems which are common to the construction of all index numbers.

1. Items

We shall first have to select proper items to compose the index. Obviously, the index number cannot include every metal and a selection will have to be made. The metals chosen must be representative, i.e. they must enter into industry and trade on a reasonably large scale. Again, it should be possible to define the grade or quality of the included items. This is necessary because there must be no doubt as to the price of the selected items, and confusion in this respect cannot be avoided unless qualities or grades are clearly described.

We have decided that the index shall be of wholesale prices, but it is possible that the wholesale price of the same grade of a metal may be different at two places at one and the same time. Are we to include the prices ruling in the London Metal Exchange only, or to take an average of prices quoted in all the exchanges? In the case of metals, there are comparatively few markets where these are bought and sold wholesale and an average price is not difficult of attainment. In the case of some index numbers, it may be necessary to take an average of several hundred prices of the same commodity. Doubtless it is more satisfactory to use an average price rather than a single price. In any case a determined time must be agreed upon for ascertaining prices.

In connexion with prices, a further point arises. In the calculation of the index shall we use the actual price or a relative price? It will probably be more convenient to calculate the *price relative* from the actual price before proceeding with the construction of the index. The price relative is the ratio of the price at one period to the price at another. Actually, this expression is a price index for each separate item. If we assume that prices in 1926 shall be our standard and the average price of steel in that year was £12 per ton, then in 1928 when the price of steel was £9 a ton the price relative was $\frac{9}{12} = 0.75$, and the index number for steel $\frac{9}{12} \times 100 = 75$.

2. Weighting

After deciding the items to be included and the methods of obtaining and expressing the price of these items, we must next consider the relative importance to be attached to each. In other words, if our index is to be a weighted index we must decide upon the weight to be assigned to each item. Very few satisfactory index numbers can be obtained without some system of weighting and the greater the difference in importance between the various items, the greater the need for a system of weighting.

In our example steel will naturally be among the included items; we may decide to include vanadium, a metal which, though not common, is finding increasing uses in industry. Now the amount of steel sold in a year is far greater in volume and also in value than the amount of vanadium sold in the same period. It would obviously be unfair for an increase of 50 per cent in the price of vanadium to have as much effect on the final index as an increase of 50 per cent in the price of steel. As a general principle, each item should have an effect on the final index commensurate with its importance in the metal markets of the country. If it were possible to ascertain the value of each metal sold in the country in a recent normal year, a satisfactory scheme of weighting could be drawn up therefrom. The weights could then be proportional to the amount of the item sold. But in constructing an index number there is no need to strain after great accuracy in weighting, for it has been shown that slight variations in weights have much less effect on the final index than those variations in actual items which are unavoidable in many cases. It is desirable that the weights should be, as far as possible, convenient numbers. When weighting is used, the weights are more easily applied to price relatives or individual index numbers than to actual prices.

3. The Base

When an index is quoted, two dates are understood because an index number is a comparative figure and the figure with which it is compared, if not given, is always implied. The latter figure is the base. In constructing an index number for the prices of metals or for any other index, the base should be prices ruling in an average year, i.e. when prices were neither unduly high nor low. The prices at the period chosen will then be taken as 100. The choice of a suitable base is important in order that the resulting index numbers shall not be artificially high or low. For prewar years, 1930 might prove a very suitable base year as it is the last year before the price of most metals fell very considerably. After deciding upon the base, it should be clearly set out. If we use 1930 as the base year it must be clear whether the average prices ruling in 1930 are used for the basis of comparison, or whether prices at a given date in 1930 are being considered.

When the base has been decided upon there are two methods of linking the base with successive index numbers.

THE FIXED BASE METHOD

In this case the index numbers for each period is compared with a fixed base. If 1930 were chosen as the fixed base, the index for this would be 100, and all future indices would refer to 1930 as base. It would, of course, be possible to change the base if future circumstances warranted it, but this would not be done as part of a regular plan.

THE CHAIN BASE METHOD

Although the fixed base method is convenient, it has certain disadvantages. As time elapses conditions which were once important become less significant and it becomes more difficult to compare accurately present conditions with those for a remote period. It may be too that new items should now be introduced or that other items should be deleted from the list. For these reasons, instead of using the prices of a fixed base period, the prices are calculated as percentages of the prices ruling at the same time in the previous year. Thus the prices for July 1946 would be compared with those for July 1945, the latter being taken as 100. This method is known as the chain base method and it is particularly suitable for use in business, where information as to the immediate past is of more importance than a comparison with a remoter period. Again, index numbers calculated by the chain base method are more free from seasonal variations than those obtained by the other method. One disadvantage of this method is, however, obvious; comparisons between distant periods are not immediately evident. To enable such comparisons to be made, chain base indices must be converted into fixed base indices. This may be done as follows:

Yearly chain base index numbers		Corresponding indices converted to a fixed base	
1930	100	1930 as base	100
1931 (1930 as base)	87	1930 as base	87
1932 (1931 as base)	78	1930 as base $\dfrac{87 \times 78}{100} = 68$	
1933 (1932 as base)	80	1930 as base $\dfrac{68 \times 80}{100} = 54\frac{1}{2}$ etc.	

4. The Average Employed

An index number is a kind of average, since it represents in a single figure the characteristics of a group of items. We saw in Chapter 7 that a group of items could be represented by a number of averages, the arithmetic mean, median, mode, etc., the choice of the particular average depending upon the information required. The same considerations which determine the choice of average in the case of statistical groups also apply to index numbers.

The arithmetic mean has the defect we have already noticed in discussing averages in allowing too much importance to a few very large or very small items. Further, if the price of any item increases, the arithmetic mean tends to exaggerate the effect of the rise. For these reasons, the geometric mean, which is not so markedly influenced, is often used. It is more difficult to calculate than the arithmetic mean, but where the number of items is small this difficulty is not overwhelming.

AN EXAMPLE OF THE CONSTRUCTION OF AN INDEX NUMBER

We give one example in this chapter of the construction of an important index number. It will be seen that it illustrates most of the foregoing points. We shall also have occasion to refer to other important index numbers and their calculation in future chapters.

Before we discuss the example, however, we should repeat that index numbers may be calculated either from actual prices, or from price relatives. If a series of indices is required it is more usual to employ price relatives which are themselves index numbers or production relatives, etc., depending upon the purpose of the index. Most of the official index numbers referred to in this book are calculated from relatives of one type or another. A simple illustration of an index number calculated directly from prices is first given.

The average prices of certain minerals in £s per ton is given as follows:

Year	Iron Scottish pig	Cleve-land	Common bars	Copper Stan-dard	Tin Straits	Lead English pig	Coal Walls-end in London
1867–77	$3\frac{1}{2}$	3	$8\frac{1}{4}$	75	105	$20\frac{1}{2}$	$1\frac{1}{10}$
1930	$3\frac{3}{4}$	$3\frac{3}{8}$	10	$54\frac{3}{4}$	145	$19\frac{1}{2}$	$1\frac{1}{4}$
Weights	10	5	3	1	1	10	10

Calculate a price index for 1930 based on 1867–77 average price as 100.

Multiplying the 1867–77 prices by the weights assigned and finding the total we get

$$35 + 15 + 24\tfrac{3}{4} + 75 + 105 + 205 + 11 = 470\tfrac{3}{4}$$

Repeating this with 1930 prices:

$$37\tfrac{1}{2} + 16\tfrac{7}{8} + 30 + 54\tfrac{3}{4} + 145 + 195 + 12\tfrac{1}{2} = 491\tfrac{5}{8}$$

The ratio of prices in 1930 to those in 1867–77 is therefore

$$\frac{491\tfrac{5}{8}}{470\tfrac{3}{4}}$$

The respective index will be

$$\frac{491\tfrac{5}{8}}{470\tfrac{3}{4}} \times 100 = 104\cdot4$$

And now to return to an official index. *The Economist* used to publish monthly an Index of Business Activity. The following details are taken from an *Economist Trade Supplement* of some years ago This index was a composite index of employment, consumption of coal, industrial consumption of electricity, railway goods receipts, commercial vehicles in use, postal receipts, building activity, consumption of cotton, consumption of iron and steel, imports of raw materials, exports of manufactures, shipping movements, provincial bank clearings, and town bank clearings. This list is fully representative of general business activity, and had the advantage that the relevant figures were fairly easy to obtain, at least. in normal times. The base is the average of these separate indices for 1935, which are all taken as 100. For April 1936, the following individual indices were obtained, all corrected for seasonal variations. (This means that if the final index shows any change from the previous one, this change is not due to seasonal influences.)

For the calculation of the final index, the geometric mean is used mainly for the reason we have already stated – the disadvantage possessed by the arithmetic mean in exaggerating the effect of a rise in any constituent item.

Table 33. *Construction of 'The Economist' Index of Business Activity*

Item	April 1936 index	Weight assigned
Employment	$103\frac{1}{2}$	10
Consumption of coal	103	4
Consumption of electricity	111	2
Railway goods receipts	$106\frac{1}{2}$	4
Commercial vehicles in use	$104\frac{1}{2}$	2
Postal receipts	102	3
Building activity	$106\frac{1}{2}$	2
Consumption of iron and steel	126	2
Consumption of cotton	110	1
Imports of raw materials	$110\frac{1}{2}$	2
Exports of manufactures	101	3
Shipping movements	$98\frac{1}{2}$	2
Provincial bank clearings	101	4
Town clearings	97	1
		$\underline{\underline{42}}$

By using four-figure logarithm tables, we can quote the final index, and at the same time we shall illustrate the calculation of the geometric mean. (For the month in question, *The Economist* quoted the index as 105.)

$$
\begin{aligned}
\text{Log } 103 \cdot 5^{10} &= 2 \cdot 0149 \times 10 = 20 \cdot 1490 \\
\text{,, } \quad 103^{4} &= 2 \cdot 0128 \times 4 = 8 \cdot 0512 \\
\text{,, } \quad 111^{2} &= 2 \cdot 0453 \times 2 = 4 \cdot 0906 \\
\text{,, } \quad 106 \cdot 5^{4} &= 2 \cdot 0273 \times 4 = 8 \cdot 1092 \\
\text{,, } \quad 104 \cdot 5^{2} &= 2 \cdot 0191 \times 2 = 4 \cdot 0382 \\
\text{,, } \quad 102^{3} &= 2 \cdot 0086 \times 3 = 6 \cdot 0258 \\
\text{,, } \quad 106 \cdot 5^{2} &= 2 \cdot 0273 \times 2 = 4 \cdot 0546 \\
\text{,, } \quad 126^{2} &= 2 \cdot 0969 \times 2 = 4 \cdot 1938 \\
\text{,, } \quad 110^{1} &= 2 \cdot 0414 \times 1 = 2 \cdot 0414 \\
\text{,, } \quad 110 \cdot 5^{2} &= 2 \cdot 0607 \times 2 = 4 \cdot 1214 \\
\text{,, } \quad 101^{3} &= 2 \cdot 0043 \times 3 = 6 \cdot 0129 \\
\text{,, } \quad 98 \cdot 5^{2} &= 1 \cdot 9934 \times 2 = 3 \cdot 9868 \\
\text{,, } \quad 101^{4} &= 2 \cdot 0043 \times 4 = 8 \cdot 0172 \\
\text{,, } \quad 97^{1} &= 1 \cdot 9868 \times 1 = 1 \cdot 9868 \\
\hline
& \qquad\qquad\qquad\quad \underline{84 \cdot 8789}
\end{aligned}
$$

Since the geometric mean is $\sqrt[42]{103 \cdot 5^{10} \times 103^4 \times 111^2}$, etc., the total of the logarithms must be divided by 42:

$$\frac{84 \cdot 8789}{42} = 2 \cdot 0209$$

$$\text{Antilog. } 2 \cdot 0209 = 104 \cdot 9$$

i.e. 105 nearly, the figure quoted by *The Economist*.

This indicates that the level of business activity in April 1936 was about 5 per cent above the average level for 1935.

It must be recorded, however, that few, if any, important index numbers now make use of the geometric index. It was very widely used in prewar days but its popularity has since waned.

STUDENT WORK

1. What is meant by an index number? Give an account of the problems which arise in the construction of index numbers.

2. Compare the utility of chain base and fixed base index numbers. Show how chain base index numbers may be converted into fixed base index numbers.

3. Compare the utility of the arithmetic and geometric averages in the calculation of index numbers.

4. Calculate the cost-of-living figure from the following statistics for 1 January 1937 (using the arithmetic average).

	Food	Rent and rates	Fuel	Clothing	Other items
Index	36	59	90	92·5	77·5
Weight assigned	$7\frac{1}{2}$	2	$1\frac{1}{2}$	1	$\frac{1}{2}$

5. Calculate the index of business activity for November 1936, using the weights and method indicated in Chapter 12, from the indices given in *The Economist Trade Supplement*, 26 December 1936:

Employment 107, Consumption of Coal 101, Consumption of Electricity $117\frac{1}{2}$, Merchandise on Railways $105\frac{1}{2}$, Commercial Motor Vehicles in use $107\frac{1}{2}$, Postal Receipts 107, Building Activity 105, Consumption of Iron and Steel 125, Consumption of Cotton $100\frac{1}{2}$, Imports of Raw Material 130, Exports of Manufactures $100\frac{1}{2}$, Shipping Movements 106, Metropolitan, etc., Bank Clearings $109\frac{1}{2}$, Town Clearings 111.

6. The following are figures of national expenditure on Social Services. The figures are in £s million and are for the year ended 31 March. If now the total expenditure in 1924 (£262·5) is taken as 100, calculate the index for each item and each total.

	1924	1931	1932	1933
Unemployment insurance	48·0	101·6	122·8	117·6
Health insurance	30·9	38·6	37·5	37·5
Pensions except war pensions	24·0	72·1	78·4	81·3
Education	86·6	104·8	103·3	101·5
Housing	16·6	40·0	42·6	42·6
Poor relief	41·9	42·5	41·2	44·1
Miscellaneous	14·5	19·5	20·0	21·3
	262·5	419·1	445·8	445·9

Chapter 13

Sources of Statistical Information

IT is proposed in the next few chapters to illustrate the statistical methods already described by discussing some of the more important published statistics and principally those issued by government departments. Although small in volume compared with the statistical data available today, the statistics collected and published by these departments prior to 1939 were adequate to meet the functions of the Government as then understood. Most of these statistics, including the decennial census of population, short-term vital statistics, and the quinquennial censuses of production, were obtained (and still are) under statutory powers. Statistics of foreign trade have long been collected by virtue of such authority; their collection is, however, continuous and regular, unlike that of the nationwide censuses. Various Mines Acts permitted the collection of statistical information on output, manpower, accidents, and the like, in coal and metalliferous ore mines, and quarries. Statistical data relating to the agricultural industry have long been collected and published by the Ministry of Agriculture.[1] Employment and unemployment statistics issued by the Ministry of Labour were reasonably comprehensive in prewar days. Details of the income and expenditure of the Central Government and Local Authorities were, as now, readily available. Price information was collected and issued by many private organizations, primarily for the benefit of their members. This information related, in the main, to raw materials and primary manufactures handled in the organized produce markets. Short-term production series were few, and apart from those relating to mining were generally the result of voluntary returns made by firms to their trade association or controlling body. Iron and steel production and

[1] Now (1964) known as the Ministry of Agriculture, Fisheries and Food.

tonnage of shipping launched were among the best known of such figures. Statistics of retail sales, mainly in the form of indices, were published by the Board of Trade and the Bank of England. Commercial activities were measured by a number of indicators; perhaps the note circulation of the Bank of England and total Bank Clearings were the most important of these. Railway traffic receipts provided a useful pointer to the state of trade and production generally.

The census of population and census of production results lent themselves to much useful statistical analysis, but these censuses were comparatively infrequent. The Board of Trade produced a quarterly index of industrial production for the main industries covered by the census of production. The information available on wholesale prices was combined by this government department into an index of wholesale prices, the object of which appeared to have been the measurement of changes in the general price level. Changes in working-class cost of living were assessed by the Ministry of Labour Cost-of-Living Index which was started before the First World War. Indices were computed by the Board of Trade to show changes in the volume as opposed to the value of Britain's overseas trade. Assessments of the country's balance of payments and national income were made, for the most part, by economists not completely identified with government service.

This not inconsiderable statistical information was brought together in the *Annual Abstract of Statistics* issued by the Board of Trade. Students would be well advised to obtain access to one of these Abstracts in order to assess the changes which have taken place in the country's economy over the last twenty-five or more years.

At the outbreak of war the volume of statistics issued for general circulation was reduced, but the statistical activities of some government departments tended to grow. Quite early in the war the Central Statistical Office was set up to provide the country's administrators with the data required to plan the war effort and to measure achievements against target. In 1941 the first of the series of White Papers[1] giving official estimates of the national income and expenditure was issued. Towards the end of the war the whole future of the government statistical service was reviewed. The need to maintain a high and stable level of employment was accepted by all political parties and this, of necessity, involved a more positive direction of the many and varied

[1] In the early 'fifties these became 'Blue Books'.

economic activities of the country. Such control could only be effectively carried out if assisted by adequate statistical information.

Accordingly, the Central Statistical Office was established on a permanent basis to direct and co-ordinate the collection and analysis of official statistics. For administrative purposes every major production and commercial activity of the country was placed under the 'sponsorship' of a government department. The iron and steel, non-ferrous metal, and engineering industries were made the special province of the Ministry of Supply,[1] building and the production of building materials, that of the Ministry of Works,[2] and the textile and many other non-metal processing industries, together with retail trade, that of the Board of Trade. The Statistics of Trade Act was passed in 1947 to enable these government departments to collect statistics on a statutory basis if they so desired. Three reasons for the collection of statistics are stated in the Act, viz. the appreciation of economic trends, the provision of a statistical service for industry, and the discharge by government departments of their particular functions. The Act also provided for an annual census of production and for periodical censuses of distribution.

PRESENT POSITION (1965)

Naturally, there has been an enormous growth in the volume of statistics collected by government departments. Most of these new statistics are of the short-term variety, relating to a month's or a quarter's production or trade. Not all of them are published but a large proportion is made available in one form or another. For purposes of identification and comparison it was found necessary to devise and adopt a new industrial classification. This classification is called the Standard Industrial Classification. Employment and unemployment figures published by the Ministry of Labour now follow this classification. In 1958 this Classification was revised, but the revision was not put into operation until 1960. Output tables from the census of production also follow this classification. Shortly after the end of the war a monthly publication, the

---

[1] In 1959, the iron and steel industry was under the sponsorship of the Ministry of Power, the engineering industries under the Board of Trade (with the exception of aircraft and electronics). The sponsorship functions of the Ministry of Supply passed to the Ministry of Aviation in 1959.

[2] Now the Ministry of Public Buildings and Works.

Monthly Digest of Statistics, was launched and it has continued to grow in size and scope since then. At the end of this chapter an idea of the contents of this publication is given. The general layout of the manufactured goods tables in the *Monthly Digest* is as shown below. The publication of this digest is intended to form part of the statistical service for industry. Economists, industrialists, trade union leaders, social workers, and those interested in market research are thereby provided with a valuable compendium of up-to-date statistics, the departmental source of which is stated at the foot of each table.

The publication of the *Annual Abstract of Statistics* was resumed sometime after the end of the war. As now issued by the Central Statistical Office, it contains annual figures for as long a period as possible for the tables shown in the *Monthly Digest*, but with the addition of many more dealing witn Area and Climate, Population and vital statistics, Social Conditions, Education, etc. Sections which are common to both the *Monthly Digest* and *Annual Abstract* are more fully covered in the latter. For example, the latest census of production reports are shown in summary form, as are the Blue Books on National Income and Expenditure. This publication is on sale about a year after the last year to which it relates. A fuller idea of its contents is given at the end of this chapter. Separate Digests for Scotland, Wales, and Northern Ireland are now published, but at half-yearly or longer intervals.

Statistical information shown in the *Monthly Digest* and *Annual Abstract* must of necessity be in summary form unaccompanied by descriptive material. For more detailed information on any one section one would need to consult the publications of the government department responsible for the collection and analysis of the figures. Thus, reports issued from time to time by the Registrar-General show different aspects of the population situation as it existed in 1961. Regular quarterly reports issued by the Registrar-General give the latest statistics of births, marriages, and deaths for Great Britain as a whole. Detailed information of commodity exports to individual destinations is frequently required. Such detail is to be found in the *Accounts relating to the Trade and Navigation of the United Kingdom*.[1] This document is published monthly by the Board of Trade. It gives also a comparison with earlier years both monthly and cumulatively. In the same way, the

---

[1] As from the beginning of 1965 called 'Overseas Trade Accounts of the United Kingdom.'

Table 34. *Specimen table in 'Monthly Digest of Statistics'*
ELECTRICITY GENERATING PLANT AND ROTATING ELECTRICAL MACHINES

Monthly averages or calendar months

	Deliveries of electricity generating plant						Production of rotating electrical machines[1]							
	Hydraulic turbines		Steam turbo-alternators 10,000 kW and over		Steam turbines less than 10,000 kW		Fractional horse-power		A.C. motors		A.C. generators		D.C. machines	
	Total	Export	Total	Export	Total	Export	Total	For export	Total	For export	Total	For export	Total	For export
	Thousand B.H.P.		Thousand kW				£ thousand							
1960	94·7	77·0	428·9	155·9	13·6	6·2	1,248	228	—	—	—	—	—	—
1961	55·1	33·9	396·6	144·9	14·1	8·6	1,229	190	—	—	—	—	—	—
1962	46·8	27·4	334·2	138·2	10·8	3·3	1,187	174	—	—	—	—	—	—
1963	54·5	52·7	407·1	158·4	14·2	4·4	1,318	186	—	—	—	—	—	—
1963:														
1st qtr.	39·7	39·7	305·8	116·0	14·0	7·3	1,294	193	—	—	—	—	—	—
2nd qtr.	15·8	15·8	417·5	111·0	22·6	7·7	1,316	200	—	—	—	—	—	—
3rd qtr.	62·6	55·6	370·8	166·7	11·4	—	1,209	169	2,801	526	325	79	1,083	194
4th qtr.	99·8	99·8	534·2	241·0	8·8	2·3	1,454	183	2,813	606	614	197	1,189	205
1964:														
1st qtr.	43·3	43·3	331·7	215·0	8·9	4·0	1,494	195	2,981	557	623	142	1,134	238
APRIL	130·0	130·0	864·1	360·0	} 7·6	} 3·9	1,672	257	2,901	620	541	92	1,304	277
MAY	1·1	1·1	205·0	60·0			1,511	226	2,678	496	568	126	1,184	298
JUNE	—	—	350·0	—			1,601	223	2,960	455	539	152	849	237
JULY	130·0	130·0	1,449·8	80·0	} 11·6	} 4·1	1,387	219	2,662	517	407	121	1,194	312
AUG.	—	—	275·0	—										
SEPT.	135·8	135·8	125·0	125·0										

[1] Earlier figures showing the classification by horse-power were last published in the *Monthly Digest* for September 1964.

Source: Board of Trade

Census of Production Office of the Board of Trade produces detailed reports on the industries separately distinguished in the census. The Ministry of Labour provides a wide range of manpower and related statistics in their monthly publication *The Ministry of Labour Gazette*.

Some of the statistics issued by government departments are, in fact, collected through the agency of public bodies and trade associations. The Coal Board collects statistics of manpower, output, etc., which appear in the *Monthly Digest* as coming from the Ministry of Power – which department, incidentally, has its own annual statistical publication. The Ministry of Power acts in a similar way through the British Iron and Steel Federation and Iron and Steel Board. Such public or semi-public bodies often issue their own statistical bulletins. The *Statistical Bulletin* of the British Iron and Steel Federation and the Iron and Steel Board is published monthly and is supplemented by a Year Book.

An attempt is made at the end of this chapter to give an idea of the range of published statistics. It is by no means exhaustive since it is confined to economic statistics. Moreover, it may reflect the author's particular interests in the metal and engineering industries. Later chapters discuss a few of the more important analyses which have been made of this information, and, in particular, deal with the compilation of the various indices used to summarize and measure changes in related groups of figures. Before reaching this list, it will be of use to review, briefly, existing international statistics of an economic nature.

INTERNATIONAL STATISTICS

Although all advanced countries maintained their own series of official statistics before the war, international comparisons were rather difficult. This difficulty arose largely on account of the lack of uniformity in the statistical classification adopted by each country. The League of Nations Secretariat and the International Labour Office were successful in reconciling a large number of these national classifications and in producing many social and economic reports which contained international comparisons. Continuity was broken as a result of the war.

Very early in its history the United Nations Organization set up a statistical office and for a number of years now the *Monthly Bulletin of Statistics* of the United Nations has been published. More than sixty tables appeared in the monthly issues during 1965. These tables are divided into much the same groups as the *Monthly Digest of Statistics* and their layout is similar. Not every country is able or willing to provide information for every table, but the U.N. Statistical Office has been remarkably successful in securing the whole-hearted co-operation of all the members and associated countries. In recent years the U.S.S.R. has provided a fair amount of basic information to the *Bulletin*. Most tables therein need to be supplemented with footnotes which serve to record any slight differences of interpretation or classification. Specialist studies are made from time to time by the U.N. Statistical Office, as for example, *National Income Studies*, 1938–47. *World Energy Supplies*, 1965.

In order to introduce a greater uniformity into overseas trade statistics, a Standard International Trade Classification has been drawn up. This has now been adopted either as a primary or secondary classification by most of the larger trading countries.

The Economic Commission for Europe (E.C.E.) is now producing annually an *Economic Survey* for Europe. Like its U.K. counterpart this contains much descriptive material as well as statistical tables. The so-called Iron Curtain countries provide much material for this survey, and, for purposes of comparison, statistics relating to the United States are included in most of the tables.

The Organization for European Co-operation and Development (O.E.C.D.)[1] collects and disseminates to the governments of member countries a great deal of statistical material bearing upon economic and financial questions. Some of this finds its way to general circulation by way of special reports and studies.

The International Monetary Fund (I.M.F.) now produces international statistics mainly of a financial character.

SOURCES OF STATISTICAL INFORMATION

Mention has already been made of the limitations of the list which follows. It was compiled towards the end of 1965. A full Index of Sources to the Tables in the *Annual Abstract* is given in the *Abstract*.

[1] Formerly Organisation for European Economic Co-operation (O.E.E.C.).

U.K. PUBLICATIONS

1. General Economic

The *Monthly Digest of Statistics*, published by H.M.S.O., with sections on:

National income and expenditure	Manufactured goods
Weather	Building and civil engineering
Population and vital statistics	Food and agriculture
Labour	External trade
Social services	Transport and communication
Industrial production indices	Finance
Fuel and power	Wages and prices
Industrial materials and	Distribution, miscellaneous

The *Annual Abstract of Statistics*, H.M.S.O., with sections on:

Area and climate	Transport and communications
Population, vital statistics, and public health	External trade
	Balance of payments
Social conditions	National income and expenditure
Education	
Labour	Banking, insurance, company formation
Production	
Distribution	Prices

Economic Survey.[1] Annually from 1947 onwards, H.M.S.O.
Economic Trends. Monthly, H.M.S.O.
London and Cambridge Economic Service. Quarterly Bulletins until end 1951, thereafter in *The Times Review of Industry*.
Economic Review. Quarterly by the National Institute of Economic and Social Research.
Journal of the Royal Statistical Society.
Industry and Employment in Scotland. Annually.
Digest of Scottish Statistics. Twice a year.
Bank of England Quarterly Bulletin.
The National Plan (*first published 1965*) *H.M.S.O.*

[1] From 1963 onwards, called *Economic Report*.

2. *Production*

(*a*) General:

    Monthly Digest of Statistics.
    Annual Abstract of Statistics.
    Abstract of Regional Statistics.

(*b*) Census of Population. Special Reports, H.M.S.O.

(*c*) *Censuses of Production.* Reports for 1930, 1935, 1948, 1951, 1954, and 1958.

    Digest of Welsh Statistics – annually.

    Digest of Statistics – Northern Ireland – twice a year.

    1948 and later censuses of production – articles in *Board of Trade Journal. Annual Abstract of Statistics.*

    Business Monitor Series. Monthly. Board of Trade.

(*d*) Fuel and power

    Quarterly Statistical Statement. National Coal Board.

    Annual Reports of National Coal Board.

    Annual Reports of Electricity Boards.

    Ministry of Power Statistical Digest, H.M.S.O.

    Monthly Digest and *Annual Abstract.*

(*e*) Agriculture

    Agricultural Statistics of the United Kingdom. Annually, H.M.S.O.

(*f*) Iron and steel

    Monthly Bulletin and *Year Book* of the British Iron and Steel Federation and Iron and Steel Board.

(*g*) Non-ferrous metals

    World Statistics of Non-ferrous Metals. Monthly.

    Quin's Metal Handbook. Annually.

    Metal Statistics. C. Tennant, Sims & Co., New York. Annually.

(*h*) Textiles

    Cotton Board Quarterly Statistical Review.

    Reports of the International Cotton Advisory Committee.

    Wool Industry. *Monthly Bulletin of Statistics.*

(*i*) Rubber

    Rubber Statistical Bulletin. Monthly.

(*j*) Motor vehicles

    Monthly Statistical Review and *Year Book,* published by the Society of Motor Manufacturers.

(*k*) Housing

Housing Summary for Great Britain. Monthly, H.M.S.O.
Housing Return. Quarterly, H.M.S.O.

3. Manpower, Employment, Unemployment, etc.

Monthly Digest and *Annual Abstract*.
Ministry of Labour Gazette. Monthly, H.M.S.O.
Annual Report of the Ministry of Labour and National Service.
    H.M.S.O.
Annual Report of H.M. Chief Inspector of Factories. H.M.S.O.

4. Earnings and Wage Rates

Ministry of Labour Gazette.
London and Cambridge Economic Service.
Time Rates of Wages and Hours of Labour. Annually. Ministry of
    Labour.
'*Statistics on Incomes, Prices, Employment and Production*'. H.M.S.O.

5. Productivity

Reports of the Anglo-American Council on Productivity. No longer
    produced.
Economic Survey and Economic Report.

6. Vital Statistics, Health

Population Census Reports.
Registrar-General's Statistical Review of England and Wales. Annually.
Annual Report of the Registrar-General for Northern Ireland.
Quarterly Returns of births, marriages and deaths – Registrar-General.
Annual Report of the Ministry of Housing and Local Government.
    (All H.M.S.O.)

7. Defence

Statistical Digest of the War.
Statement on Defence (Command Paper).
Navy, Army, Air Force Estimates and Appropriation Accounts. Now
    Ministry of Defence Estimates, etc. (All H.M.S.O.)

8. Transport and Communications

Annual Report of the five sections of the British Transport Commission.

Transport Statistics. British Railways Board. Monthly.

Basic Road Statistics. Annually, British Road Federation.

9. Overseas Trade

Accounts relating to the Trade and Navigation of U.K. Monthly.[1]

Report on Overseas Trade. Monthly.

Board of Trade Journal. Weekly.

Annual Statements on the Trade of U.K.

Monthly Digest and *Annual Abstract.*

Balance of Payments Command Papers. (All H.M.S.O.)

10. Prices and Price Indices

Board of Trade Journal.

Ministry of Labour Gazette.

Monthly Digest and *Annual Abstract.*

Metal Bulletin.

Bulletin and *Year Book* of British Iron and Steel Federation and Iron and Steel Board.

11. National Income and Expenditure

National Income and Expenditure Command Papers and Blue Books. Both Annually.

Economic Survey and *Economic Report.*

Monthly Digest and *Annual Abstract.* (All H.M.S.O.)

12. Miscellaneous

Journal of the Royal Statistical Society – Series A, B, and C.

Bulletin of the Oxford Institute of Statistics.

Financial Statistics. Monthly. H.M.S.O.

Criminal Statistics. Annually. Home Office.

Friendly Societies' Statistical Summary. Annually.

Report of the Commissioners of Inland Revenue. Annually.

Report of the Bank of England. Annually.

[1] From 1965 *Overseas Trade Accounts of the United Kingdom.*

Statistics of Education. Annually. Min. of Education.

Reports on the Census of Distribution.

Board of Trade Journal and full-length reports.

Reports of the Registrar-General of Friendly Societies. Annually.

INTERNATIONAL STATISTICS

Monthly Bulletin of Statistics of the United Nations.

Statistical Year Book. Annually. United Nations.

Demographic Year Book. United Nations.

Yearbook of National Accounts Statistics. United Nations.

Commodity Studies – Timber, Cotton, Rubber, Coal. Annually. United Nations.

Economic Survey of Europe. Annually. Economic Commission for Europe.

Economic Survey for Asia and the Far East. Annually. United Nations.

General Statistics. Bi-monthly. O.E.C.D.

Foreign Trade. Monthly. O.E.C.D.

Industry Studies – Engineering Industries, etc. Annually. O.E.C.D.

Country Studies – O.E.C.D. Countries. Annually. O.E.C.D.

Publications of the International Labour Office, Geneva.

Digest of Colonial Statistics. H.M.S.O.

Reports of the International Metal Conference.

Trade Yearbook. Food and Agriculture Organization. Annually.

International Financial Statistics. Monthly. I.M.F.

Balance of Payments Year Book. I.M.F.

THE USE OF COMPUTERS IN THE ANALYSIS OF OFFICIAL STATISTICS

At the time the present edition was being prepared (end 1965), the use of computers for the analysis of official statistics was very widespread. All the government departments which collect a significant volume of statistics from industry, agriculture, commercial concerns, or from individuals by way of the census or similar inquiries, have installed computers for the analysis of this information.

Chapter 14

Vital Statistics

VITAL statistics, or as they are sometimes called, demographical statistics, are perhaps the most easily understood and most widely used of all published economic data. For a short period in 1961 the population census was a topic of great national importance. This topic reached its climax on 23 April when the sixteenth census was taken. As the various official reports on this census become available they will be greeted with enthusiasm by economists, sociologists, and administrators, and may evoke a mild interest on the part of the general public. But vital statistics comprise much more than an analysis of the population census, or estimates of the population at intercensal periods. They include the figures of births, marriages, and deaths issued regularly by the Registrar-General, and the isolation and interpretation of trends which these regular figures may embody.

POPULATION

Facts regarding population are obtained from the population census and from estimates made in non-census years. This most important branch of the Government's statistical work is under the control of the Registrar-General. The population census has been taken every ten years since 1801 with the sole exception of 1941 – one of the war years. Legal powers have existed for some years to take a census quinquennially. These powers will be used for the first time in the sample survey to be taken in 1966. The Registrar-General, by virtue of the information he receives from the compulsory registration of births and deaths and the records of immigration and emigration, is able to estimate the population at any time. In practice these estimates usually refer to the mid-year period.

The list of questions which formed the basis of the 1931 census has already been discussed in Chapter 2. More questions were asked in 1951. Those relating to sex, age, marital condition, relation to head of household, occupation, and usual residence were again in the questionnaire. A question on the place of work which formed part of the 1921 census was repeated in 1951. Two short questions on education were included. The first, whether the enumerated individuals were receiving full- or part-time education at an educational establishment, was a repetition of a 1921 question. The second asked those who were gainfully occupied to state the age at which their full-time education ceased. Additional and quite new questions inquired whether each household had exclusive use of, shared with another household, or lacked entirely, piped water supply within the house, cooking range and other amenities. The remaining questions related to the duration of marriage and number of children and were asked of married women under the age of 50. These women were asked to give the date of their marriage or marriages and the total number of children born to them in marriage. These questions were intended to supplement existing data on fertility, and in particular the information which, since 1938, has been collected on this subject when births are being registered.

In the main, the 1961 census contained the same kind of questions as its immediate predecessor. Among the more important differences were:

1. The extension to the entire population, of the question seeking information about the age at which full-time education ceased.

2. A new question sought information on scientific and technological qualifications held.

3. The inclusion of a new question designed to obtain information about the frequency, amount, direction, and characteristics of population movements.

4. The information sought on kitchen facilities was restricted to households sharing dwellings.

5. A new question dealt with housing tenure – whether premises were owner-occupied, part of business premises, or rented from a Council or private landlord.

There was one most important departure from earlier practice. It will be recalled that a number of the provisional analyses relating to the 1951 census were obtained from a 1 per cent sample of the forms collected.

In 1961 there were two kinds of forms distributed; a shortened form to be completed by nine out of ten householders and occupants of hotels, hospitals, and similar institutions, and a more lengthy form which had to be filled in by the remaining one-tenth. This was the first time in our history that sampling procedures had been used in the collection of census information. The sample was so arranged as to be fully representative over the country as a whole and everyone had the same possibility of being included. The questions chosen for sample treatment were those relating to occupation, employment, place of work, status in employment, scientific and technological qualifications, together with those relating to change of usual residence and duration of stay at recorded residence.

As with all questionnaires, the value of the information obtained from the census depends upon the correctness of the answers to the questions. On the whole, the information is reliable because not only are examples given on the form for the guidance of the public, and skilled enumerators give assistance where necessary, but what is more important, the census has behind it the compelling power of the law from which no one is exempt. Even so, a certain amount of erroneous information creeps into the census forms. A small proportion of people give their ages in round numbers rather than their exact age; ages of 41 or 42, for example, are set down as 40. Ladies are notoriously unwilling to state their exact age and a proportion understate it. However, these inaccuracies are very small and unimportant in comparison with the great mass of accurate and valuable information obtained.

The Preliminary Report was issued within two months of the taking of the census. Space does not permit the discussion of more than a few of the more outstanding facts revealed by it. Some of these can best be shown in tabular form page 144.

As members of the Armed Forces, Mercantile Marine, and civilians serving or living abroad were not enumerated, the 1961 total is rather lower than the population estimate made by the Registrar-General for mid-1961, viz. 52,216 thousands for the United Kingdom. The resident population in England and Wales represents a density of 790 persons per square mile – a density which, with the exception of Holland, is higher than nearly every country in the world. For Great Britain as a whole the density is 580 persons per square mile.

Population Changes 1951–1961

Table 35 shows that population grew much faster in England and Wales than in Scotland and Northern Ireland. The national increase in the population was augmented, particularly towards the end of the period, by a comparatively large number of immigrants. The Birthplace

Table 35. *Population of United Kingdom, 1951 and 1961*

(Numbers in thousands)

	England and Wales		Scotland		Northern Ireland		United Kingdom	
	No.	%	No.	%	No.	%	No.	%
1951								
Males	21,016	48·1	2,434	47·8	668	48·8	24,118	48·1
Females	22,742	51·9	2,662	52·2	703	51·2	26,107	51·9
Total	43,758		5,096		1,371		50,225	
1961								
Males	22,304	48·4	2,482	47·9	695	48·8	25,482	48·3
Females	23,801	51·6	2,697	52·1	731	51·2	27,229	51·7
Total	46,105		5,179		1,426		52,711	
Increase between 1951 and 1961								
Males	1,288	6·1	48	2·0	27	4·0	1,364	5·7
Females	1,059	4·7	35	1·3	28	4·0	1,122	4·3
Total	2,347	5·4	83	1·6	55	4·0	2,486	4·9

The 1961 distribution of males and females implies that in the United Kingdom there were 1,043 females per 1,000 males.

and Nationality Tables show that in 1961, no fewer than $1\frac{1}{2}$ million of the population of England and Wales (46,105,000) were born abroad. By mid-1964, the population of the United Kingdom had grown to more than 54 million and that of England and Wales to 47·40 million. Immigration accounted for a significant proportion of this increase. There was also a small but steady movement from Scotland to England during the intercensal period and this flow has continued. The more rapid growth in the male than in the female population is a reflection of the slightly greater number of male than female births.

Geographical Changes

(See Fig. 27.) The rate of growth varied considerably from region to region. In general, the population of the southern half of England grew at a faster rate than the northern half, while in Wales the growth was hardly noticeable. The tendency of population to move south has now persisted for over 40 years and may, in the next few years, create economic and social problems in the south-east. The population increase in the Home Counties and the areas immediately around London was well above the average for the country as a whole, although the population of Greater London, returned as 8,172,000, was less than 1931 and significantly less than in 1939. This is accounted for by the tendency of families to move out of the London conurbation to the Home Counties.

An interesting feature of postwar social policy has been the establishment and growth of 'New Towns'. Twelve such towns are distinguished in the Preliminary Report for England and Wales. Four of these, Basildon, Crawley, Harlow, and Hemel Hempstead had populations of over 50,000 in 1961. The population of the twelve New Towns grew from 135,000 in 1951 to 426,000 in 1961, and their growth continues.

Of the cities outside the County of London, Birmingham headed the list with a population of 1,106,000, followed by Glasgow with 1,055,000. Both these cities returned somewhat lower figures than in 1951, as also did Liverpool, 747,000, and Manchester, 661,000. The movement of families to areas outside city boundaries is the cause of this decline. Only one other city, Leeds, 511,000, had a population of over half a million.

It is of interest to note that the latest population estimates for all cities, towns, and urban district council areas can be found in the Quarterly Housing Return produced by the Ministry of Housing and Local Government and published by H.M.S.O.

The 1961 census shows that more than half the total population and two-thirds of the urban population of England and Wales live in comparatively dense units containing more than 50,000 persons. This crowding into large towns is further shown by the fact that 50 per cent by number, of the towns are small and contain less than 8 per cent of the total population, or 10 per cent of the urban population; the latter as defined in the Local Government Act of 1929.

Employment of Scientific and Technological Personnel

The 1961 census schedule which was completed by one household in ten included a question directed to all persons with stated qualifications in science and technology. Such persons were asked to state the relevant academic and/or professional qualification held and the main branch of science and technology in which these qualifications were held. In the recent past there have been a number of inquiries concerned with these topics but this was the first time such a question had been asked in a census schedule. On account of the importance placed by the Government on this information, its tabulation and analysis was given priority and a report was published about fifteen months after the census date.

This report gives the number of persons holding scientific and technological qualifications and related these to the sex, occupation, industry in which employed, age, and marital condition of the holders. Nearly 288,000 persons or just over one half of one per cent of the population of Great Britain held such qualifications. Of these, 40,000 were economically inactive, i.e. retired, not gainfully occupied or out of employment at the time of the census. The proportion of males aged 25–34 with such qualifications was $2\frac{1}{2}$ per cent. The teaching profession is the largest single employer of such qualified persons. Teaching and other professional and scientific services including public administration and defence absorbed 40 per cent of the gainfully occupied population with scientific and technological qualifications. Of those employed in industry, the majority were working in the chemical, aircraft, electronics, and electrical engineering industries.

Age Distribution of the Population

At the time of writing, i.e. towards the end of 1965, a number of analyses had not been published. For the latest age distribution of the population, reference can be made to the *Digest of Statistics* which gives this distribution for the middle of 1964. A comparison of the position in 1931 and mid-1963 is shown in Fig. 27. This period covers a decade or so of comparatively low birth-rates, followed by two decades of significantly higher rates. The lower birth-rates of the early thirties account for the fall in the proportion of persons in the 15–34 age group. The range 15–64 contain nearly all those who are in employment and on whom the economic life of the nation is mainly dependent. Having regard to the fact that many more young persons in the 15–34 age group are now in full-time education than in 1931, it will be seen that the economically active proportion of the population is now appreciably smaller than in 1931. The growth in the proportion of the '65 and overs', particularly females, is very pronounced. One in seven of all females in the United Kingdom are in this group. Once the age of 75 is reached, the female population exceeds the male by at least two to one.

Other Features of the Census

Earlier editions of this book have commented upon the social and economic facts brought out by the 1951 census. It was pointed out that in England and Wales in 1951, the percentage of households with more than two persons per room was only one-third of the 1931 figure. One would expect that less overcrowding existed in 1961 than in 1951. As in the latter year, this tends to be higher in the north than in the south. The 1951 census revealed that three out of eight households had no fixed bath and that $7\frac{1}{2}$ per cent shared with others. Published 1961 figures show that fewer than one-quarter of households are without baths and less than 5 per cent share.[1]

Comment was made on the earlier marriage age compared with 1931. By 1951, nearly half the women in the 20–24 age group and four out of five in the 25–34 group were married. This trend towards earlier marriage has continued. The total in civil employment increased by about one-tenth between the two census years. Employment in manufacturing industry as a whole has remained constant in total but within this total, employment in engineering has increased and that in textiles, declined. Substantial increases have taken place in employment in the distributive traders, professional and financial services and in construction. Employment in agriculture and mining have continued to decline.

BIRTHS, MARRIAGES, AND DEATHS

Particulars of every birth, marriage, and death must be lodged with the local registration authorities within a limited time from the happening of the event. From these registrations, birth, death, and marriage rates are obtained for the United Kingdom as a whole as well as for individual areas. For the country as a whole the Registrar-General obtains the figures, while for local authorities the Medical Officer of Health usually compiles them.

Birth Rates and Death Rates

Birth rates are expressed as so many live births per 1,000 of the estimated population at the middle of the year. The Registrar-General, who receives all statistics of births and deaths, is in a good position to make

[1] See Housing Tables, Parts I and II.

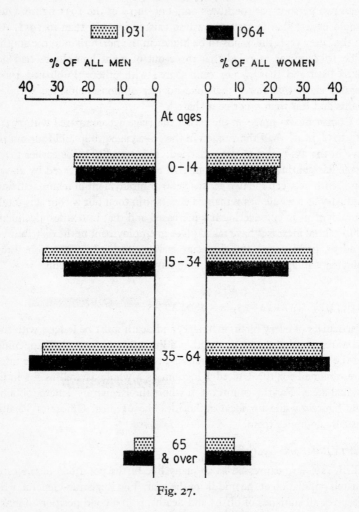

DISTRIBUTION OF POPULATION
BY AGE GROUPS

GREAT BRITAIN

▦ 1931   ■ 1964

% OF ALL MEN   % OF ALL WOMEN

40 30 20 10 0   0 10 20 30 40

At ages

0–14

15–34

35–64

65 & over

Fig. 27.

REGIONAL CHANGES IN POPULATION
1931 – 1961
Changes as percentages per annum

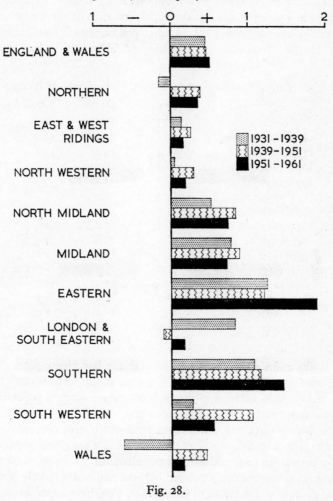

Fig. 28.

an accurate estimate of the population of the country at any given time. In fact, the Registrar's estimate for the population at the time of the census is usually very close to the figure revealed by the actual census, allowing for H.M. Forces serving overseas.

In the same way the general death rate is the number of deaths occurring in a year per 1,000 of the population alive in the middle of the year. The marriage rate gives the corresponding figure for marriages.

Table 36, which refers to England and Wales, shows how greatly

Table 36. *Birth, death, and associated rates – England and Wales*

Year	Birth rate	Death rate	Survival rate
1871–1880 (average)	35·4	21·4	14·0
1881–1890 ,,	32·4	19·2	13·2
1891–1900 ,,	29·9	18·2	11·7
1921–1930 ,,	18·9	12·5	6·4
1935	14·7	11·7	3·0
1939–1941 ,,	14·3	12·9	1·4
1942–1945	16·4	11·6	4·8
1946–1949 ,,	18·5	11·5	7·0
1950–1959 ,,	15·7	11·6	4·1
1960	17·2	11·5	5·7
1961	17·6	11·9	5·7
1962	18·0	11·9	6·1
1963	18·2	12·2	6·0
1964	18·4	11·3	7·1

the births and deaths have changed over the last ninety years. The difference between these two rates is known as the survival rate. This rate gives some indication of the probable future trend in population, but the indication is not a very precise one.

The higher birth and stable death rates which have operated since 1942 have been the main cause of the dissipation of the gloom which was felt in prewar days about the future population of this country. Nevertheless, as we have already pointed out, the number of elderly people in the country will continue to grow and this will have important social consequences.

INFANT MORTALITY RATE

Another frequently quoted death rate is the infant mortality rate. This is the death rate of children under one year of age per 1,000 live births. Although still considerably higher than the general death rate, the infant mortality rate has shown a spectacular decline this century. This may be taken as evidence of the great improvement in medical knowledge and skill and of the value of the child and pre-natal welfare services. In the decade 1871–80, this particular rate averaged 150. By the beginning of the century it was as high as 145. Since then it has fallen continuously and more and more rapidly. It was 80 in 1920, 64 in 1930, 57 in 1940, 33 in 1950, and 22 in 1960. The 1964 figure was 20.

One might expect from the laws of chance that the number of male and female births taken over a period would be the same. But for a long period now the ratio of male to female births has been of the order of 1,050 to 1,000, i.e. 21 boys are born to every 20 girls. For 1935, for example, the ratio was 1,059 to 1,000, for 1962, 1,061 to 1,000. The higher death rates of male children bring the population of males and females into equality in the age groups 20–24. Thereafter, there is a greater number of females than males.

CRUDE AND CORRECTED DEATH RATES

The death rates for local areas, as quoted by their Medical Officers of Health, are really crude death rates because they take no cognizance of the age distribution of the population in these areas, and as such are not strictly comparable. Thus, we may find that the crude death rates of such health resorts as Cheltenham, Bath, and Harrogate are actually higher than those for many London residential suburbs. This is due to the fact that the former towns contain a high proportion of elderly people who have retired to them and the death rate is consequently higher than in the case of certain London residential suburbs containing a large proportion of young married couples. The average age of the population of England and Wales was 32·7 years in 1931, for Cheltenham the average age was 36·0, for Bath and Harrogate 37·0 each. Coming to more recent times it can be said that the average age in 1963 was 36·0. The average age of the population of the 'New Towns' was no doubt much lower than this.

F

If we wish to make a comparison of the death rates on an equitable basis, we must calculate the corrected death rates and use these for the purpose of comparison. The corrected death rate is a weighted mean, and as a rule the weights assigned in calculating it bear a definite relation to the age distribution of the population in the country as a whole. In order to make the point a little clearer, let us use the following symbols and obtain from them an expression indicating a corrected death rate.

Let the total population of the country be P, of whom

p_1 are between the ages of   0 and   4 years

p_2 ”   ”   ”   ”   5 ”   9 ”
p_3 ”   ,   ,   ”   10 ” 14 ”
p_4 ”   ”   ”   ”   15 ” 19 and so on.

If now we are considering the corrected death rate of a town, we must know the death rates for each of the age groups 0–4 years, 5–9 years, 10–14 years, etc.

Let these be represented by – d_1, d_2, d_3, etc.

Then the corrected death rate will be:

$$\frac{p_1d_1 + p_2d_2 + p_3d_3 + \ldots}{P}$$

Of course, age distributions other than the one named above might be used, but as the census publications (and intercensal) estimates give the total population of the country divided into those same groups, this distribution is most commonly employed. The practical effect of the method is to weight the death rate for each age group with the proportion of people in the country as a whole in each of the particular groups. Thus the actual age distribution in the town considered is immaterial in the calculation of the corrected death rate. If the percentage of people in each age group is known, the calculation of the corrected death rate will be considerably shortened.

STUDENT WORK

1. Calculate:

    (a) The crude death rate in a town.

    (b) The death rate in each age group.

    (c) The corrected death rate.

    (d) The infant mortality rate, assuming the following figures:

Population of the town in June of the year considered								62,960
Number of deaths during the year								845
Age group	0–4	5–14	15–24	25–34	35–44	45–54	55–64	65 and over
Population in each group	10,080	12,402	6,370	8,950	8,310	7,528	5,170	4,150
Deaths in each group	251	177	54	80	82	81	60	60
% of total population of Great Britain in each group	12·1	17·7	15·8	15·1	14·0	11·6	7·7	6·0
Number of live births	1,020							
Number of deaths of children under 1 yr.	71							

Chapter 15

Manpower, Employment, and Related Statistics

THIS is now a well-documented field of economic activity – at least from the statistical point of view. As we have seen, the population censuses of 1951 and 1961 both contained questions on personal occupations and from the answers to these questions the occupational tables in the census reports are prepared. A standard classification 'Classification of Occupations, 1960' was used for the relevant tabulations arising from the 1961 census. But much more frequent statistical information on labour matters is required and arrangements have long been in operation to collect regular statistics on employment and unemployment. The operation of the comprehensive system of social services introduced in 1948 and the importance accorded to manpower in the planning of the nation's resources have provided both the need for, and the means of, obtaining further statistical data. All matters relating to manpower and employment come within the purview of the Ministry of Labour.

THE WORKING POPULATION

The starting point of an assessment of the country's labour supply and its industrial distribution is the total working population. This is defined as 'all persons aged 15 or over at work, or registered as available for work'. At a date in June 1964, the total working population of Great Britain was given as 24,981,000. It is not a static figure, of course. Young people enter the category when registering for, or taking their first job, older people leave it by marriage, retirement, or death. Married women who take up employment swell its ranks, and so on. The working population is made up of four main categories, as shown in Table 37.

The assessment of the numbers in H.M. Forces presents no particular statistical difficulties and the changes in their total must necessarily reflect the international situation. We will content ourselves by saying that at mid-1939, the Armed Forces numbered 480,000. At the middle of 1945 they reached a peak of 5,090,000. After September 1945, there

Table 37. *Distribution of manpower in Great Britain, June, 1964*

	Thousands	
H.M. Forces and Women's Services		424
of which, Males	408	
Females	16	
Men and women on release leave		—
Registered unemployed		322
of which wholly unemployed		317
Total in civil employment		24,240
of which, Males	15,798	
Females	8,442	
Total working population		24,981
of which, Males	16,446	
Females	8,535	

was a rapid decline as demobilization gathered strength. After the end of 1946 this decline became much slower, but continued until the middle of 1950, when the total was 690,000. Thereafter, and as a consequence of the worsening of international relations, an increase in the size of the Armed Forces was decided upon and the length of military service increased. By the middle of 1952 the numbers in the Forces had risen to 872,000. Thereafter, a steady decline ensued and by mid-1964 the numbers had fallen to 424,000. Conscription had been abandoned some years earlier.

TOTAL IN CIVIL EMPLOYMENT

The computation of this figure and its distribution into industries provide a big statistical problem. Prior to 1948 the figures quoted under the heading were incomplete and included a large element of estimation. The comprehensive national insurance scheme which came into operation in July 1948 provided the means for a more complete assessment. The main basis of the figures of total in civil employment is the annual exchange of employment cards. Since 1948 it has not been possible to have a simultaneous exchange of all cards. Instead, they are exchanged in four quarterly groups. In allocating the cards to the groups, arrangements have been made to ensure a random distribution of the different cards among the insured population. Consequently, the total in civil employment at the quarterly exchange of cards is deemed to be four times the number of cards exchanged. One addition has to be made to the total so obtained, that of established civil servants whose insurance contributions are paid by other means and who do not have cards.

The June exchange is rather more comprehensive than the other three and yields an additional analysis by way of employment in industries. At this point it becomes necessary to refer again to the Standard Industrial Classification. This is a list of some 170 industries and services grouped in 24 main categories. Every industrial, commercial, and service establishment is classified to one of these 170 divisions. The classification assigned depends upon the major product made by the establishment or the most important service it renders. Thus, an establishment (i.e. factory premises) may produce electric motors only, in which case it will be classified to the electrical machinery industry. If it were to make wireless sets and wireless valves as well it would be classified either to the wireless apparatus and valve, or electrical machinery, industry, depending upon which was the more important product. But the essential thing to note is that the entire employment at that establishment will be registered to the industry to which the establishment has been classified. The insurance card of every employee bears the code number of the industry to which the establishment at which he works belongs. This is made use of to obtain an accurate figure for employment in each of the 170 industries and services.

At the June exchange of cards ('B' cards) employers of five or more persons make a return of the total number of cards held by them, distinguishing the number of 'B' cards. These returns provide the equivalent of a complete count for the employers who render returns, and a 75 per cent sample of the total number of current cards. From this very large sample the numbers employed in each industry or service can be estimated with but a negligible margin of error.

The results of the June count can therefore be taken as authoritative both as regards total in civil employment and its distribution over industries. The total figure is accurately estimated at quarterly intervals by the other three counts. Changes in the industrial pattern of employment between one June count and the next have to be estimated by other means. The basis of this particular estimation is the monthly employment return completed by industrial and other establishments employing more than 100 workers and by a sample of 1 in 4 of establishments employing 11 to 100 workers. This return, commonly known as the 'L' return,[1] can be used to estimate employment, at a date in each month, of a large proportion of the 170 industries and services of the Standard Industrial Classification. The 'L' return asks for the number of employees, male and female, at each establishment and bears the code number of this establishment. The 'L' return also makes possible a monthly estimate of the total in civil employment, and, occasionally, the total on defence work.

The results of all these estimates are shown in the *Ministry of Labour Gazette* the *Monthly Digest of Statistics*, and *Statistics on Incomes, Prices, Employment and Production*. The total in civil employment rose slowly from mid-1948, when it was reported as 21·6 million to the mid-1951 figure of 22·3 million. The mid-1952 figure was given as 22·1 million. There was a fall in the early months of 1952 on account of temporary unemployment in the textile trades. From the end of 1952 until the middle of 1957 the total in civil employment rose steadily to 23·2 million. From then until the end of 1958 a slightly downward trend occurred and the December 1958 total was 22·9 million. For the next three and a half years, the total slowly rose to just over 24 million. There was a sharp set back in early 1963, but the slow rise was soon resumed. Perhaps the most noticeable feature of the 1948–64 period was the steady expansion in the chemical and engineering and metal-using trades, attributable to the continued high level of demand, at home and abroad, for metal goods, coupled, from 1950 to 1955, with the effect of rearmament. Employment in the textile, mining, and agricultural industries has slowly declined since 1954. The total employed in manufacturing, changed but little between 1954 and 1964. There were significant increases in building and construction, distribution and the other services. A regional analysis of employment and unemployment by industries is published annually by the Ministry of Labour, largely from the June exchange of books.

[1] See Chapter 2, p. 12.

REGISTERED UNEMPLOYMENT
Total

So far we have dealt with three of the main sub-sections of the total working population. There remains a fourth – registered unemployment. So long as a person is in work his or her employment card remains with his employer (except during the annual exchange). If this person becomes unemployed the card is lodged at the local employment exchange. From these lodged cards the unemployment statistics are compiled. Analyses showing the industrial and regional distribution of unemployment can therefore be made. They relate to a specific date round about the middle of the calendar month. The industrial analysis follows the Standard Industrial Classification; the regional one can be in accordance with local areas and their combination into the nine standard regions of Great Britain used in official statistics.

For obvious reasons unemployment statistics attract more general attention than do figures relating to employment. The introduction of the new series of statistics from mid-1948 onwards has not reduced the comparability of prewar and postwar statistics of unemployment quite so much as in the case of civil employment and industrial analyses.

The average unemployment in the first quarter of 1926 was 1,140,000. During the three years 1927–29, this average was about 1,100,000 in the summer months and rather higher in winter on account of seasonal variations. Unemployment rose rapidly during 1930 and exceeded $2\frac{1}{4}$ millions in the last quarter of that year. The rise went on until 1933, during the first quarter of which year it averaged 2,845,000. Thereafter the trend was downwards and by the last quarter of 1937, the average was a little above $1\frac{1}{2}$ million. 1937 must be reckoned the best of the prewar years from the production and employment point of view. 1938 saw a rise in unemployment, but the quickened pace of rearmament in 1939 and the outbreak of the war in September quickly reduced the figures. Table 38 shows the mid-year unemployment totals from 1938 to 1965.

As can be seen from the table, unemployment in Great Britain virtually disappeared after 1941 and in the postwar period remained at a very low level in comparison with prewar days. There is still a seasonal pattern; the lower level of building activity in the winter months causes an increase in unemployment. This was particularly true of the early months of 1963. The August, and to a less extent, the January[1] figures, may be swollen on account of school-leavers who have not found employment when the returns are compiled. Over the past twelve years, there has been a certain amount of cyclical variation in unemployment. There were slight recessions in 1952, in 1958, and again in 1962–63. These were partly due to steps taken by the Government to ease inflationary pressures which were particularly severe just prior to these dates. Unemployment at the end of 1958 and 1962 exceeded half a million. Measures taken to encourage expansion soon followed and the figure dropped to the postwar average. The decline in textiles and shipbuilding have brought temporary increases in unemployment in the areas engaged in these industries.

Table 38. *Registered unemployment in Great Britain*

Mid-year figures: Thousands

1938	1,803	1950	282	1961	266
1940	645	1952	440	1962	397
1942	87	1954	240	1963	480
1944	54	1956	223	1964	322
1946	383	1958	429	1965	276
1948	286[2]	1960	305		

Unemployment by Regions

In prewar days, the percentage level of unemployment differed widely from region to region. It was heaviest in the coal-mining, shipbuilding, and iron and steel trades, and since these tend to be somewhat localized, Wales, Scotland, the North-East and North-West areas of England had particularly heavy rates of unemployment. Thus, in November 1936, 27 per cent of the insured population of Wales was unemployed. For London, the percentage was 6·7. Now that the unemployment position is so much less severe these differences, although they still exist, are less striking, except, perhaps, in Northern Ireland. Successful attempts have been made to steer new factories to the areas of comparatively heavy unemployment (now called Development Areas). Table 39 shows the unemployment percentage, by region, in the middle of August 1964, when the total unemployment figure was 400,000. For a

[1] From 1964 onwards, this no longer applies.
[2] New series; on the old basis the figure was about 276.

fair comparison of the level of unemployment over fairly long periods, the number of persons registered as unemployed as a percentage of the total employees should be used. This percentage averaged 2·0 in Great Britain in 1952; in 1955 the percentage was only 1·1. Since then it has varied between.

Table 39. *Percentage unemployed – Regional Analysis, August 1964*

London and S.-E.	0·9	Northern	3·4
Eastern and Southern	1·0	Scotland	3·4
South-Western	1·3	Wales	2·5
Midlands	1·0	Great Britain	1·6
Yorks and Lincs	1·3	Northern Ireland	6·2
North-Western	2·1		

Duration of Unemployment

Each month a table appears in the *Ministry of Labour Gazette*[1] showing the composition of the unemployed population at a given date in accordance with the duration of unemployment. The divisions shown are wholly unemployed for two weeks or less, over two weeks but not more than five weeks, more than five weeks but not more than eight, over eight weeks and temporarily stopped.

LABOUR TURNOVER

An interesting series of statistics has become available since the war as a result of quarterly returns made by employers to the Ministry of Labour. This series relates to the rates of labour turnover and the results are published quarterly in the *Gazette*. Labour turnover is shown by a figure of the number of engagements, and the number of discharges or losses, in a month as a percentage of the numbers employed at the beginning of the month. These two percentages are given for males, females, and total workers for each Standard Industrial Classification industry coming within the scope of manufacturing industries. The rate of labour turnover is higher than one might expect. Engagements averaged about 2·8 per cent per month and discharges about the same during 1964. This implies an annual labour turnover

[1] Most of these employment and unemployment statistics are also shown in the *Monthly Digest, Annual Abstract* and *Statistics on Incomes, Prices, Employment, and Production*.

rate of over 30 per cent. As is to be expected, the rate of turnover of female labour is appreciably higher than for male. Fairly wide variations exist between industries.

UNFILLED VACANCIES, SHORT-TIME AND OVERTIME

Among the various indicators of the demand for labour, statistics of unfilled vacancies, and of the number of operatives on short-time or overtime, together with the aggregate hours of short-time and overtime, have pride of place. The relation of the number of unfilled vacancies to total unemployment is regarded by some authorities as of special significance. If vacancies exceed unemployment, a state of overfull employment is said to exist. Monthly figures of unfilled vacancies, classified in accordance with the Standard Industrial Classification and by Standard Regions, are given in the *Ministry of Labour Gazette*. This publication also shows the amount of short-time and overtime during one week in each quarter classified industrially. Fig. 29 illustrates total unfilled vacancies and total unemployment on the same graph and thereby illustrates the changes in inflationary pressure from 1961 to 1964.

TIME LOST THROUGH INDUSTRIAL DISPUTES

The Ministry of Labour publishes this information monthly in the form of an aggregate number of working days lost in each major industry during the month in question. This information is supplemented by a résumé of the causes, progress, and impact of the principal trade disputes. Statistics of working days lost also appear in the *Monthly Digest* and *Annual Abstract*. Some 2·1 million days were lost on the average in the years 1935 to 1938. In the five years 1948–52 the average was 1·7 million days. The total in civil employment had increased appreciably since prewar days, the incidence of disputes was therefore less than the averages imply. In the period 1953 to 1956 the average number of days lost was rather higher, 2·6 million in fact. The average of the seven years 1957–63 was even higher at 4·4 million. In 1963 only 1·8 million days were lost compared with over 5,500 million days worked. 2·3 million days were lost in 1964.

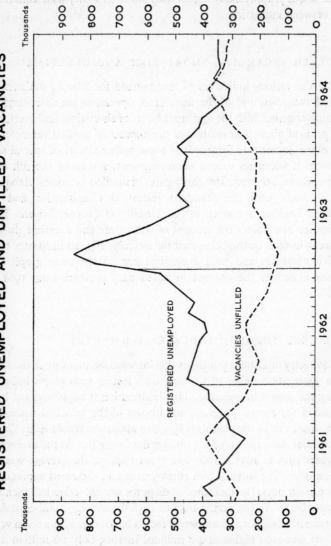

Fig. 29. *Registered unemployment and unfilled vacancies (Economic Trends, September, 1964)*

HOURS WORKED AND EARNINGS

No study of manpower and related statistics would be complete without reference to hours worked and earnings. The official statistics of these are obtained by means of a six-monthly inquiry made by the Ministry of Labour. The inquiry relates to a week in April and a week in September or October, and the present series goes back to 1938. Earlier

Table 40. *Average weekly earnings and hours worked*

		Earnings					Hours worked	
Date		Men			All workers		Men	All workers
				1938 =		1938 =		
		s.	*d.*	100	*s.*	*d.*	100		
October	1938	69	0	100	53	3	100	47·7	46·5
July	1940	89	0	129	69	2	130	—	—
,,	1944	124	4	180	96	8	182	51·2	48·6
April	1946	120	9	175	101	0	190	47·6	46·2
,,	1950	145	9	211	124	1	233	47·0	45·6
,,	1954	197	8	286	166	6	312	48·3	46·5
,,	1958	253	2	367	214	2	402	48·0	46·2
,,	1962	312	10	453	263	0	493	47·3	45·7
,,	1964	352	5	511	294	8	553	47·8	46·1

inquiries at less frequent intervals have also been made. Practically all manufacturing industries and a number of important service trades now come within the scope of the inquiry, which is, however, limited to wage-earners. More than 6½ million employees were covered by the inquiry of April 1964, the results of which appeared in the August 1964 issue of the *Ministry of Labour Gazette*. Only the broadest summary of these results can be quoted here and these are shown in Table 40.

It is clear from this table that the increases in weekly earnings since 1938 have been smaller for men than for other workers. The largest percentage increase has been in the earnings of girls, but the increase in boys' and women's earnings has also been greater than of men. These differential increases were obtained during the war and in the early postwar years. In more recent years, however, these differentials have been reduced. Some information on the extent of payment by results is also sought in the inquiry on hours worked and earnings. The

October inquiry in alternate years beginning with 1947, has included a question on payment by results. The percentage of employees so remunerated rose from 28 per cent in October 1947, to 34 per cent four years later. Since then the proportion has tended to decline, and by 1957, it had fallen to 31. The percentage varies considerably from industry to industry and as one would expect it is higher in manufacturing industry than in the service and similar trades. In 1938, only 25 per cent of employees were paid by results. Analyses of earnings by occupations and by regions are now published along with the other six-monthly series.

Table 41. *Ministry of Labour Index of Weekly Rates of Wages*

31 Jan. 1956 = 100
30 June 1947 = 64·1

Monthly averages

1948	67·8	1959	117·0
1950	71·0	1960	120·0
1952	83·3	1961	125·0
1954	91·0	1962	129·6
1956	104·7	1963	134·3
1958	114·0	1964	140·8

INDICES OF WAGE RATES

Earnings are, of course, affected by overtime or short-time working. Wage rates in the present context refer to average rates for the normal or standard working week. Two such indices are now available; one computed by the Ministry of Labour, and the other by the London and Cambridge Economic Service. The former is now based on wage rates in operation on 31 January 1956. It replaces and improves upon an index based on rates ruling on 30 June 1947. It is possible to link the two indices by a factor obtained from an examination of the indices for 1956 which have been quoted on both bases. The current index is given for 'All Industries and Services' and for 'Manufacturing Industries' and separate figures are quoted for men, women, juveniles and all workers. The index measures the average movement from month to month in the level of full-time weekly rates of wages in the principal industries and services in the United Kingdom. The percentage increases in the various industries are combined in accordance with their relative importance as measured by their total wage bill in 1955. Table 41 shows how the Ministry of Labour Index of Rates of Wages has moved from mid-1947 to the middle of 1964, for 'all workers'.

The above table shows that in the sixteen years from mid-1947 to mid-1964 weekly wage rates more than doubled; the increase, in fact, was 120 per cent or an average of 5·1 per cent per annum.

An index calculated by the London and Cambridge Economic Service was published quarterly in the Supplement to *The Times Review of Industry* based on mid-June 1950 = 100. This index was known as the 'Quoted Full-time Weekly Wage Rate Index'. In its earlier form it had been known as the Bowley Index; it had been devised by the late Sir Arthur Bowley. By linking successive series this index could be carried back for many years. In September 1961, this index and its sub-indices were replaced in *The Times Review* by a monthly series of index numbers for each major industrial group. These indices were carried back to 1949. The originators were economists at Manchester University. Figures from 1961 onwards have appeared from time to time in *The Times Review*.

PRODUCTIVITY

Productivity is usually considered in relation to labour employed and is assessed in terms of output per man-hour, man-week, or man-year. Unfortunately very little information exists on this most important development in statistical measurement. The difficulties are many, output in real or physical terms cannot readily be measured, nor can the amount of labour which has been applied to this output be assessed. We shall see later when we discuss the census of production that net output per person gives another measure of productivity, but comparison between successive years' figures cannot properly be undertaken until the effect of price changes has been eliminated. All these aspects were considered in most of the reports of the Anglo-American Council on Productivity during the active life of this body. The only regular productivity figures published in this country relate to output per man-shift in the coal mines. These are given monthly in the *Digest of Statistics* and in the publications of the National Coal Board. The *Economic Review* and the various regular bulletins issued by the Economic Section of the Treasury nowadays may quote changes in output per man for manufacturing industry as a whole. The first issue (1958) of *Economic Review* issued by the National Institute of Economic and Social Research contained estimates of changes in productivity over a number of years in a wide range of industries.

'Wage Drift'

For a considerable time now, average hourly earnings have increased faster than average wage rates. This is because hourly earnings reflect the effect of higher overtime rates, payment by result schemes, and local settlements which provide higher earnings than do national ones. The difference between earnings and wage rates is known as *wage drift*. Some idea of its extent may be obtained from the fact that in the three years 1960 to 1963 hourly wage rates for men increased by 15 per cent, but hourly earnings by nearly 20 per cent.

Qualified Manpower

Reference has already been made to the information obtained in the 1961 census on the holders of scientific and technological qualifications. Since 1956 triennial inquiries have been carried out by the Ministry of Labour to determine the stock of such persons employed in industry, education, government departments, and the public sector, the kind of work they do and the immediate and short term requirements for such personnel. The results of the 1962 inquiry were published in Cmnd. 2146, *Scientific and Technological Manpower in Great Britain*. A further inquiry was carried out early in 1965.

STUDENT WORK

1. Draw up the following tables and, by using the current issues of the *Ministry of Labour Gazette*, insert the appropriate figures.

   (a) A table to show the variations in the unemployment percentages in the various administrative districts for a period of six months.

   (b) A table to show the variations in the unemployment percentages in the main industries for a period of six months.

2. Write an account of the Standard Industrial Classification.

3. Draw a graph to illustrate the following quarterly averages of the registered unemployment in Great Britain (1926–36) (figures in millions):

1926	1st	1·140	1929	4th	1·281	1933	3rd	2·397
	2nd	1·390	1930	1st	1·543		4th	2·268
	3rd	1·584		2nd	1·762	1934	1st	2·303
	4th	1·493		3rd	2·045		2nd	2·110
1927	1st	1·259		4th	2·297		3rd	2·115
	2nd	1·031	1931	1st	2·622		4th	2·109
	3rd	1·050		2nd	2·574	1935	1st	2·255
	4th	1·107		3rd	2·734		2nd	2·030
1928	1st	1·149		4th	2·668		3rd	1·960
	2nd	1·119	1932	1st	2·666		4th	1·901
	3rd	1·288		2nd	2·714	1936	1st	2·022
	4th	1·355		3rd	2·843		2nd	1·746
1929	1st	1·353		4th	2·757		3rd	1·630
	2nd	1·113	1933	1st	2·845		4th	1·621
	3rd	1·152		2nd	2·573			

4. Explain how the figure for total unemployment is arrived at.
5. Compare current earnings, hours of labour, and the extent of payment by results with the conditions obtaining in 1938.
6. Describe the computation of the current index of rates of wages.
7. Compare the working days lost through industrial disputes in the post-war decade with those of prewar days.

Chapter 16

Overseas Trade Statistics

SOURCES OF STATISTICS

THE collection and analysis of the statistics of Britain's foreign trade are under the supervision of the Board of Trade. These statistics have been collected and published now for very many years. Indeed, some records of imports and exports go back to the thirteenth century. Britain, in common with most other countries, has accordingly maintained more detailed figures of overseas trade than of any other branch of economic activity. This is largely because the figures are obtained as a by-product of other operations – the records made for the levying of customs duties. Although in essence they are 'secondary data' their scope is so wide and their contents so detailed that they permit of an enormous number of useful tabulations and analyses.

Importers and exporters are required by law, under penalty, to enter upon the appropriate forms full particulars of the goods imported or exported by them in accordance with *the official classification*. Exported goods must be entered for customs purposes either as 'exports – produce and manufactures of the United Kingdom', or 're-exports of imported merchandise'. The latter category includes only goods, materials, or articles exported in the condition they were imported, or having undergone minor operations which leave them essentially unchanged – as, for example, blending or bottling. The official classification is important. For imports, this is known as the Import List,[1] for exports, the Export List. These are issued annually and differ slightly from year to year, the tendency being towards greater detail in the commodity section. It will be sufficient if the contents of the Export List are discussed as the Import List is similar in content.

[1] From 1959 onwards the Import List has been renamed 'Statistical Classification for Imported Goods'.

Since the fourth edition of this book was issued Britain, along with many other countries, has adopted the Standard International Trade Classification (S.I.T.C.), thereby greatly improving the comparability of overseas trade statistics. This was revised in 1963 to bring it into line with the Brussels tariff nomenclature. In this classification there are ten main commodity classes designated by the numbers 0 to 9. Each of these classes is further subdivided into a very large number of commodities, some of which are further split up into types. Exporters must indicate the heading in the Export List, which is most appropriate to the goods being exported. From the beginning of 1959 they must also give the correct statistical code number for the heading selected. They must quote the units required by the List which will generally be one or more units of quantity together with value, and also the place and country of final destination. The tabulation, each month, of the enormous number of documents which arise from Britain's overseas trade provides a task of great magnitude. It is performed by the Statistical Section of H.M. Customs and Excise. By means of an electronic computer,[1] preliminary totals are available to the President of the Board of Trade about the middle of the next month. Thus, total imports and exports together with some analyses of country of origin and destination for June are known by the middle of July. About a week later the *Trade and Navigation Accounts* are on sale. These show in detail the imports and exports by commodity and country, for a fair proportion of the items shown in the Export and Import Lists. Monthly totals, the cumulative total for the year to date, and comparisons with previous years' figures are also shown. The student of economic statistics should familiarize himself with the content of the *Accounts relating to the Trade and Navigation of the United Kingdom* – to give the full title[2]. They are among the most used official statistics and they form the basis for many of the routine and *ad hoc* analyses of Britain's overseas trade which are a feature of present-day announcements. Summaries of exports and imports by groups, together with comment on trends and changes, appear in the *Board of Trade Journal*. Year Books, which give a run of annual trade figures, are also published after the lapse of an interval.

[1] Before 1964 a punched card system was used.

[2] From the beginning of 1965 called 'Overseas Trade Accounts of the United Kingdom'.

International comparisons of imports and exports are to be found in regular O.E.C.D. publications, limited mainly to the trade of O.E.C.D. countries, and also in the Statistical Bulletin of the United Nations.

GENERAL NATURE OF BRITISH OVERSEAS TRADE

Preoccupation with the level of imports and exports, their nature, and country of origin or destination, has been an outstanding characteristic of the postwar era. These are all facets of the balance of payments problem, about which more will be said later in the chapter. With the greater degree of currency convertibility which came into operation at the beginning of 1959, the geographical distribution of imports and exports is not so important as it was in the early postwar years. There has also been a considerable change in the nature of British imports and exports as compared with prewar.

It is still true to say – as it was at the beginning of the century – that Britain's imports consist mainly of foodstuffs and raw materials, together with a sizeable and growing proportion of manufactured goods, including an increasing volume of textile goods and machinery. In volume, total imports are not very much greater than in prewar days. (See Table 43.)

In 1963,[1] total imports into the United Kingdom were valued at £4,820 million divided as follows. Food, beverages, and tobacco amounted to £1,680 million, basic materials to £1,000 million, fuels to £550 million, and manufactures to £1,580 million.

Exports, unlike imports, are very much higher than in prewar days. Now, as then, they consist very largely of manufactured goods, but there has been a significant fall in the tonnage of coal exported. The export of petroleum and petroleum products is now important, and in 1962, their value was more than three times that of coal, coke, and briquettes. Textiles are relatively less important now and metal goods much more so. In 1929 textiles and clothing represented 28 per cent of Britain's exports, by 1951 the proportion had fallen to 18 per cent, and in 1963 these commodities made up only 8 per cent of total exports. Metals and metal goods increased their share from 28 per cent in 1929 to 50 per cent in 1951, and to 58 per cent in 1963. This change is illustrative of a

[1] The 1964 total was £5,400 million.

world movement in the export of manufactured products. World trade in consumer goods, of which clothing and textiles are good examples, tends to fall as many countries begin to make them for themselves. The growth of industrialization increases the demand for machinery and capital equipment, however, and this increases the volume of world trade in metal goods. U.K. exports in 1964 totalled £4,230 million.

TRENDS IN IMPORTS AND EXPORTS

The most obvious way of comparing imports and exports is in value terms and a fairly long series of annual figures is given below. Nineteen twenty-nine, the earliest year for which figures are quoted, was the last year before the onset of the great depression of the 'thirties, 1937 marks the best year of that decade. During the war the greater part of Britain's export trade was temporarily lost. Imports had, of course, to be maintained at as high a level as possible consistent with other claims on our shipping and financial resources. The wartime import figures are inflated by the unusually large volume of finished munitions which they contain. Exports rose rapidly after the war, imports much more slowly, at least until 1951, after which year there was a fall, partly due to lower import prices. The immediate impression one gets is the vastly higher level of foreign trade during the 'fifties compared with two decades earlier. There was a substantial increase in exports even in real terms, but the total increase shown in the table is due even more to increases in prices which have taken place since 1938. On the other hand, falling prices in the early 'thirties provide a partial explanation of the large fall in the value of overseas trade which took place between 1929 and 1935. More is said about this aspect in the next section. Throughout the period recorded imports are very much higher than the corresponding exports. This feature is also the subject of comment later in the chapter.

Year by year comparisons of imports and exports are affected by price changes, as we have seen. Other difficulties appear when comparisons between successive or near months are attempted. This is because the number of working days in the month may vary from one month to the next or between the same months in successive years. This variation may be due to public holidays or a different number of Sundays in the months being compared, or to the incidence of dock strikes. When one remembers that imports during 1964 averaged £18·5 million and exports £14·7 million per working day, a difference of two or three days can obviously make a substantial rise or fall in the monthly total. Short-term comparisons should therefore be on the basis of an equal number of working days.

Table 42. *U.K. exports and imports by value (£s million)*

Year	Exports	Retained imports [1]	Year	Exports	Retained imports [1]
1929	729	1,111	1949	1,789	2,221
1930	571	957	1950	2,174	2,525
1931	391	797	1951	2,582	3,778
1932	365	651	1952	2,585	3,334
1933	370	626	1953	2,582	3,238
1934	396	680	1954	2,674	3,273
1935	426	701	1955	2,905	3,765
1936	441	787	1956	3,172	3,740
1937	521	953	1957	3,325	3,942
1938	471	858	1958	3,208	3,633
1939	440	870	1959	3,330	3,852
			1960	3,555	4,399
			1961	3,682	4,260
1946	915	1,251	1962	3,791	4,329
1947	1,135	1,735	1963	4,080	4,666
1948	1,579	2,016	1964	4,254	5,360

VOLUME OF IMPORTS AND EXPORTS

For a number of reasons it is desirable to eliminate from the import and export figures the effect of changing prices. If this is done, it is possible to make comparisons of the 'quantum' or volume of imports and ex-ports. We can see from the table that the value of exports in 1964 was nine times as great as in 1938. It has been estimated that the price of 1964 exports was approximately three and three-quarter times those of 1938. Making allowance for this price change (by dividing it into the value ratio) we see that the volume of exports in 1964 was 2·4 times that of 1938. This kind of information enables the Government to assess the current effort devoted to exports compared with that in previous years. It also makes possible comparisons of the real quantity of imports we

[1] Imports, less re-exports.

are receiving. The last twenty years have witnessed great price changes and these inevitably obscure the real changes which have taken place.

In order to convert into volume terms, imports and exports expressed in value, a price index must be used or implied. Currently the volume index numbers of imports and exports are calculated thus. An estimate is made of the value of goods imported (or exported) in the period in question at the prices of a chosen base year and this estimate is compared with the value of goods actually imported or exported in the base year. In this way the volume index numbers give a measure of the

Table 43. *Indices of imports and exports by volume (1954 = 100)*

Year	Imports	Exports	Year	Imports	Exports
1938	104	58	1956	110	113
1947	80	63	1957	114	116
1950	89	101	1958	114	111
1951	100	100	1959	122	116
1952	92	94	1960	138	122
1953	99	96	1961	135	125
1954	100	100	1962	139	128
1955	111	107	1963	144	133

NOTE. – 1964 shows the highest postwar volume figures for both imports and exports – 160 and 138, respectively.

changes in the value, at constant prices, of imports and exports. The calculation is made monthly and is based on the quantity and value particulars in the Trade and Navigation Accounts. The prices used are in fact the average values per unit calculated from the Trade Accounts. The base year in the series calculated and published at the beginning of 1965 is 1961, and the calculation of the volume index of imports and exports in the first quarter of 1959 consists of expressing a large sample of the imports and exports during the quarter at prices ruling in 1961, as shown in the Trade Accounts for that year. The result of this calculation is expressed as a percentage of the value of these same imports and exports at 1961 prices.

The current (1965) series of volume index numbers has been worked forward to 1963 and backwards to 1947. An earlier series provides a link with 1938. Index numbers are now calculated for total imports and exports and also for each of the main classes based on 1961 = 100. The compilation of these index numbers is done by the statisticians in the

Board of Trade, the figures are published in the *Board of Trade Journal*, *Monthly Digest of Statistics*, *Annual Abstract of Statistics*, and also the monthly Board of Trade publication *Report on Overseas Trade*. Annual figures are quoted in Table 43 for Imports and Exports based on 1954 = 100. The volume indices for 1938 have been obtained by linking the current series with earlier ones based on 1947 = 100, and 1954 = 100.

THE BALANCE OF PAYMENTS

It is common knowledge that the recorded value of Britain's imports exceeds that of her exports. The figures in Table 42 show this very clearly. One reason for this is that they are valued at a different point. Exports are valued F.O.B. (free on board), i.e. when loaded on the ship ready to leave the country. Imports include the cost of carriage and insurance to the port of discharge, i.e. they are valued C.I.F. (cost, insurance freight). Imports have to be paid for; exports represent earnings. Any nation whose imports exceed its exports is normally compelled to live partly on its past savings, or pile up new debts. These past savings take the form of money invested in foreign countries. Between September 1939 and June 1944 no less than £1,000 million of overseas assets were sold by Britain to pay for her large excess of imports. During the latter half of the war. Lease-Lend aid and grants from the Commonwealth helped to bridge the gap between expenditure and earnings. After the war, a loan of some £1,000 million from U.S. and one of £280 million from Canada were raised, in order to tide Britain over the time required to rebuild her export trade and balance her overseas accounts. When these loans were exhausted, Marshall Aid, mainly by way of direct grants, was fortunately forthcoming. More recently, defence aid on a modest scale has been received from U.S.A., but interest on the postwar loan is now being repaid. Defence aid ceased in 1958.

Before we can arrive at the difference between earnings and expenditure, i.e. the balance of payments, we must make some adjustment to the visible trade deficit. This adjustment is in respect of 'invisibles' – international transactions involving earnings on capital and payments for services. British shipping earns large sums by carrying goods for other countries. Banks, insurance companies, civil airlines perform services for foreign firms and nationals and thereby earn commissions and fees. Although much of the British capital invested abroad was exchanged for British Government stock during the war and much has since been lost in China and Egypt, Britain is still receiving substantial sums in this way.

At the same time debts are being incurred by this country in respect of interest and profits earned by foreign firms and foreign governments. British tourists spend more abroad than foreign tourists do in this country. The maintenance of British Forces overseas adds to the pay-

Table 44. *Net invisible earnings in 1934 (as estimated by the Board of Trade) (£s million)*

Income earned by our shipping (estimated)	70
Commissions, profits, etc., earned by banks and insurance companies from foreign countries (estimated)	30
Income from British capital invested abroad	175
Repayment by other countries of loans previously made to them	9
Net receipts from other sources	10
	294

ments which have to be made to foreign countries. However, invisible earnings still exceed their expenditure counterpart. It is not easy to compare invisible earnings, by category, with those of prewar days. Below we give estimates for 1934 and those for four recent years. It must be emphasized that these can only be estimates. They are computed by expert statisticians – but often have to be amended in the light of later study or further information.

Net invisible earnings, 1961–64 (£s million)

	1961	1962	1963	1964
Shipping	−28	−12	−11	−27
Interest, profit, and dividends	244	329	377	435
Travel	−19	−20	−45	−43
Private transfers	9	1	−14	−20
Government transactions	−335	−363	−387	−431
Other net[1]	255	252	242	265
Total	126	187	162	179

[1] All other transactions including overseas transactions of oil companies, insurance, and banking services, civil aviation, royalties, commissions, etc. Services rendered by the 'City' in 1961 earned, it is estimated, about £150 million.

It will be noted that invisible earnings are a much smaller percentage of total international transactions than they were in prewar days and are significantly lower than a decade ago. This latter fall is due to a fall in shipping earnings and an increase in Government transactions. There remains the task of bringing together the balances on visible and invisible trade in order to arrive at the estimated balance of payments. These can be compared with prewar estimates. Table 45 brings them together.

Table 45. *Estimated balance of payments (£s million)*

1929	+100	1955	−157
1932–35 (average)	− 2	1956	+209
1936–38 ,,	− 40	1957	+216
1946–48 ,,	−312	1958	+345
1949	+ 31	1959	+153
1950	+300	1960	−258
1951	−403	1961	− 1
1952	+170	1962	+115
1953	+151	1963	+113
1954	+121	1964	−374

The reader may well ask, 'What is the cause of these violent fluctuations, and how are the deficits settled?' These questions are economic rather than statistical, but to leave them unanswered would be unreasonable.

There is a chronic tendency in the British economy for increased purchasing power to be devoted to imports unless checked or thwarted. The American Loan was used up in this way, hence the deficits of 1946 and 1947. The three succeeding years were characterized by strenuous and successful efforts to bring the situation under control – largely by stabilizing imports and increasing exports. Greater freedom to buy from abroad and easier foreign travel granted in 1950, together with attempts on the part of the Government to build up stocks of imported commodities in spite of their increased price, led to the huge deficit of 1951. The following year saw attempts made to rectify the situation, and for three years the balance of payments showed a surplus. The steadily increasing pressure of home demand experienced in 1955 led to an increase in imports and a check on exports; the result was a deficit on overseas account. In the three years after 1955 remedial measures to check home demand and encourage exports met with success and satisfactory surpluses were achieved. Although 1958 was a year of slight recession in world trade, the fall in import prices which occurred in that year led to a balance of payments surplus of record proportions. These cyclical movements were repeated in 1960–62 and 1963. Nineteen-sixty-four was a particularly bad year.

As regards the second part of the question, the answer is that much of the postwar deficits – at least until 1951 – were offset by foreign aid mainly from U.S.A. But Britain also increased her overseas liabilities which had become formidable as a result of the war. These liabilities known as the Sterling Liabilities are credits allowed us by other countries, mainly members of the Commonwealth. These balances tend to decline when Britain is achieving a surplus on her balance of payments account and to grow when a deficit is being built up. At the end of 1951 these Sterling Liabilities amounted to the formidable sum of £3,900 million, three-quarters of which represented credits allowed to us by the Commonwealth. By the end of 1962 these liabilities had been reduced to £3,600 million, but by the end of 1964 they had risen to over £4,000 million. This is a huge burden of debts and to it must be added our liabilities in respect of postwar American and Canadian Loans.

Deficits on balance of payments may also be offset by the running down of the country's gold and dollar reserves. Deficits tend to reduce these reserves and surpluses to increase them. A great deal of attention is now paid to the level of the gold and foreign currency holdings which is issued by the Bank of England at monthly intervals. The level of the reserves is regarded as the most important indicator of the financial strength of the country. But these reserves are also affected by the amount of foreign lending which the British Government and private individuals have undertaken. These were particularly heavy in 1964. Moreover, they also depend on the willingness of other countries to maintain banking and currency reserves in London. The gold and dollar reserves rose steadily from £437 million in September 1948 to £1,381 million in the middle of 1951. Since then the total has fluctuated considerably, it was £757 million at the end of 1955 and £1,096 million at the end of 1958. After a slight fall in 1959, the total had risen to £1,185 million at the end of 1961. Thereafter, a decline tended to occur and by the end of 1963 the total was £949 million. The end-1964 total was £827 million, but this total owed a great deal to the massive loans and credits arranged during the autumn of this year. These became necessary as a result of the financial crisis which came to a head in November 1964.

STUDENT WORK

1. Explain why the value of our imports as revealed by the Board of Trade returns always appears considerably in excess of that for exports.
2. Using the most recent figures and estimates available, draw up a statement showing how this difference is accounted for.
3. Describe and account for the trends in British Overseas Trade since 1926.
4. How is the volume index of exports arrived at?
5. Give an account of the trends in our terms of trade since 1945 and compare the current figure with that for 1938.

Chapter 17

Statistics of Prices

STATISTICS which show the movements in the prices of individual commodities are very numerous. Many of these statistics are not, however, of general interest and may concern only individuals or firms handling the commodity in question. What does interest the business community as a whole is the movement of groups of related prices as, for example, the materials used in the mechanical or electrical engineering trades, or prices of capital equipment. The general public, on the other hand, is more particularly concerned with the changes in retail prices. The only method by which price movements in the aggregate may be assessed and compared is by the use of index numbers. During the last few years a very large number of price indices have been computed and published by various government departments. In the main these fall into four classes: price indices of materials used in industry, indices of the output of certain industries, or groups of industries, retail price indices, and import and export price indices. In addition, a composite *Price Index of Manufactured Products* is being published. A number of non-government bodies used to publish wholesale price indices, but no longer do so.

The attitude of the economist and administrator towards such indices has changed in recent years. The first important wholesale price index to be produced in this country dates back more than three-quarters of a century. This is the 'Sauerbeck' index, still continued as the 'Statist' index. The first wholesale price index published by a government department appeared in 1903 and the calculations were carried back to 1871. Broadly speaking the object of these indices was to measure changes in the general level of prices, and therefore in the purchasing power of money as understood in the Quantity Theory of Money. The relevance of such a concept, as well as the belief in the possibility of calculating it, have now been discarded in favour of a family of index numbers each covering a smaller but more precisely defined sector of the economy. Hence the appearance of the many new series already referred to.

Articles on the method of compilation of these index numbers have appeared from time to time in the *Board of Trade Journal* and current indices are quoted there. *The Monthly Digest of Statistics* and *Annual Abstract* also give the more important of these indices. In the succeeding paragraphs an example from each of the four main classes is discussed. This description is, however, preceded by a note on the oldest existing wholesale price index number.

GENERAL WHOLESALE PRICE INDEX NUMBERS

The 'Statist' Index

This long-standing index is computed from the prices of 45 commodities, 19 of which are foodstuffs and 26 materials. The base period is 1867–77. The arithmetic mean is used and no weighting is deemed necessary. Movements in this index give some indication of the long-term price changes of the most important commodities entering into international trade. It is still computed monthly. The index for 1963 stood at 374. Sub-indices for various groups of commodities are also published.

Wholesale Price Index Numbers which are no longer published

Within recent years two once important index numbers of Wholesale Prices have ceased to be calculated and published – viz. *The Economist* Index and that produced by the Board of Trade. The reason for their cessation is the wealth of information on sector price index numbers and the scepticism of the value of general wholesale price index numbers. A short description of the method of calculating these two indices is of interest in showing that the prevalent ideas about the methods which should be employed in index number calculation have also tended to change.

THE 'ECONOMIST' INDEX. This contained the prices of 58 items. It had a fixed base, the average of 1927 prices being taken as 100. The geometric mean was employed for computing the final average, which combined sub-indices for Cereals and Meat, Other Foods, Textiles, Minerals, and Miscellaneous Products. The series was carried back to 1913.

THE BOARD OF TRADE INDEX OF WHOLESALE PRICES. As in the case of the two foregoing index numbers, this one also had its origin in the days when a general index of wholesale prices was thought to fulfil a useful economic function. In its construction the prices of 150 commodities in ten main groups were used. Each group contained a varying number of prices, the number depending upon the relative importance attached to the group. Price relatives were calculated on the chain base principle, each figure being computed in association with the corresponding one for the previous year. The average employed was the geometric mean. This is of particular advantage if, as often happened, a comparison of wholesale prices over a period was required and the index has to be linked to a fixed base. Various years have been chosen for period comparisons, 1930, 1938, and 1949, have been used during the last three decades.

PRICE INDICES OF MATERIALS USED IN INDUSTRY

A number of such indices are now being published monthly by the Board of Trade. They include separate indices for materials used in mechanical engineering, electrical engineering, building and civil engineering, house building, textiles, and chemicals.

The selection of items for use in such indices has been made after an examination of the 1951 census of production schedules which required manufacturers to specify the weights and value of the chief raw materials used in their productive processes. Unlike the general Wholesale Price Index Number, these indices are arithmetic averages of price relatives. The census of production schedules also provided the data on which the weighting system is built up. Fuels are included along with the materials used. The base period for these series of index numbers is the average of 1954. This will be found to be common to other index numbers since it was a year in which a full census of production was taken. The current series replace earlier ones based on prices ruling on 30 June 1949, but they can be linked with these earlier indices.

The particular value of these index numbers is the light they throw on the trend of costs in industry. If they can be associated with index numbers of wage rates a fairly complete picture of the trend in industrial costs can thereby be obtained. Many commercial contracts include a price variation clause which permits of changes in the contract price if raw materials undergo a price change or wage rates are put up. Such indices can often supply the requisite data for such price variations. *The Monthly Digest of Statistics*, the *Annual Abstract* and the *Board of Trade Journal* regularly publish these index numbers.

There has been a considerable divergence, since 1954, in the main index numbers in this family group. For example, the July 1964 index numbers (1954 = 100) ranged from 135·0 in the case of materials and fuel used in the mechanical engineering industries, to 97·7 for materials used in textile production. The latter tends to reflect charges in import costs of raw materials, the former is much more closely tied to home produced materials and components.

Among this family is a price index for 'basic materials and fuel used in manufacturing industry', the 1964 value for which was 107·0.

PRICE INDICES OF INDUSTRIAL OUTPUT

These are useful when a comparison by volume of output is required at two different periods for which output figures are given in value terms. Thus, suppose the output of internal combustion engines and parts is £45 million in one year and £50 million in the next. By value, this represents an 11 per cent increase but if the price of internal combustion engines rose by 8 per cent during the year, the increased output is only 3 per cent in real terms.

A large number of price indices of industrial output is quoted monthly in the *Board of Trade Journal*. The selection of the items and the weights assigned to them have again been made from the results of the 1954 census of production. The base is the average of 1954 prices, and each index is a weighted arithmetic average of the price relatives it includes.

These industrial output index numbers are of two kinds. Some relate to the output of broad sectors of industry and are therefore composite index numbers of a large number of products produced in these industries. Examples are: price index numbers of the output of chemical and allied products, of textiles and of iron and steel products. The other kind consists of price index numbers of selected commodities, but commodities manufactured in the United Kingdom. These commodities could be boots and shoes, radio sets, or hand tools. Fewer quotations go to the preparation of these index numbers, but the index numbers themselves cover a very wide range of commodities.

Included in the first of these kinds of price indices of industrial output is one which covers the prices of 'all manufactured products' divided into total sales and home sales. By and large, therefore, this total sales index number relates to manufactures generally. Its trend is shown by the following: 1954, 100·0; 1955, 102·7; 1956, 106·7; 1957, 110·4; 1958, 111·1; 1959, 111·4; 1960, 113·1; 1961, 115·7; 1962, 118·0; 1963, 119·8; 1964, 123·6. If these kind of index numbers cover the same field as those for which materials used are calculated, it may be of interest to see how prices and costs are related to each other.

RETAIL PRICE INDICES

Of all the price indices, this type is the one which attracts most attention. Since the everyday transactions of the general public are carried on at retail prices this is only natural. It is therefore proposed to describe at some length the origin of the present index, its relation to its predecessors, and its method of calculation. Apart from its general appeal the current index is worthy of our attention because it illustrates a number of statistical principles. In a sense it can be regarded as measuring changes in the purchasing power of money in the hands of the public, and, as such, it often provides the basis for wage and salary claims. Indeed, in some trades, wages are linked with the index and a rise of a certain number of points in this index is automatically accompanied by what is considered as an equivalent increase in wages.

Prior to 1947 changes in retail prices were officially measured by the Ministry of Labour Cost-of-Living Index. This had its origins in the conditions of sixty-odd years ago as revealed in an examination of some 2,000 urban working-class family budgets of weekly expenditure. This expenditure averaged 36s. 10d. a week, of which 22s. 6d. went on food. This particular inquiry provided the selection of items used in the index, the weighting system used within each of the main groups, and also the one which linked these group indices into a final figure. For this final index, the groups were weighted thus: Food, 7½; rent and rates, 2; clothing, 1½; fuel and light, 1; other items, ½. A wide range of price quotations was obtained from over 5,000 retailers of all kinds situated in

G

some 509 towns and villages. The first step in the calculation was the assessment of the percentage increase in the current price of the selected items as compared with prices ruling at July 1914. Then these increases were weighted to give a group increase and, finally, these group indices were combined to give a final figure. This was then quoted as 'the average increase in the cost of maintaining unchanged the pre-1914 standard of living of the working classes'. Consider for a moment the figures for December 1935. Food showed an increase of 31 per cent, rent and rates 58 per cent, clothing 85 per cent, fuel and light 80 per cent, and other items 70 per cent. The final Cost-of-Living Index was then:

$$\frac{(31 \times 7\frac{1}{2}) + (58 \times 2) + (85 \times 1\frac{1}{2}) + (80 \times 1) + (70 \times \frac{1}{2})}{12\frac{1}{2}}$$

Trends in the Cost-of-Living Index

Table 24 on page 100 shows the trend in the index from 1928–34. In this section the seasonal variations of the index were discussed; the elimination of these variations showed clearly the downward trend from 1928 to 1933. Evidence of a reversal of this trend appeared in 1934. Table 46 shows how this rise was continued over the next few years.

Table 46. *Variations in the cost-of-living figures 1935–39 (Figures indicate percentage increase over the figures for July 1914)*

Year	Jan.	Feb.	Mar.	Apr.	May	June	July	Aug.	Sept.	Oct.	Nov.	Dec.
1935	43	42	41	39	39	40	43	43	43	45	47	47
1936	47	47	46	44	44	44	46	46	47	48	51	51
1937	51	51	51	52	52	52	55	55	55	58	60	60
1938	59	57	56	56	56	56	56	56	56	56	56	56
1939	55	55	53	53	53	56	55	55	55	60	65	73

Soon after the outbreak of the war, the Government began to control retail prices with the hope of limiting the rise in the cost of living. In order to compensate manufacturers and wholesalers for increasing costs, a system of subsidies was introduced and extended. This control was most complete and effective in the case of food and rent, and the amount of money devoted to food subsidies grew steadily. The Cost-of-Living Index, heavily weighted as it was by food items, rose only slowly, and suspicion which had long been in existence that the index really understated the rise in the cost of living, became stronger. This was because the prices of a large number of commodities and services, which had become part of the working-class standard of living, but which were not represented in the index, rose faster than the prices of included items. There was a general belief that the Cost-of-Living Index measured changes in the cost of subsistence and that Government intentions expressed by way of subsidies and price control were directed at keeping this as stable as possible, while allowing the prices of luxury or semi-luxury goods to rise more quickly.

Table 47. *Variations in the cost-of-living figure, 1940–47*

Date	Food	Rent and rates	Clothing	Fuel and light	Other items	Final index
Jan. 1940	57	62	150	100	90	74
July 1940	64	64	185	112	119	85
Jan. 1941	72	64	230	123	122	96
July 1941	66	64	280–285	128	130	99
Jan. 1942	63	64	300	130	133	100
July 1942	60	64	305	132	164	100
Jan. 1943	64	64	270	144	168	99
July 1943	68	64	245–250	144	186	100
Jan. 1944	68	64	240–245	144	191	90
July 1944	69	64	245	153	191	101
Jan. 1945	68	64	245–250	164	191	102
July 1945	76	66	245–250	175	191	107
Jan. 1946	73	66	245–250	175	191	105
July 1946	74	67	245–250	176	193	106
Jan. 1947	74	67	245–250	176	193	106

The inadequacy of the coverage of the index had been revealed by an inquiry made in 1937–38, into both urban and rural working-class budgets. This had been on a fairly large scale and had been carried out by the Ministry of Labour. Table 48 shows how the spending patterns had changed in thirty years and indicates that the increased purchasing power in the hands of the working classes had been expended mainly in non-food products and in services. The outbreak of the war caused the postponement of a new index which was finally introduced in the summer of 1947. By this time independent experts estimated that the Cost-of-Living Index was understating the change in working-class cost of living by as much as 20 to 25 per cent. The new index was called the Interim Index of Retail Prices. The intention presumably was to emphasize the provisional nature of the index and to blunt the impression that it measured changes in the cost of living.

Compared with the data used for the calculation of the Cost-of-Living Index, it appears that much of the emphasis on postwar working-class budgets has switched from food to 'other items'. From the beginning of 1940 an increasing number of food prices came under the control of the Government. These controlled prices were in many cases

Table 48. *Spending patterns 1937–38*

	Total expenditure %	Food %	Rent and rates %	Clothing %	Fuel and light %	Other items %
Agricultural households	100	47·9	8·2	10·1	8·5	25·3
Industrial households	100	39·5	12·6	10·8	7·4	29·7
Employed in Cost-of-Living Index Calculation	100	60·0	16·0	12·0	8·0	4·0

very little in excess of pre-1940 prices (at least until the end of the war). 'Other Items' have been, for the most part, free of Government control. Indirect taxation may have caused an increase in their price level, in addition to that due to excess of demand over supply. It does seem, therefore, that the Cost-of-Living Index, as stated throughout the war, had been somewhat low. On the other hand it is true that the commodities and services included among 'Other Items' are only conventional necessaries.

The Interim Index of Retail Prices

To a very large extent this was based on the results of the 1937–38 inquiry. It was thought, however, that this inquiry underestimated the amounts spent on drink and tobacco. Moreover, it was known that expenditure patterns were somewhat different in 1947 than ten years earlier and these points were taken into consideration when the new index was first introduced. Basically, however, the index measured the changing cost of buying the basket of goods and services that made up the family budget of 1937–38. It covered practically the whole expenditure of wage and small salary earning households. Some 250 items, 84 of which were food-stuffs, were regularly priced. These were further subdivided into grades and qualities. Twenty-four sorts of biscuits and five kinds of breakfast foods were included, for example. A new departure as compared with the old index was the inclusion of the costs of services, in which, *inter alia*, railway, bus, and tram fares are considered. The items covered were divided into eight main groups – food, rent, and rates, clothing, fuel, and light, household durable goods, miscellaneous goods, services and drink and tobacco. The base date was 17 June 1947, and the index took the form of a weighted arithmetic average of price relatives.

In their reading about index numbers, students may see a reference to the Laspèyre formula. This type of index number is one in which the weights employed are those known to be operative at the base date. The Interim Index of Retail Prices was of this type. Clearly such an index needs revision from time to time because the weighting system at the base date may no longer be appropriate after a few years have elapsed. In the case of the index we are considering other equally compelling reasons, some of them political, exist for keeping it constantly under review. To this end the Minister of Labour invited the Cost-of-Living Advisory Committee, in 1950, to consider if changes in the index were desirable. This Committee reported in two stages. In 1951 it recommended that a new family budget inquiry should be held to obtain information which would provide an up-to-date and more permanent basis for an index of retail prices. Pending the holding of such an inquiry a number of minor adjustments to the Interim Index were suggested. These were put into operation in 1952, and the Interim Index as so revised, was calculated until 1956.

By that time the Advisory Committee had held a full-scale inquiry into postwar household spending in 1953–54, and the results had become available. Nearly 13,000 households, carefully selected to provide a representative sample, were paid a small fee for keeping full records of their expenditure. In February 1956 the Advisory Committee submitted their report on this inquiry and their recommendations for the replacement of the Interim Index by a more up-to-date one. These recommendations were accepted by the Minister of Labour, and the new Index known as the Index of Retail Prices with a base date of 17 January 1956, came into operation shortly afterwards. It is of interest to note that the two indices of wages discussed in an earlier chapter were based on the same date as the two price indices. For full details of the method of compilation of the latest index the student is referred to the pamphlet *Method of Construction and Calculation of the Index of Retail*

188   AN OUTLINE OF STATISTICS

Prices, produced by the Ministry of Labour and published by the Stationery Office.

Some slight variation in the method of calculation was introduced in 1962. The group indices were rebased to January 1962, and a new set of weights derived from the continuing Family Expenditure Survey for the three previous years was adopted. From 1963 onwards, the weights are revised each February on this basis. The index is therefore now based on a pattern of expenditure which approximates to the time to which it refers: more of a Paasche than a Laspèyre type. The 'index' is now quoted on a 1962 base, but a link with the 1956 base is quite easy to establish.

Table 49. *Weights allocated to each main group in the Interim Index and index of retail prices.*

	Interim index of prices	Index of retail prices	
	1947–56	1956–62	1964
Food	399	350	314
Alcoholic drink	78	71	63
Tobacco	90	77	74
Housing[1]	72	87	107
Fuel and light	66	55	66
Durable household goods	62	66	62
Clothing and footwear	98	106	95
Miscellaneous goods	44	59	63
Transport and vehicles ⎱	91	68	100
Services ⎰		58	56

Elaborate and careful arrangements are made to collect price information from all kinds of shops and service trades spread over the United Kingdom for an enormous range of goods and services. The goods and services are such as are bought by the average family in which the head earned in 1953–54 up to £1,000 per annum. Within these prescribed limits the Retail Price Index is as near perfect as it could be for the very large effort involved in the collection of the data, and the construction of the sub-indices and final index. Table 49 shows the weights assigned to the sub-indices in the two latest indices of retail prices.

[1] In the Interim Index, this item was called Rent and Rates. In the later index it includes cost of housing repairs and decorations.

Generally speaking, the changing pattern of expenditure reflects the current higher standard of living compared with earlier periods, particularly in relation to luxury goods.

The pamphlet on the *Method of Construction and Calculations of the Index of Retail Prices*, gives the factor which should be used for linking this index with the one it supersedes. The Interim Index, in its turn, can be linked with the old Cost-of-Living Index. At 17 January 1956 the Interim Index (17 June 1947 = 100) stood at 153·4, the Index at 100. Clearly, then, the Interim Index can be put on the basis of 17 January 1956 = 100 by dividing by 153·4, or the current index can be rebased to 17 June 1947 = 100 by multiplying by this same factor. Table 50 provides a series of annual figures running back to 1938. The 1938 and 1946 figures must, however, be treated with reserve on account of the deficiences in the Cost-of-Living Index.

Table 50. *Trends in retail prices 17 January 1956 = 100*

1938	Cost-of-living Index	39	1956		102·0
1946	basis	62	1957		105·8
1947		65	1958		109·0
1948		70	1959	Index of retail	109·6
1949		72	1960	prices	110·7
1950		74	1961		114·5
1951	Interim Index basis	81	1962		119·3
1952		89	1963		121·6
1953		91	1964		125·7
1954		93			
1955		97			

On this basis, retail prices in 1964 were, on the average, about three-and-a-quarter times those of 1938. There are considerable differences in the trend in the sub-indices even since 1956, arising partly from the operation of the Rent Act, higher rates, and the changes in rates of purchase tax. At the end of 1962 the final index stood at 120·2, while the sub-indices read: Food, 113·2; Alcoholic drink, 108·8; Tobacco, 123·6; Housing, 147·9; Fuel and light, 138·6; Durable Household goods, 102·9; Clothing and footwear, 110·0; Miscellaneous goods, 129·6; Transport and vehicles, 126·3; services, 133·3.

An interesting general point arises from the operation of base-weighted index numbers (Laspèyre's index) of retail prices. The calculation compares the cost of a fixed basket of goods at the current date with that at the base date. But keen shoppers will vary their purchases in accordance with prices. When eggs are cheap more will be bought; when butter is dear, margarine will take its place. The keen shopper can in this way 'beat the index', the cost of his purchases will not rise *pari passu* with the index. With the more frequent reweighting of the index this will not be so easy.

INDEX NUMBERS OF IMPORT AND EXPORT PRICES

About one-fifth of the total costs in the manufacturing industry is derived from imports and about 28 per cent of the output of manufactured goods is exported. Import prices are therefore an important factor in the determination of production costs and export prices affect the selling value of output. Some measure of the change in these prices is also an obvious necessity in the study of trends in imports and exports in real terms.

Monthly index numbers of these prices are now calculated. In the case of imports, separate index numbers are calculated for Food, beverages and tobacco, Basic materials, Fuels, and Manufactured goods, and these are combined into an 'All items' index. Export price index numbers for Metals, Chemicals, Machinery, and Transport equipment, Textiles and Other exports are similarly worked out and combined into an index covering exports as a whole. The current series (1964) is based on average prices in 1961 = 100, and as with other index numbers, the series can be linked with earlier calculations. About 200 items are used in the calculation of the imports index and 250 in the exports. They are selected from the monthly 'Trade and Navigation Accounts' on two basic principles. They are sufficiently homogeneous for the average or unit value calculated from the Trade Accounts to behave like a true price, having regard to the weights assigned to them. Moreover, they are judged to be a representative sample of the pattern of trade in the base year.

Based on 1961 = 100 import prices (or unit value index numbers as they are sometimes called) averaged 88 in 1950. They rose to 117 in 1952, fell to 104 in 1954 and by 1957 had again risen to 111. From then, until 1963, there was a steady fall to 99, followed by a rise to 103 in 1963 and 107 in 1964. Export prices rose sharply from 76 in 1950 to 94 in

1952. By 1954 they had fallen to 89 since when they have steadily risen to 106 in 1964.

TERMS OF TRADE

By this is meant the relation of export to import prices. Within recent years Britain has come into line with most other countries in expressing terms of trade in this way; formerly the reverse relation was used. A rise now indicates a favourable movement, with export prices rising faster than import prices. Based on 1961 = 100 the terms of trade rose steadily from 87 in 1954 to 102 in 1962; 1964 shows a slight fall to 99. In the early postwar years they were very unfavourable, but by 1962 it is thought that they had completely recovered the prewar level.

OTHER PRICE INDICES

In addition to the price indices already discussed, the *Monthly Digest of Statistics* and *Annual Abstract* contain regular information, in terms of indices, about tramp shipping freights and agricultural and livestock products. *The Financial Times* publishes a daily index of stock and share prices. There is thus a wide variety of price information in the form of index numbers. The reader must, however, have noticed a significant omission – no mention has been made of price indices of capital equipment. The measurement of price changes of machinery is clearly difficult since continuous changes are made in design. Such an index would be of considerable use to accountants since it would give an indication of the current replacement cost of machinery. This would facilitate the calculation of the financial provision which should be made in addition to depreciation allowances computed on the basis of original cost. It is believed that Government departments are collecting such information, but it is not known whether such an index will be made generally available. However, *The Times Review of Industry and Technology*, referred to on page 165 gives a quarterly index of the price of capital goods, based on 1958 = 100. It even carries back the computation to 1913 for which a figure of 15 is given. The 1964 figure is 109.

STUDENT WORK

1. In a certain month the average percentage increases in prices over
   July 1914 figures were as follows. Using the weights quoted below,
   calculate the food index for the month:

Article	% Increase in price	Weight	Article	% Increase in price	Weight
Beef	14	48	Sugar	12	19
Mutton	22	24	Milk	90	25
Bacon	21	19	Butter	3	41
Fish	102	9	Cheese	3	10
Flour	25	20	Margarine	−21	10
Bread	41	50	Eggs	81	19
Tea	28	22	Potatoes	45	18

2. In January 1936 the percentage increases in the average prices of the
   items making up the groups – food, rent and rates, clothing, fuel and
   light, and other items – were: 31, 58, 85, 75, 70 respectively, while the
   weights assigned were $7\frac{1}{2}$, 2, $1\frac{1}{2}$, 1, and $\frac{1}{2}$. Calculate the cost-of-living
   figure for the month.

3. Give an account of the construction of an index of wholesale prices.

4. Using the figures quoted in Table 46, show graphically the variation
   in the cost-of-living figure from 1935 to 1939.

5. Give an account of the construction of the Interim Index of Retail
   Prices.

6. Do you consider that the Index of Retail Prices accurately measures
   changes in working-class cost of living?

7. Graph the index of rates of wages from June 1947, to the present time
   alongside the index of retail prices.

Chapter 18

Production Statistics

A VAST amount of statistical information on production is now regularly issued, much of it by government departments. By virtue of the responsibilities placed with these departments by the Statistics of Trade Act 1947, short-term statistics are collected in respect of a large range of products and industries. A large proportion of these appear in the *Monthly Digest* and *Annual Abstract*. It is again emphasized that these two publications are essential works of reference for the student, or user, of economic statistics. But for general planning purposes this great range of information needs to be summarized. As the student will now have realized, this is best done by means of indices of production. It will be one of the main purposes of this chapter to consider these indices. There is, however, another source of statistical information on production which should be known to all who are in any way concerned with production figures, namely the full census of production. This full census is very wide in scope and very detailed in operation. It is important, therefore, to spend some time in studying it. We do not propose to comment any further on short-term production statistics, but intend to devote the rest of this chapter to a discussion of the two major topics just propounded.

INDICES OF PRODUCTION

In the more immediate prewar days, the Board of Trade calculated, quarterly, an index of production. The weights used were derived from the net output figures derived from the 1930 census of production and these were applied to production and related statistics received from various sources. In a few cases employment data or figures of the consumption of raw materials were used if production statistics were not available. The index was built up from ten groups: mines and quarries, iron and steel, non-ferrous metals, engineering and ship-building, building materials, textiles, chemicals, leather and footwear, food and drink. It was a weighted arithmetical average of the group indices. This index fell into abeyance during the war. It might be noted in passing that the use of employment data or raw material consumption figures in a production index may tend to give a downward bias over a long period. This is because technological progress usually results in the more economical use of manpower and raw materials.

The Interim Index of Industrial Production

After the war the index was completely revised and its computation undertaken by the Central Statistical Office. This new index was named the Interim Index of Industrial Production. As in the case of the Interim Index of Retail Prices, the weighting system was derived from prewar studies adjusted in the light of known changes. The index was a weighted arithmetic average of price relatives. Its base was the average monthly output for 1946 and it incorporated about 400 individual groups. These were representative of seventeen industrial groups of the Standard Industrial Classification. Where possible, monthly output was measured in physical terms – tons of coal mined or steel produced, numbers of bricks or passenger cars produced, or the structure weight of aircraft delivered. In many cases this was not possible, particularly for many sectors of the engineering industry. Output measured in terms of value was the most usual substitute. The use of value figures necessitated the use of some form of index to eliminate the effect of price changes. The index used for this purpose was obtained by combining changes in wage rates and costs of raw materials. In a few cases the quantities of raw materials used provided a measure of finished output. For some series, building and contracting and shipbuilding, in particular, estimate of the work-in-progress as well as finished output were used in the production series. Whatever monthly output figures were used they were adjusted to a standard number of working days per month.

In general, the weights assigned to the seventeen industrial groups were in proportion to the estimated net output in these groups in 1946. Although a partial census of production was taken for 1946, the incompleteness of this census and the time taken to analyse the results made it impossible to use them. Instead, the net outputs from the 1935 census of production were extrapolated to 1946 by multiplying them by an employment/earnings factor. If employment in 1946 in any industry was one-and-a-half times as great as in 1935 and the average level of earnings twice as great, then the employment/earnings factor was three.

The interim index series was continued over a period of six years with but minor changes. New series were occasionally introduced and existing ones dropped out as figures ceased to be available. By 1952 the results of the complete census of production for 1948 had become available. Many more short-term statistics were being collected than in 1946. The time had obviously come for the replacement of this index by a more reliably based one. A revised index was therefore launched in the middle of 1952.

The Index of Industrial Production

The 1948, 1954, and 1958 censuses of production provided the weighting system for this index which for the first ten years of its existence was based on output in 1948. However, in 1958 the base year was changed to 1954 and revised weights revealed by the full census of production of 1954 were adopted. The opportunity was also taken of redefining industries in accordance with the Revised Standard Industrial Classification. Then, in 1962 the index was moved to a 1958 base using the information from the 1958 census. The description which follows relates to the Index of Industrial Production based on 1958; it follows closely that given in the Supplement to the *Monthly Digest of Statistics* as revised in January 1964.[1]

The index is prepared by the Central Statistical Office in collaboration with the Statistics Divisions of government departments. It is intended to provide a general measure of monthly changes in the volume of industrial production in the United Kingdom. Mining and quarrying, manufacturing, construction and gas, electricity and water are included; but agriculture, trade, transport and finance, and all other public and private services are excluded. The index covers the production of capital goods and consumption goods for the home market, for export and for the Armed Forces.

[1] This Supplement provides many useful descriptions of the compilation of many of the index numbers dealt with in the second part of this book.

The index is a weighted arithmetic average. In combining the individual production series, the method used has been to give each industry a 'weight' proportional to its net output in 1958 as shown by the census of production for that year. The net output figures given in the published reports of the census have been adjusted by deducting the estimated amounts paid for services rendered to the industries by firms outside the field covered by the index, such as advertising and insurance, since these represent production in the 'services' sector of the economy.

About 880 production series, individually weighted, are incorporated in the index. Although some are quarterly, the majority are for weeks or calendar months. Most of the series represent physical quantities produced. For some industries including, for example, parts of the engineering groups, construction, clothing, china, and glassware, it has been necessary to use series of the value of production adjusted for changes in prices. For some other industries for which output figures are not available, alternative series, such as the use of raw materials or numbers of persons employed, have been used. For construction and shipbuilding, where production of individual products extends over a long period, monthly figures of deliveries of finished products are not a reliable measure of current output, and the index makes allowances for the amount of work in progress.

The level of production is expressed as a percentage of the average monthly production in 1958. To ensure comparability between different months, adjustments have been made (where the basic figures refer to calendar months) for variations in the number of days in each month, excluding for each industry those which are not normally working days, for example, Sundays and Saturday afternoons. The index thus compares the average weekly rates of production in the different months. It reflects, however, any change in production resulting from public and other holidays and from seasonal factors, for which no adjustments have been made.

ADJUSTMENTS FOR SEASONAL VARIATIONS. The monthly index numbers for 'All industries' and 'All manufacturing industries' are now quoted corrected for seasonal variations. These series are designed to eliminate normal month to month fluctuations and thus show the trend more clearly. They are particularly valuable when, as in late 1958, early 1959, and again in 1963, the index was eagerly scanned for signs of an upturn. The correction for seasonal variation is obtained in two steps. First, the movement in the indices arising from public holidays and from annual holidays taken in the constituent industries is arrived at by an examination of as-long-a-run of figures as possible. Then, the remaining seasonal variation is calculated by the method of moving averages. The average deviations from the smoothed trend line provide a measure of this part of the seasonal variation. In August the seasonally corrected index for 'All industries' is shown as 14 per cent above the uncorrected one; that for October, 4 per cent below it.

Table 51 shows the constituent industrial series of the Index of Industrial Production and changes in the series from 1959 to 1964.

It will be noticed that reweighting the index on the 1958 census of production has involved only small changes in the 'All industries' figure from that computed on the 1954 census weights. The difference in weights between 1954 and 1958 reflects the decline in importance of the textile and clothing industries and the growing importance of the chemical, engineering, and vehicle industries.

Industrial production in 1963 was very roughly double the 1946 level and about 50 per cent higher than in 1948. Non-official estimates of 1938 industrial production suggest that it was about 2 per cent below that of 1946. For 1963 industrial production would therefore seem to be about 103 per cent higher than in 1938. The rapid growth in industrial production in the postwar years received a check in 1952, but recovered strongly again in the years 1953 to 1955. During the next three years little change was recorded. There was a leap forward in 1959 and 1960, little change in 1961 and 1962 and a large increase in 1963 and 1964.

CENSUSES OF PRODUCTION

The only way of obtaining complete and detailed information on all aspects of production is by means of a census. The first census of production was taken in respect of the year 1907. Thereafter, such a census was taken at roughly five-year intervals except during war years. Three were taken between the two wars – for the years 1924, 1930, and 1935, each by virtue of a special Act of Parliament. In addition, an inquiry taken under powers possessed by the Import Duties Advisory Committee provided a great deal of industrial production information for the year 1937. A census covering a small number of industries was taken in

Table 51. *Index of industrial production: Base average 1958 = 100*

	Weights	1959	1960	1961	1962	1963
All industries (a) (b)	1,000	105	112	114	115	119
Manufacturing industries	748	106	115	115	115	120
Mining and quarrying	72	97	94	93	95	95
Food	55	102	104	107	110	112
Drink and tobacco	31	107	112	116	116	121
Chemicals and allied industries	68	111	122	124	129	138
Ferrous metals	55	104	121	113	106	111
Non-ferrous metals	13	107	123	116	114	119
Engineering and electrical goods	167	105	114	121	123	126
Shipbuilding and marine engineering	22	94	85	86	87	77
Vehicles and aircraft	79	109	118	109	111	120
Metal goods, n.e.s.	42	100	112	105	101	108
Textiles	58	106	110	107	105	110
Leather, leather goods, and fur	4	103	102	102	97	99
Clothing and footwear	30	111	120	122	118	120
Bricks, cement, etc.	17	107	120	129	129	131
Pottery and glass	11	106	116	115	121	127
Timber, furniture, etc.	20	112	114	116	111	113
Paper, printing, and publishing	55	107	119	120	122	128
Other manufacturing industries	22	108	120	116	118	126
Construction	126	106	111	120	121	121
Gas, electricity, and water	54	103	110	116	125	133

(a) First half 1964, seasonally corrected, 127; full year, 128.

(b) To one place of decimals the 1959, 1960 figures are 105·2 and 113·9. On the 1954 base adjusted to 1958 = 100, they would have been 105·9 and 113·2.

1947 in respect of the year 1946. The Statistics of Trade Act, 1947, directed the Board of Trade to take an annual census of production. The first of these annual series was taken in 1949 and related to production in 1948. It was a complete and very detailed census. Those for 1949 and 1950 were complete, but not nearly as detailed. That for 1951, taken in 1952, was both complete and detailed. The censuses for 1952 and 1953 covered much the same ground as those of 1949 and 1950, but only a sample of small firms was included. The full census of 1954 was also conducted on a similar sample basis.

A committee was appointed in 1954 to advise the Government on the future of censuses of production and distribution. This Committee, known as the Verdon Smith Committee, favoured the continuation of annual censuses of production, but suggested that full censuses should be taken at less frequent intervals than three years. In any census small firms employing less than twenty-five persons should be asked only for employment figures.

A census of production can only be taken under statutory powers. It requires all manufacturing concerns within the ambit of the inquiry to furnish a return to the Board of Trade on the prescribed form. The questions, for the most part, relate to the year's trading. Calendar years are preferred, but establishments are given the option of providing financial year's figures. The scope and nature of a complete census can best be appreciated if the contents of an actual questionnaire are discussed. For this purpose, the 1963 census is taken as an example, reference being made to changes as compared with 1951. (See Table 52.)

As with the population census, the amount of information obtained is very great indeed, and even with the aid of mechanical and electronic methods of sorting and tabulating, the results take a long time to produce. The census of production is at a further disadvantage in that the replies are received over a period of six months or more. The main features of the 1958 census were published during 1960 and 1961, although some of the information gathered was available to government statisticians by the end of 1959.

The results of partial or simplified censuses such as those for 1959, 1960, 1961, and 1962 became available by the end of the year in which the census was actually taken.

CENSUS DATA

The information published in the *Board of Trade Journal*, 27 December 1963 on the 1962 census can be taken as typical of that relating to years in which a simplified census is taken. The information given related to main industry groupings of the Standard Industrial Classification and

Table 52. *Summary of information required by Census of Production*

1951	1963
DECLARATION that information given is correct and complete.	The same.
Statement of nature of work done, and average number of persons employed, by firms employing ten persons or less. (These firms do not complete the remainder of the questionnaire.)	The same but limit raised to 25.
ESTABLISHMENT TABLE, to be completed if the return relates to more than one industrial establishment, calling for the address of each and a summary of the principal details.	The same.
YEAR OF RETURN, showing period to which information relates.	The same.
1. WORKING PROPRIETORS requires the number of working proprietors (males and females separately) in September of year of return.	Number only.
2. EMPLOYMENT. Table (i) – Details of persons on pay-roll at a given date in September, divided into (*a*) Operatives and (*b*) Administrative, technical, and clerical employees. Each group shows separately males and females, and subdivides each into Under 18 years, and 18 years or over. Table (ii). Average number of persons on the pay roll in year.	Average number for each group only required, but with additional group for transport workers.
Part B. Average number Outworkers employed during year.	The same.
3. WAGES AND SALARIES. Amounts paid during year to (*a*) Operatives and (*b*) Administrative, technical and clerical employees.	The same, but with the addition of transport workers.
4. PLANT, MACHINERY, AND VEHICLES. A – Cost of new and second-hand items acquired during year, and B – Proceeds of items disposed of during the year, both divided into Plant and Machinery and Vehicles. Further question as to amount of second-hand above.	Much the same, but other capital equipment included with plant and machinery.

Table 52—*Continued*

1951	1963
5. NEW BUILDING WORK. The cost of new building or constructional work charged to capital account during the year.	Cost of land and buildings acquired and proceeds of disposals also required.
6. POWER EQUIPMENT AND FUEL CONSUMPTION. A – (i) Prime movers and generators, (ii) Electric motors available for use in September of year, subdivided in tabulated form. B – Consumption of purchased fuel in year, subdivided into types.	6 and 7 not required.
7. SHIFT WORKING. Details of shifts worked in specified week in September.	
8. MATERIALS AND FUEL. (*a*) Total value of materials and fuel purchased in year. (*b*) Quantities of specified materials used.	The same. Many materials specified.
9. WORK GIVEN OUT IN YEAR OF RETURN. Total amount paid.	The same.
10. STOCKS AT BEGINNING AND END OF YEAR OF RETURN. Value at beginning and at end of year of (*a*) Products on hand, (*b*) Work in progress, (*c*) Materials and fuel.	The same.
11. OUTPUT IN YEAR OF RETURN. A – Quantities and values of specified parts actually made during year.	The same.
B – Quantities and values of specified finished products, or groups of products sold during the year.	The same.
12. TRANSPORT PAYMENTS. Amounts paid for transport services to: (*a*) Other firms and undertakings and (*b*) to own separate transport organization.	Other work and expenses, such as repairs, rates, depreciation, postage, etc., included.

consisted of value of goods sold and work done, stocks and work in progress, and fixed capital expenditure. In the case of a full census, reports on each industry are published. They give very detailed information on the output of individual products and materials used in the year covered by the census, and indicate how the gross output, net output, and net output per person are distributed over the industry by size of firms and location. Reference should be made to the actual reports as it is quite impossible to give an adequate description of their content in a few lines. We should, however, pause a moment to consider the concepts of gross output, net output, and output per person. The gross output of an industry is the total value of the invoiced sales adjusted for the change in stocks of finished products and work in progress which have taken place during the period covered. Thus, the total sales of the Radio and Other Electronic Apparatus trade in 1958 amounted to £303 million. At the end of the year, however, stocks of finished products and the value of work in progress were £7 million higher than at the beginning. Hence, gross output for 1958 was £310 million. This, then, is the total output of the firms classified to the Radio and Other Electronic Apparatus trade. In attaining this gross output, raw materials such as steel, non-ferrous metals, and glass, purchased components and materials such as cable and paper, have been used up, and fuel and electricity consumed. If the value of these is deducted from the gross output, net output remains. In a general way it is true to say that net output represents the value added by the industry to the materials, etc., which it consumes. This added value comes about as a result of the joint efforts of labour and management acting with industry's capital equipment. When the net output is divided by the average number of persons employed, the net output per employee is obtained. In the case we are discussing the cost of materials was £161 million, giving a net output of £149 million. As the average number of persons employed was 172,000, the net output per person for 1958 was £865.

In a sense, net output per person is a measure of productivity. Labour is used more economically in industries with high net outputs, mainly because these industries are well supplied with capital equipment. The net output per person in the Mineral Oil Refining trade, which uses a good deal of continuous operation plant, was £2,287 in 1957. Comparisons of net output between one census and the next can show whether output per man, and therefore productivity, is increasing. In the Radio and telecommunications trade,[1] the net output per person was £246 in 1937 – when the partial census was taken under regulations made by the Import Duties Advisory Council. Twenty years later it was £782. A large part of the apparent increase between 1937 and 1957 was due to higher selling prices. Price indices of industrial output are therefore of great value in the measurement of changes in net output, at constant prices. In order to eliminate price changes entirely we should apply a price index of industrial output to the gross output and a price index of materials to the materials used.

RESULTS AND APPLICATIONS OF THE 1958 CENSUS OF PRODUCTION

By the end of 1961 all the results of the 1958 census had been published by way of reports for each 'census' industry. The Revised Standard Industrial Classification had been employed throughout.

The publication of these industry reports has provided the material for reweighting the Index of Industrial Production. This has been the case for each revision of the Index – to a 1948, 1954, and 1958 base. Probably the 1963 census reports will be used for a further revision. However, the index numbers of wholesale prices have been retained on the 1954 base. These are due for a revision when the 1963 census figures are available.

STATISTICS OF RESEARCH AND DEVELOPMENT

This is perhaps the best place to include a note on this topic. Research and development may be carried on in establishments which specialize in this kind of work, in which case the employment concerned is included in S.I.C.879 'Research and development services' – a subsection of 'Other Professional and Scientific Services'. Or it may be carried alongside production work when the employment concerned will be regarded as part of the work of the factory and classified as such. In the first category are a fairly large number of government owned, or controlled, establishments of which the Royal Aircraft Establishment is

[1] This became 'Radio and other electronic apparatus' in the 1958 revision of the S.I.C. – S.I.C.364.

perhaps the best known, but many industrial companies possess separate and specialized research and development establishments.

Statistically speaking, this type of work is of two kinds: work done for payment as part of an order or contract and work undertaken for and financed by, the firm itself. The former is properly treated as 'Output in year of return' in the Census of production questionnaire; the latter cannot be regarded as output. Specialist government research and development establishments are not included in any census of production. Research and development work of the former kind is undertaken mainly for government departments, public bodies, and public corporations.

A number of inquiries, at roughly triennial intervals, have been made into the nature and volume of research and development work, and a further inquiry is due in 1965. The results of the 1962 inquiry are given in the Annual Report of the Advisory Council on Scientific Policy 1961–62 Cmnd. 1920. The national total of research and development work in 1961–62 is shown to be £634 million compared with £300 million in 1955–56 and £478 million in 1958–59. Outside government establishments, the bulk of research and development work is carried on in four industries – aircraft, electronics, chemicals, and electrical engineering.

STUDENT WORK

1. Using the weights quoted in Table 51 arrive at the 'All Industries' index for 1956, 1957, and 1958, from the individual industry indices for these years.
2. Explain, briefly, the type of information which is obtained in a full census of production.
3. Distinguish between gross and net output. To what extent can 'net output per person employed' be regarded as a measurement of productivity?

Chapter 19

National Income Statistics

STUDENTS of economics are well aware that the present and future well-being of the individual and the community depends a great deal upon the size of the national income and how this income is shared among its claimants – personal consumption, capital investment, and government expenditure. One of the main objects of economic planning as we know it in Britain is, in fact, the expansion of the national income and its allocation in such a manner that the current and future welfare of the State is increased. This planning obviously necessitates a knowledge of the level of this income and its constituent parts during the past few years. Much attention has therefore been given to this side of the economic statistician's work during the past two decades. It should be pointed out, however, that as presented in the *Economic Report* or the *National Income* Blue Books, the figures may appear precise and firm. This apparent precision is for presentation purposes only; some of the figures, at best, can only be estimates. Continuous efforts are being made to improve them as more basic data become available and greater experience and skill are forthcoming to handle these data. It is only fair to say that national income accounting, as this branch of economic statistics is sometimes called, has made tremendous progress in recent years not only in Britain but in all advanced industrial communities. The 1964 Blue Book, *National Income and Expenditure*, contains 110 pages of tables and notes. Later in this chapter a list is given of the table headings. No student of economics can afford to neglect these Blue Books since they throw light on so many aspects of economic activity. From 1956 onwards, quarterly estimates have been made of the main constituents of national income and expenditure and these are published in *Economic Trends* and the *Monthly Digest*.

The earliest estimates of the national income were made by economists with a bent towards statistics. The late Sir Arthur Bowley and the late Lord Stamp estimated the national income for 1924 (a census of production year). Mr Colin Clark, then of Cambridge University, continued the Bowley–Stamp estimates through the 'twenties and 'thirties. In 1941 the Chancellor of the Exchequer introduced the first official estimates of the national income, and for the next ten years these estimates were put forward in a White Paper, *National Income and Expenditure of the United Kingdom*, issued about the time the Budget was introduced. These contained first estimates for the year ending on the previous 31 December, and repeated, or more generally revised, estimates for earlier years. Early in the 'fifties the White Paper was replaced by a much more comprehensive Blue Book preceded by preliminary estimates of the major items in national income accounting contained in a short White Paper. The whole field of current national income statistics is in the hands of the Central Statistical Office, assisted by other government departments. A number of university research workers have in recent years, made estimates of national income right back to 1688.

DEFINITIONS AND CONCEPTS

For any discussion of this somewhat difficult branch of economic statistics some definitions are essential. So much so that the Central Statistical Office have produced a large book, *National Income Statistics: Sources and Methods*. We can discuss only one or two main concepts. We will begin with the *Gross National Product*.

Gross National Product

This is the total value of the goods and services produced by industry, commerce, and the service trades and professions, plus net income from abroad. Multiple counting is the greatest pitfall in assessing the gross national product. An addition of the gross outputs of each separate industry would yield a very much inflated figure since the value of the raw materials might be counted several times: steel in the output of the steel industry, a part of this output again in the value of major components such as ball bearings and internal combustion engines incorporated in finished engineering products, and a good deal of it in the production of these finished engineering products. Multiple counting can only be avoided by aggregating the net output of individual industries. The value of the output of the service trades and the professions can only be measured by the net incomes of the people employed in them. For national income purposes, the output of the Civil Service, for example, is reckoned to be equal to the salaries paid to its members.

Table 53. *Gross National Product by industry (at factor cost) (£ million)*

	1948	1957	1963
Agriculture, forestry, and fishing	643	862	972
Mining and quarrying	383	707	739
Manufacturing	3,737	6,869	9,070
Construction	571	1,130	1,716
Gas, electricity, and water	209	473	838
Transport and communication	887	1,619	2,171
Distributive trades	1,393	2,422	3,175
Insurance, banking, and finance (including real estate)	283	498	868
Other services	972	1,823	2,977
Total production and trade	9,078	16,421	22,526
Public administration and defence	709	1,166	1,563
Public health and educational services	257	700	1,187
Ownership of dwellings	296	567	1,006
Domestic services to households	113	97	86
Services to private non-profit-making bodies	72	131	215
Less Stock appreciation	−325	−185	−208
Residual error	−19	269	−216
Gross domestic product at factor cost	10,181	19,166	26,159
Net income from abroad	187	245	377
Gross National Product	10,368	19,411	26,536

It should be clear from the foregoing that the gross national product represents the additional wealth which accrues to the community during a period of time by virtue of the efforts of its members for which payment is made either in money or in kind. Table 53 shows how the g.n.p., as it is often abbreviated, was made up in the years 1948, 1957, and 1963.

It will be noted that the figures are quoted 'at factor cost'. This means that the total g.n.p. is the aggregate of the real value of the output and services of its component parts. An element of artificiality may be introduced into the figures by government action. The factor cost of a packet of cigarettes is the value of all the work done in manufacturing and distributing it. But as we know, the price of the packet is very much in excess of the value of this work added to that of the raw materials to which it is applied. The bulk of the price is made up of taxation. On the other hand, the factor cost of certain agricultural products may exceed the price paid because the latter is kept low by government subsidies. If the effect of such government action, which merely affects the price without changing the real value, is brought into account the result is the g.n.p. at market prices. Since indirect taxes are much greater than subsidies, this is appreciably greater than at factor cost. For 1953 g.n.p. amounted to £14,773 million; it exceeded £26,500 million ten years later. Preliminary estimates for 1964 give a figure of £28,900 million.

Net National Income

A moment's thought will lead to the conclusion that the gross national product is always translated into incomes, some of which will accrue to individuals, others to corporate bodies such as industrial companies and public enterprises. The wages component in manufacturing industry, for example, is the same as the wages received by persons in this group of industries. The net addition to costs attributable to distribution becomes the wages, salaries, and profits of those engaged in distribution, and so on. Thus, the national income could also be computed by aggregating personal and corporate incomes. However, purely transfer incomes such as pensions and family allowances must be excluded. One further adjustment is required. Some part of the nation's productive effort is used up in maintaining its stock of capital equipment and not, therefore, in the production of new wealth. The financial provision for this is known as depreciation. When this is deducted from the g.n.p. the result is stated as the net national income. This can be at factor cost or at market prices. For the years 1948, 1957, and 1963 capital consumption, i.e. depreciation calculated in accordance with certain accepted conventions, amounted to £890 million, £1,691 million, and £2,324 million, respectively. In the latter year, gross fixed investment was about £4,833 million, and so half the investment in 1963 represented replacement of existing assets and half represented a net addition to capital assets.

It follows from the foregoing that the national income estimates can be built up from aggregate incomes of the various factors of production. Table 54 shows the results of this form of approach.

Table 54. *National income (at factor cost) £ million*

	1948	1957	1963
1. Wages and salaries	6,185	11,730	16,310
2. Pay and allowances of the Armed Forces	233	392	421
3. Employers' insurance contributions, pension funds, etc.	348	804	1,341
4. Professional earnings	209	288	386
5. Income from farming	301	453	530
6. Profits of other sole traders and partnerships	810	1,058	1,304
7. Trading profits of companies	1,798	3,091	3,988
8. Trading surpluses of public corporations	118	323	835
9. Profits of other public enterprises	106	128	74
10. Rent of land and buildings	419	818	1,394
11. Net income from abroad	187	245	377
12. *Less* Stock appreciation	−317	−185	−208
13. Residual error	—	269	−216
14. G.n.p. at factor cost	10,397	19,411	26,536
15. Depreciation	890	1,691	2,324
16. National income	9,507	17,720	24,212

It will be noted that the 1948 figures of g.n.p. differ slightly in Table 53 and Table 54. This is because the 1948 figures were taken from two different issues of the Blue Book *National Income and Expenditure*, the 1957 and 1958 issues to be exact. This point illustrates the endless striving which occurs to correct the estimates of national income and expenditure as new and more reliable ways of gathering information are discovered. Even so, an item 'Residual error' still appears.

The student may well inquire the source of the figures in Table 54. There is no one source for any of these figures. They are estimates made by experts who apply their ingenuity to such information as is available and to the task of increasing this information. Returns made to the Inland Revenue provide a basis for estimating wages and salaries. Tabulated data from this source refer to a year or two ago, but current estimates can be made by applying to this basic information the effect of changes in wage rates and employment totals. Trading profits of companies can be estimated in a similar fashion.

To supplement this information a large sample of the largest firms provides quarterly estimates of profits made. Government expenditure is readily available on a quarterly basis. Trading surpluses of public corporations are given in the annual return which these corporations must make to Parliament. Farming income has to be estimated annually by the Minister of Agriculture as a basis for the annual review of farm prices.

The reference to 'stock appreciation' calls for comment. The incomes and profits quoted in the table for the three years are inflated on account of this factor which has arisen as a result of the increase in raw material prices during the years in question. The compilers of the national income statistics rightly decided that this element, viz. the enhanced value of stocks held arising from price increases, should not be regarded as forming part of profits. Conversely, if prices fall, stock appreciation is positive.

Students of economics will be interested in the changes in the share of the national income accruing to the various factors of production. Table 54 indicates that wages and salaries accounted for 65 per cent of the national income in 1948 and 67 per cent in 1963. Rent of land and buildings received less than 5 per cent in 1948 and 5·8 per cent in 1963. If the total stock appreciation in line 12 of the table, and depreciation in line 15 are deducted from the sum of items 5, 6, and 7, it will be seen that profits excluding stock appreciation made up 18 per cent of the national income in 1948 and 14 per cent in 1963.

Such students should also find Table 53, which gives the sources of g.n.p. of considerable interest. The relative proportions of g.n.p. showed from agriculture, mining, and manufacturing are most instructive. It may come as a surprise to find that manufacturing (including gas, water, and electricity), contribute only 37 per cent to g.n.p.

AVAILABLE RESOURCES AND THEIR ALLOCATION

We have seen that the g.n.p. is made up of the national income plus depreciation charges, and that the national income is the sum of personal and corporate incomes. But the national income rarely equals the resources available for consumption, investment in Britain and government uses. If Britain has a deficit on her balance of payments, that deficit adds to our available resources since it means that we are realizing our foreign assets, building up debts with other countries, or receiving grants from them. In fact, all the three processes may be in operation at once. On the other hand, if we have a surplus on our balance of payments we are using part of our national income to pay off debts or to increase our overseas investments. Table 55 shows the total available

Table 55. *Available resources and their allocation (£ million)*

	1948	1963		1948	1963
Gross national product at factor cost	10,397	26,536	Exports and income received from abroad	2,392	7,184
Imports and income paid overseas	2,412	6,921	Public authorities' current expenditure on goods and services	1,762	5,107
Indirect taxes and local rates	2,023	4,048	Subsidies	573	583
			Gross domestic capital formation		
			(a) fixed investment	1,455	4,833
			(b) increase in value of stocks, etc.	500	343
			Personal consumption	8,475	19,663
				15,157	37,713
			Less stock appreciation	375	208
Total available resources at market prices	14,832	37,505	Total expenditure	14,832	37,505

Source: *National Income Blue Book*, 1964.

resources in 1948 and 1963, and how they were allocated between the three main claimants.

By the use of suitable price index numbers the components of the gross national product can be expressed at constant prices. A table in the Blue Book does this and enables calculations to be made of the real increase over a period. Thus, the gross national product in 1963 was 49 per cent greater than in 1948, consumption was 45 per cent higher, while gross fixed investment had increased by 110 per cent. Changes in the volume of imports and exports are dealt with in an earlier chapter. The price index numbers used for the purpose are given in the Blue Book. It is interesting to note that the Retail Price Index is not used for this purpose. A currently weighted index known as the Consumer Price

Index is employed instead. The use of a base weighted index has some disadvantages, it reflects the pattern of consumer spending at the base period, but the pattern may change as prices change. This point was discussed in the chapter on statistics of prices.

Table 56. *Financing of Investment 1948 and 1963* (£ million)

	1948	1963
Investment		
Gross fixed capital formation at home	1,455	4,883
Value of physical increase in stocks and work in progress	175	135
Stock appreciation, i.e. rise in stocks due to price increases	325	208
Net investment overseas	139	113
Total gross investment	2,094	5,339
Financed by:		
Savings –		
Persons	128	1,842
Companies	928	2,609
Public Corporations	61	570
Central Government:		
Surplus on revenue account	524	232
Transfers from other capital accounts (including grants from overseas)	226	50
Local Authorities	78	244
Additions to dividend, interest, and tax reserves	141	8
Residual error, i.e. balance not accounted for	8	−216
Total savings	2,094	5,339
Capital consumption – i.e. depreciation	890	2,324

As the list of tables at the end of this chapter shows, detailed analyses are found in the Blue Book of each component in the gross national product.

Economists are interested in the methods of financing the gross capital formation given as £2,094 million in 1948 and £5,339 million in 1963. The Blue Book provides estimates for these. Table 56 shows these estimates in summary form. It will be seen that voluntary private saving in 1948 covered only a small fraction of the amounts required to finance capital formation. The bulk of the sums required still comes from firms who save by setting aside large sums for depreciation and who build up reserves for general and specific purposes. This means that company shareholders provide much of the financial capital currently required. It is true, also, that the tax-payer is called upon to help. A Budget surplus is a form of involuntary saving forced on the tax-payer who, however, loses control of his involuntary savings. But when the country is running a deficit on its balance of payments other countries help to finance our capital formation, and in so doing release a larger proportion of the national income for personal consumption. A surplus on balance of payments implies additional investment.

DISTRIBUTION OF TOTAL INCOME BY SIZE OF INCOME

We conclude our survey of national income statistics by a short study of the size distribution of incomes. These particular data are obtained by an examination of returns made to the Inland Revenue authorities by persons liable for income tax. Table 57 shows the latest information available at the time of writing and is taken from the 1964 Blue Book on national income and expenditure. This table illustrates, in a striking fashion, the social revolution which has been taking place during the last twenty-five or so years. The number of incomes in the £250–£999 range increased enormously between 1938 and 1962, while the proportion of incomes over £10,000 retained after the payment of tax fell appreciably during the same period. It is now more or less generally agreed that the taxation of high incomes has been carried about as far as it can be, and that the bulk of direct taxation is, and must inevitably be, collected from the middle income ranges. Indeed, surtax payers were given considerable reliefs in 1962.

In passing we might make a reference to the Lorenz Curve which is often employed to measure the concentration of wealth or income. This is a form of cumulative frequency curve expressed in terms of percentages. Since no reliable figures are available for the number of incomes under £250 per annum we cannot illustrate the Lorenz Curve from the data given in Table 57, but the method of computing it can be indicated. The figures in columns (1) and (2) need to be arranged in the form of cumulative percentages of their totals. Thus, in column (2)

Table 57. *Distribution of personal income by ranges of income*

Range of income before tax		Number of incomes[1] 1,000's (1)	Income before tax £ million (2)	Income after tax £ million (3)	(3) as per cent of (2) % (4)
1938					
Not under £	Under £				
50	250	..	2,700	2,696	99·8
250	300	750	204	201	98·5
300	400	780	267	259	97·0
400	500	360	160	151	94·4
500	600	210	114	105	92·1
600	800	220	151	134	88·7
800	1,000	109	96	83	86·5
1,000	1,500	130	157	130	82·8
1,500	2,000	53	90	72	80·0
2,000	3,000	46	112	87	77·7
3,000	5,000	33	126	91	72·2
5,000	10,000	18	123	78	63·4
10,000	20,000	6	76	39	51·3
20,000 and over		2	87	30	34·5
Total		..	4,463	4,156	93·1
Income not included in the distribution by ranges		..	615	..	..
Total personal income		..	5,078	..	..
1962					
Not under £	Under £				
50	250	4,710	840	839	100·0
250	300	1,380	385	383	99·5
300	400	2,300	799	777	97·2
400	500	2,315	1,040	997	95·8
500	600	2,300	1,265	1,194	94·4

[1] A married couple is for income tax purposes counted as one individual.

Table 57—*Continued*

Range of income before tax		Number of incomes[1] 1,000's (1)	Income before tax £ million (2)	Income after tax £ million (3)	(3) as per cent of (2) % (4)
1962					
Not under £	Under £				
600	700	2,200	1,430	1,334	93·3
700	800	2,230	1,666	1,542	92·6
800	1,000	3,710	3,323	3,056	92·0
1,000	1,500	4,415	5,260	4,711	89·6
1,500	2,000	895	1,510	1,293	85·6
2,000	3,000	412	984	780	79·5
3,000	5,000	209	787	576	73·2
5,000	10,000	97	638	406	63·7
10,000	20,000	22	286	138	48·3
20,000 and over		5	177	49	27·7
Total		27,200	20,390	18,075	88·6
Income not included in the distribution by ranges		..	3,581	..	..
Total personal income		..	23,971	..	..

incomes under £250 account for 60·4 per cent of total 1938 incomes; those under £500, for 74·7 per cent, and so on. If the percentages for number of incomes are plotted on the horizontal axis and percentages of total incomes in money along the vertical, the result is a Lorenz Curve. The smaller the gap between the straight line joining nil and 100 per cent and the Lorenz Curve between nil and 100 per cent, the more evenly are incomes distributed. There is evidence that earned incomes are now more evenly distributed than in prewar days and the effect of direct taxation has been to increase slightly the degree of equality in incomes after tax.

[1] A married couple is for income tax purposes counted as one individual.

H

SUMMARY OF CONTENTS OF NATIONAL INCOME BLUE BOOKS

The wealth of statistical material in the annual Blue Books has already been commented upon. The list of table headings which follows indicates the scope and nature of the material, only a fraction of which has been touched upon in this chapter. An interesting series, from the point of view of the economist, is the one dealing with *Industrial Input and Output*.[1] Input–output analysis is a comparatively new study which aims at determining the kind and extent of inter-industry dependence. A typical input–output problem might be: 'If the output of defence equipment is doubled, what effect would this be expected to have on imports, capital investment, exports, and the output of specific industries?' Another problem might be to determine the contribution of each major industry and service to every £100 worth of output in the engineering industries. Analyses of this latter type are to be found in the series on *Industrial Input and Output*.

Table 58. *National Income and Expenditure, 1964*

1. *Summary Tables*

Gross national product
Personal income and expenditure
Corporate income appropriation account
Current account of Central Government including National Insurance Funds
Current account of local authorities
Combined capital account of the United Kingdom
Transactions with the rest of the world
Shares in the gross national product
The composition of final output
Gross national product by industry
Gross national product by category of expenditure
Gross national product by sector and type of income

[1] These have now been extended and issued in 1961 as a separate document, *Input–Output Tables for the United Kingdom, 1954*.

Table 58—*Continued*

2. *Output and Expenditure at Constant Prices*

Output and expenditure at 1958 prices
Index numbers of output at 1958 factor cost
Index numbers of costs and prices

3. *Industrial Input and Output*

Gross domestic product by industry and type of income
Wages and salaries in manufacturing industry

4. *The Personal Sector*

Consumers' expenditure:
  at current prices
  revalued at 1958 prices
Taxes on expenditure and subsidies by category of consumers' expenditure
Distribution of personal income before and after tax
Categories of personal income
Capital account of the personal sector
Revenue account of life assurance and superannuation funds, etc.

5. *Companies*

Appropriation account
Capital account
Appropriation account of non-nationalized companies
Combined appropriation and capital account of companies excluding insurance, banking and finance
Appropriation account of companies in insurance, banking and finance
Trading profits by industry

6. *Public Corporations*

Operating account
Appropriation account
Capital account
Analysis of appropriation accounts by industry
Analysis of capital accounts by industry

Table 58—*Continued*

7. *Central Government including National Insurance Funds*

Current account
Capital account
Revenue account of National Insurance Funds

8. *Local Authorities*

Current account
Capital account

9. *Combined Public Authorities*

Combined current and capital account
Analysis of current expenditure on goods and services
Housing subsidies
Taxes on expenditure and subsidies: allocation by type of expenditure
Taxes on income, national insurance contributions, and taxes on capital:
　　allocation by type of income, property, and sector

10. *The Public Sector*

Current and capital accounts
Analysis of public expenditure

11. *Financial Accounts*[1]

Net acquisition of financial and overseas assets:
　summary analysis by sector
　analysis by sector and type of asset, 1963
　personal sector
　banking sector
　public sector
　overseas sector
Net acquisition of financial assets of the public sector: analysis by
　　sector acquiring assets

12. *Capital Formation*

Gross fixed capital formation at home:
　analysis by sector at current and 1958 prices
　purchases less sales of land and existing buildings by sector

[1] New Tables

Table 58—*Continued*

analysis by sector and type of asset
analysis by type of asset –
    at current prices
    at 1958 prices
analysis by industry group –
    at current prices
    at 1958 prices
analysis by industry and type of asset
Capital consumption:
    analysis by type of asset
    analysis by sector
Net fixed capital formation:
    analysis by type of asset
    analysis by sector
Gross capital stock at 1958 prices, new:
    analysis by industry and type of asset[1]
    analysis for manufacturing and construction, distribution and other
      services[1]
Capital formation in stocks and work in progress:
    increase in book value analysed by industry
    value of physical increase at current prices analysed by industry
    value of physical increase at 1958 prices analysed by industry
    analysis by sector

13. *Definitions of Items in Summary Tables*

STUDENT WORK

1. Define: gross national product at factor cost; net national income at
    market prices; stock appreciation as used in national income statistics.
2. What is meant by a Lorenz Curve? Show how it may be used to indicate
    the degree of inequality in incomes.

[1] New Tables.

Chapter 20

Statistics of Distribution

ONE of the most interesting postwar developments in the field of economic statistics is the growth in our knowledge of the retail trade. This has come about as the result of the censuses of distribution taken in 1951, 1958, and 1962 (in respect of the years previous), and the establishment of short term statistics on retail sales. This branch of the statistical work of government departments is wholly in the hands of the Board of Trade. The President of the Board of Trade appointed a Committee in 1945 to consider the need for, and the scope of, a census of distribution. This Committee reported in 1946, and its recommendations included the taking of a census of distribution in 1949 in respect of the year 1948, and thereafter one every five years. The first census was, in fact, taken in 1951, in respect of the year 1950. The Verdon-Smith Committee, which reported in 1954, recommended that the census be taken every ten years, with sample surveys in certain intermediate years. The first census under this latter recommendation was taken in 1958 in respect of 1957, the second in 1962. These three censuses have provided basic data for the compilation of short term statistics of retail sales. These statistics are obtained by asking a sample of retailers to supply monthly information on their sales. This information is then grossed up from the sample to the estimated whole for each class of retailer, and the results combined by a weighting system derived from the census.

CENSUS OF DISTRIBUTION, 1950

The first complete census of distribution was taken in 1951 in respect of the trading which took place in 1950. A short report on the Retail Trade appeared early in 1953. This provides a quick reference to the main features of the retail trade and at the time of publication provided a most valuable addition to our knowledge of retail distribution. Prior to this, the Board of Trade had published a report on the number, type, and geographical location of the retail shops in Great Britain. This report called *Britain's Shops* was prepared from the mailing list assembled for the purpose of sending out blank census forms. These two publications contained the sum total of our information on retail outlets until the preliminary results of the 1957 Census of Distribution became available. Most of the facts derived from the 1950 census have been incorporated into the preliminary report of the 1957 census discussed in the next paragraph. The 1950 census also covered Wholesale establishments. The information derived about this sector of distribution appeared in the Board of Trade publication *Census of Distribution and Other Sources, 1950,* Vol. III. *Wholesale Trades.* A summary table also appears in the *Annual Abstract of Statistics,* 1958. This quotes number of establishments, receipts, sales, number of persons engaged, and wages and salaries paid for the wholesale trade. This trade is divided, for census purposes, into about a dozen types of trader, and the tabulated information shows the trade in some twenty types of commodities.

CENSUS OF DISTRIBUTION, 1957. SELECTION OF THE SAMPLE

Unlike the 1950 census, which covered all retailers, the 1957 census took the form of a sample survey. It covered in all nearly 12 per cent of the total number of retail organizations. All known multiple retailers – those operating ten or more branches – were included in the survey and so were all but the smallest co-operative societies: a sample of twenty-two of the smallest co-operative societies (who account for only 1·3 per cent of total co-operative sales) was included. The department stores and similar large clothing, household goods and general stores were also included 100 per cent., the aim being to cover substantially all traders with a turnover of more than about £100,000. All known mail order houses and credit traders calling on customers were also included, since it was thought desirable to produce separate figures for these types of trading.

The remainder of the retail field was covered by means of selecting a sample of areas and enumerating only those areas. The details of this area sampling scheme were quite complicated. They were fully described in the *Board of Trade Journal* for 2 January 1959. This article points out that estimates made from a sample are subject to sampling errors. The standard errors for the various estimates are given. The theory of sampling is touched upon in Appendix I (page 239).

Table 59. *Retail and Service Trades: 1950, 1957, and 1961*

	Number of establishments			Turnover			Percentage change in turnover	
	1950	1957	1961	1950	1957	1961	1950–57	1957–61
				£ million	£ million	£ million	%	%
TOTAL RETAIL TRADE	583,132	577,495	580,151	5,000	7,587	8,949	+52	+18
Grocers and provision dealers	143,692	150,552	150,098	1,223	2,031	2,361	+66	+16
Other food retailers	139,884	124,602	129,642	997	1,552	1,794	+55	+16
Confectioners, tobacconists, news-agents	74,606	77,437	70,802	503	703	801	+40	+14
Clothing and footwear	97,162	94,448	93,068	930	1,146	1,350	+23	+18
Household goods	65,795	65,323	73,689	537	830	1,040	+55	+25
Other non-food retailers	60,352	61,360	59,125	374	563	681	+51	+21
General stores	1,641	3,683	3,727	436	762	922	+75	+21
SERVICE TRADES:								
Boot and shoe repairers	18,467	14,458	11,186	19	23	25	+20	+12
Hairdressers	33,113	34,458	40,472	38	62	98	+64	+57
Laundries, launderettes, and dry cleaners	‥	‥	4,614	‥	‥	113		

CENSUS OF DISTRIBUTION, 1961

This was a complete census on the lines of the 1950 inquiry. All the half-million odd retailers in Great Britain were called upon to complete the questionnaire. It covered all trades engaged in the retail sale, repair, and hiring out of consumer goods, hairdressing and manicure services, and for the first time in any census of distribution—laundries, launderettes, and dry cleaners. The first results were published in the *Board of Trade Journal* on 8 February 1963, just over a year after the end of

Table 60. *Retailers grouped by form of Organization*

	Turnover			Percentage change	
	1950	1957	1961	1950–57	1957–61
	£ million	£ million	£ million	%	%
TOTAL RETAIL TRADE	5,000	7,587	8,949	+52	+18
Co-operative societies	571	905	959	+59	+ 6
Retailers with 10 or more branches	1,093	1,884	2,586	+72	+37
Retailers with 5–9 branches			⎧ 461 ⎫		
Other large retailers (a)	3,335	4,799	⎨ 657 ⎬ +44		+13
Other independents			⎩ 4,286 ⎭		
FOOD SHOPS	2,220	3,583	4,155	+62	+16
Co-operative societies	432	707	729	+64	+ 3
Retailers with 10 or more branches	408	730	1,036	+79	+42
Retailers with 5–9 branches			⎧ 135 ⎫		
Other large retailers (a)	1,380	2,146	⎨ 122 ⎬ +56		+11
Other independents			⎩ 2,132 ⎭		
NON-FOOD SHOPS	2,780	4,004	4,794	+44	+20
Co-operative societies	139	198	230	+42	+16
Retailers with 10 or more branches	685	1,154	1,550	+69	+34
Retailers with 5–9 branches			⎧ 325 ⎫		
Other large retailers (a)	1,955	2,652	⎨ 535 ⎬ +36		+14
Other independents			⎩ 2,154 ⎭		

(a) Retailers with 1–4 branches and having 25 or more persons engaged.

the period to which most of the returns referred. Various other analyses were published in the *Journal* during 1963. The whole of the census results are to be published in three volumes; these will provide a wealth of information for market researchers on retail outlets in towns and cities, gross margins and employment in retailing. Detailed figures are being given for sixty-one groups of commodities forming part of the retail trade.

Two tables taken from the *Board of Trade Journal* of 8 February 1963 are given here—by way of illustrating the summary information derived from the census.

Part of the increase in turnover between 1950 and 1961 is, of course, due to higher prices. A price index could be devised from the constituent parts of the Index of Retail Prices which would show the per cent price change between 1950 and 1961, and by applying this to the turnover figures, the increased turnover at constant prices could be calculated. Another point of interest is the proportion of total retail sales obtained by each organization listed in Table 60 and changes in this proportion which have taken place between 1950 and 1961. It is clear from the percentage change in turnover that the multiple retailers have made most progress and that co-operative societies have tended to lose ground relatively, particularly between 1957 and 1961.

STATISTICS OF RETAIL SALES

We have already pointed out that the census of distribution has made possible the compilation of an index of retail sales from returns of sales made by a large number of retailers. Thus, a series of index numbers of weekly sales based on average 1950 = 100 and 1961 = 100 was established when the results of the two censuses became known. *The Annual Abstract of Statistics*, 1964, contains a table which provides information by means of index numbers of these sales analysed by kind of business and by type of shop. Monthly figures, in some detail, are given in the *Digest of Statistics* and also the *Board of Trade Journal*. It is of interest to note that a few years ago a *Digest* table issued before the results of the 1957 census were available, showed total retail sales in 1957 to be 53 per cent higher than in 1950 and sales of co-operative societies to be 64 per cent greater. Table 60 shows that these were very good estimates – an indication of the accuracy that can be obtained from a carefully selected sample, but also of the need for a periodical census to provide completely accurate bench-mark information.

During 1963 the series of retail statistics based on 1957 = 100 were replaced by two series based on 1961 = 100. Seasonally corrected indices for retail sales as a whole and unadjusted indices for some fourteen types of shops, are given monthly; at current prices, retail sales in 1963 were 8 per cent higher than in 1961; at constant prices the increase was 3 per cent. The corresponding figures for 1964 were respectively 13 per cent and 6 per cent.

This kind of information, besides being most useful as an indication of changes in retail sales, is used by the national income statisticians in arriving at their quarterly estimates of the gross national product and its component parts.

STATISTICS OF RETAIL STOCKS

The Monthly Digest of Statistics includes a monthly index of stocks for which the relevant information is obtained from a representative sample of retailers – having regard to type of organization, type of shop, and commodities sold. At the beginning of 1965, this index was based on end-1956 = 100. Naturally this index shows a seasonal variation. Stocks are built up to meet the summer holiday shopping peak, and even more so, to meet the Christmas rush. The average stock held by retailers in 1963 was 37 per cent higher than at the end of 1956, while the average for 1964 was 48 per cent higher.

TRANSPORT STATISTICS

Transport is one aspect of distribution and it is therefore appropriate that some reference should be made to this statistically well documented field of information. Tables in the *Monthly Digest* show: New registrations and current licences for road vehicles of all kinds; index numbers of road traffic and inland goods transport; road casualties; detailed statistics of public road passenger transport; traffic receipts of British Railways and London Transport from passengers and freight; receipts from freight on inland waterways; register of merchant vessels in the Commonwealth; shipping movements; U.K. passenger movements by sea and air; details of aircraft miles flown, mail and freight carried by U.K. Airlines.

The table of index numbers of road traffic and inland goods transport is of particular interest. When the relevant indices from this table are associated with special inquiries made by the Ministry of Transport, it is possible to assess the relative volume of goods carried by road and rail and see how the proportion has changed since 1952.

In 1963, the Ministry of Transport issued a booklet *Survey of Road Goods Transport 1962.* This was the third of the series; earlier surveys had dealt with conditions in 1952 and 1958. These surveys were derived from sample inquiries addressed to road goods transport operators. They were designed to collect information on the characteristics of the goods vehicle fleet and on the work performed by road goods transport. The surveys in question covered one week in the year, the one in 1962 related to 2–8 April. This week was considered to be a 'normal', i.e. unaffected by any special features such as holidays, weather difficulties, and the like. Since 1959 the Ministry of Transport and the Road Research Laboratory have carried out continuous traffic counts at various points. These counts linked with the 1958 *Survey* provide the road traffic data in the *Digest* table referred to. These consist of indices of vehicle miles travelled for about ten types of vehicles, and an index of ton-miles of road transport. Based on 1958 = 100, the all road traffic index for 1964 is 144 the ton-miles index is 153. The corresponding index for rail traffic is 92, indicating a substantial rise in road goods transport since 1958, and a significant decline in rail goods transport.

From the three *Surveys* carried out by the Ministry of Transport the following figures emerge:—

Table 61. *Proportion of inland traffic carried by road and rail – Percentages*

	Road	Rail
1952	46 %	54 %
1958	56 %	44 %
1962	68 %	32 %

The 1962 indices for inland goods transport (ton miles) as shown in the *Digest* were 89 for rail and 133 for road. Applying the changes in the indices between 1962 and 1964 to the figures given in the above table, it would appear that in 1964 road transport carried about 70 per cent of the total volume of inland transport measured in ton-miles.

STUDENT WORK

Of what value is the census of distribution to: (*a*) Market Research firms, (*b*) Statisticians wishing to compile index numbers of retail sales?

Chapter 21

The Application of Statistical Methods to Business Problems

THROUGHOUT the previous chapters an attempt has been made by the choice of examples, wherever possible, which have a commercial or industrial bias, to illustrate how statistical methods may be applied to business activities. In this chapter a greater prominence will be given to business problems. The right use of statistical data is usually of great assistance in the management of a business. We must, however, give one word of warning here. Not all statistical methods are equally applicable to problems definitely connected with business, nor can the more applicable methods be employed with equal force to all types of businesses. Most of the methods used in statistics can well be applied to business generally, and all the methods we have dealt with so far are capable of illustration from the whole field of business. This is because business activity as a whole is fairly stable, and some of its sections may be compared with other sections. This is not, however, necessarily true of each single business. The individual business, particularly if it is small, is probably liable to greater fluctuations than business as a whole and thus comparisons in the case of a single business may be more difficult. Nevertheless, even in quite small businesses some definite application of statistical method is usually possible. While the application of such methods to individual businesses is naturally very important, the reader should never lose sight of the trends and tendencies of business as a whole.

No new principles or ideas are involved in the application of the science of statistics to business problems. Generally speaking, as little time can be given to statistical inquiries in business, the same degree of exactness used by the statistician in his investigation can hardly be expected. In fact, if a sample (used in the statistical sense) gives satisfactory results there is no point in pressing for a large-scale or complete investigation. The cost in time and therefore in salaries in the conducting of statistical work must also be considered. In other words, there should be no such idea as 'statistics for statistics' sake', but the idea should be for the sake of results and conclusions obtainable therefrom. To sum up, the statistical methods which may be used in business are those previously considered and they should be used with some definite end in view.

THE SCOPE OF SUCH STATISTICAL WORK

Generally speaking such statistical work may be divided into the same classes into which we divided statistics generally in our first chapter. These divisions are, it will be remembered, the collection of observations and records, the tabulation and illustration of these records, their analysis, and the drawing of conclusions from the analysis. This latter will usually be made by the administrative officers of the firm, and they may form the basis on which the general policy of the firm is established.

RECORDS

Every public limited company is bound by law to keep its books in a prescribed manner, but the records made by most businesses are greatly in excess of those demanded by law, and they show much more than the financial position of the business.

Sales Records

So far as the financial side of the business is concerned, records of sales or output, the total sales, the sales of each type of product manufactured and the price or average price per unit of output will naturally be made. Most manufacturing businesses will also keep a record of the value of orders received and orders on hand for each class of product they manufacture. Together, these records will give some idea of how the business is faring, particularly if records of previous years are available. If the manufacturing processes take some time the records will also show the amount of work there is to be done in the immediate future.

Purchase Records

In the same way records of total purchases made for purposes of production will also be kept, together with the actual price per unit, or if this is not possible, the average price per unit, e.g. price per ton of steel. From the point of view of assessing the financial results of the business, the figure for purchases, although useful, is not so valuable as the sales figure. Purchases made by way of capital expenditure or for maintenance of the fabric of the factory buildings and for the maintenance of plant and machinery will also be kept, but records of these will be distinct from those relating to purchases of raw materials for production.

Wages

Together with purchases, wages form the chief item in prime costs. In the wages records, a distinction must be made between wages paid for work done on production, for work done in the maintenance of plant, machinery, tools, and buildings, and work done by way of provision and installation of new capital expenditure. When considering wage records it may be useful to have information regarding the average number of wage earners, both adult and juvenile, during the month, the hours of labour worked in the month both as ordinary time and overtime, as well as the total wages paid.

Records of Expenses

Within limits, the greater the subdivision which is made in the records of expenses, the greater will be their utility for statistical purposes. The amounts paid by way of salaries, fuel and lighting, rent and rates, carriage, packing materials, insurance, maintenance of plant, machinery, tools and buildings, advertising, stationery, depreciation, bad debts, etc., should all be recorded. Amounts paid by way of salaries could further be subdivided into office salaries and works' salaries, and the amounts for maintenance of plant and machinery for each individual machine could well be recorded.

THE PRESENTATION AND ANALYSIS OF BUSINESS RECORDS

Statistical methods can give much help with regard to ways in which the information obtained by records may be presented. Someone has said that a major part of a dictator's time is spent in reading reports and in listening to the advice of experts. A similar state of affairs exists, at least so far as reading reports is concerned, for the managing director of a company. The same is true, but to a less extent, of all the administrative staff in a business. The directors must have their finger on every section of the firm's activities and the only way in which this can be done is for someone to obtain the required information and present it in the clearest and most significant fashion.

Reports made to directors and administrative staffs will usually be statistical and will often be in tabular form. The greater the skill which the person presenting the reports has in the technique of classification and tabulation, the more useful will the reports be. The student would do well to refer once more to what has already been said regarding the more theoretical part of this branch of our study. The reports which are required must of course vary from firm to firm and thus it is not easy to give a practical example. However, for most firms engaged in manufacturing processes the value of orders received during the month, the sales for the month and the value of orders on hand for each class of the firm's products are of great value and give scope for a piece of good tabulation.

The Use of Graphs and Diagrams

A comparison between outputs of more than one year can usually be well represented graphically. It is not unusual for the managing director to have a large-scale graph of the value of the firm's output over a number of years pinned up in his private office.

Most firms try to plan their year's work in advance. This necessitates deciding upon a figure for the output at which to aim. It is helpful to plot the cumulative figures for the actual output alongside the output which is being aimed at (see Fig. 30). It is obvious at a glance whether the actual output is greater or less than the output aimed at.

In order to offset the influence of seasonal fluctuations or of the varying number of working days in the month, it is more useful to compare the monthly output with that of the corresponding month of the previous year, rather than with that of the previous calendar month.

In addition to plotting the actual values of orders received and outputs, it is useful to plot the cumulative figures, i.e. the total to date for both. For purposes of comparison graphs showing values of orders received and outputs which cover a number of years are also of value. If the output under consideration is one where seasonal fluctuations are particularly noticeable the general trend might be calculated by the method of moving averages and its value shown on a graph.

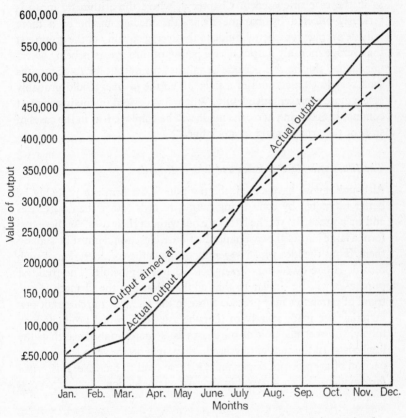

Fig. 30. *Output graph plotted against output aimed at. Output aimed at £42,000 per month or £500,000 for year*

The Use of Averages

In Chapter 7 we discussed the wide use made of averages or types in general statistical work. They are of no less value in business statistics. Thus we constantly refer to average monthly output, the average selling price for each class of output, the average value of orders received.

Of the three commonly used averages, the arithmetic mean, the median, and the mode, the arithmetic mean is the one most widely used in business. In the calculation of the averages just mentioned, the arithmetic mean would probably give the most satisfactory result. But just as in the case discussed in Chapter 7, where the arithmetic mean is seriously affected by extreme items, the median might be a more reliable average (or a better guide to the average quality of the group). If the average monthly output over a period of three years is being ascertained, and during this period the value of the output for three months sank very low on account of a strike, then the median would probably give a more representative figure. Where it is desired to obtain the most commonly occurring item, the mode will be employed, as in the cases of sizes or patterns to make as stock lines.

The Illustration of Purchases and Wages Records

Although, as we have stated, the position of the firm can probably be better estimated by considering output records rather than purchases and wages records, yet the latter are not without their uses. As these two form a large part of the cost of production, a close watch must be kept on them. Thus the idea which generally prompts the consideration of such records is one of cutting down costs wherever possible. The trend of purchases will be similar to that of the sales, but the changes in the trend of purchases may precede those in the sales. As purchases of raw materials are made merely so that the sales of finished products may follow, the cost per unit of purchases is of more importance than the total costs. In the case of purchases, then, it is desirable to have a comparison of average prices per unit; if these tend to increase, it is *prima facie* evidence of an increase in the cost of production.

AVERAGE HOURLY COST OF LABOUR

In dealing with wage records, a useful figure to have is the hourly cost of labour, i.e. the total wages for a month, say, divided by the total number of hours worked in that period. If overtime is being worked by the employees, this figure will be all the more valuable, as it will draw attention to the increased cost of such overtime. The hourly cost of labour might well be calculated monthly. It would also show the effect of replacement of one type of labour by another type, e.g. skilled by semi-skilled, in so far as it affects labour costs.

At quarterly intervals the total wages cost might be expressed as a percentage of the sales for the corresponding period. If the average length of time taken for a job to pass through the works is not more than one month, such a figure would indicate something of the efficiency of labour. For a period longer than one month as the average time of manufacture, the percentage of wages to sales should be based on more than quarterly figures, i.e. for a period of longer than three months. Other things being equal, a fall in the percentage of wages to sales indicates an increasing efficiency of labour. By the phrase 'other things being equal', the question of a rise in the average selling price is ruled out. This increased efficiency may, of course, be due to a number of factors: the introduction of new machinery, an alteration in the hours of labour, the change-over from time rates to piece rates, etc., but such an index is bound to be of use in estimating the results of such factors. (See Tables 62 and 63.)

Table 62. *Calculation of hourly cost of labour (female employees)*[1]

Month	Average number of employees	Total hours worked	Total wages paid	Average hourly cost of labour		
			£	s.	d.	
Jan.	250	42,480	2,301	1	1	
Feb.	250	37,500	2,030	1	1	
Mar.	252	42,900	2,453	1	2	
April	252	40,250	2,348	1	2	Hourly cost of labour rising through overtime being worked.
May	255	44,300	2,583	1	2	
June	255	42,860	2,679	1	3	
July	255	45,200	2,825	1	3	
Aug.	260	48,000	2,998	1	3	
Sept.	260	49,000	3,062	1	3	
Oct.	255	46,850	2,995	1	3	
Nov.	255	45,320	2,833	1	3	
Dec.	250	42,160	2,700	1	3½	

[1] As originally drawn up in first edition, 1937.

Table 63. *Wages cost as a percentage of the value of the output*

(i)	(ii)	(iii)	(iv)	
			(ii) as a percentage of (iii)	
Period	wages paid	Value of sales	%	
	£	£		
1st quarter	9,200	16,400	56	
2nd ,,	9,350	16,700	56	
3rd ,,	9,500	16,670	57	
4th ,,	9,400	16,500	57	Efficiency of labour decreasing
1st ,,	9,200	15,860	58	
2nd ,,	9,380	16,170	58	
3rd ,,	9,700	16,730	58	
4th ,,	9,800	16,900	58	
1st ,,	9,400	15,930	59	
2nd ,,	9,600	16,280	59	
3rd ,,	10,000	16,940	59	
4th ,,	10,200	17,000	60	

THE ANALYSIS OF EXPENSES

As in the case of purchases and wages, the examination of expenses will be made for the purpose of cutting down their amount wherever possible. Some expenses will vary with the scale of output, but others will remain practically the same whatever the output, providing no new plant is employed. It is advantageous then if the plant can be run continuously at full pressure because these fixed expenses will bear less heavily on the final cost of production when this is done.

As with wages, a good plan in studying the records of expenses is to express the separate expenses as a percentage of the total sales, say, every quarter or every year. A basis of comparison is then established. It may appear that an increase in output is being gained at the expense of an increase in the cost of maintaining the firm's plant in a state of efficiency or at the expense of increased fuel consumption. If now records of the cost of the maintenance of each individual machine are kept and of the fuel used in each department, the offending part of the plant or the offending department can readily be isolated and remedies applied. If also the records of work done by machines or their running hours can be made, the connexion between the cost of maintenance and the work done may provide a nice problem in correlation.

The Use of Index Numbers

The student will readily see that by expressing each expense as a percentage of output the firm is really making use of index numbers. The index number for output is taken as 100, but the base is changed from quarter to quarter or year to year depending upon the calculations made.

THE APPLICATION OF STATISTICS TO NON-MANUFACTURING CONCERNS

So far in this chapter the use of statistics in relation to manufacturing concerns has been considered, but statistical records are equally vital to purely trading businesses which may buy in bulk and sell in smaller quantities. In this case, however, the most useful records may be somewhat different in character. Most of what has been said with reference to the collection and analysis of sales, purchases, and expenses records applies equally well to trading concerns. Advertising may, however, assume a greater importance in the latter businesses while its results may not be so readily estimated as they may not become immediately apparent. Where possible the manufacturer who produces more than one type of product will try to arrive at the profit made on each. In the same way the trading concern which has several departments will no doubt require to know not only the total profit made, but also the proportions made in each department. To do this records must be departmental, i.e. the wages, salaries, heating and lighting, purchases, etc., for each department kept separate or if this is not possible, the amounts incurred by each estimated. This problem is usually easier of solution in the case of the trading concern than in that of the manufacturer.

But as the trading business buys merely to sell again, questions of the rate of gross profit and rate of turnover of stock become important. The rate of gross profit expected will naturally depend upon the number of times the stock of any particular type of goods is turned over, say, in a year. Let us consider this a little more closely.

If the average stock of a particular article is valued at £1,000 and the total sales of that article £10,000 in a year, it must follow that the stock of that article has had to be replenished ten times, i.e. that the rate of stock turnover is ten. Some types of goods, such as provisions and perishables, have a rapid turnover, while others like musical instruments, furniture, etc., have a much slower rate of turnover. The rate of gross profit expected on furniture will be much higher than that expected on such commodities as sugar or tea.

Records made by trading concerns will then include: rates of gross profits calculated usually on cost price, average stock and rate of stock turnover. To calculate the rate of stock turnover the value of the stock held at monthly intervals should be ascertained and its average value calculated. This divided into the sales for the year will give the rate of stock turnover per annum. Stock records will also show the most suitable amount, quality, and grade to be kept. Too great an average stock means that capital is locked up in stock, while too little means that orders cannot be fulfilled as speedily as they might. The calculation of the most appropriate stock level can, however, be a very complex matter.

It will certainly be of use to the firm if the amount of each separate expense is expressed as a percentage of turnover (i.e. total net sales) as such a percentage gives in a convenient form the relation between the turnover and the various expenses.

ACCOUNTANCY RATIOS

It is of interest to note that all the foregoing paragraphs in this chapter have so far remained almost unchanged since this book was first published in 1937. It is now necessary to add that within recent years accountants have tried to formalize and extend the simple ideas contained in the foregoing paragraphs. This comparatively new study is sometimes given the name of 'ratio analysis' and the ratios derived are called 'accountancy ratios'. These are merely one method of measuring business relationships and their main purpose is to assist in the interpretation of business accounts. Thus, gross profit as a percentage of turnover, ratio of stocks to turnover, and wages as a percentage of sales are all simple accountancy ratios. It is desirable to arrange these ratios into a number of more or less well-defined ratio groups: solvency, capital, cost, earnings, and dividend ratios, for example. Earnings ratios may include, among other things, the ratio of earnings to sales, to issued capital, and to capital employed. They may also include index numbers which permit a comparison to be made, in real terms, of earnings over a period of time.

More advanced techniques are now being used in this study and accountants are finding that the concept of net output or value added (see Chapter 18, p. 202) may be a useful idea in this respect. In a paper read to a conference held by the British Institute of Management,

Professor F. Sewell Bray suggested four main operating ratios, together with possible variants, as worthy of attention by business executives. These are:

1. Goods and outside services consumed, and gross output.
2. Operative and ancillary labour, and net output.
3. The variable margin, and gross net outputs.
4. Operating overheads and net output.

By the 'variable margin' Professor Bray means the difference between net output and total wages, salaries and social insurance charges. Changes over time in these ratios may well point to increased or decreased efficiency. If they can be compared with ratios calculated by other firms in the same line of business they may indicate relative efficiency. A few of these accountancy ratios, but for a very large number of named firms are published triennially by the Board of Trade in *Company Assets, Income and Finance*. Editions of this publication relating to 1951, 1960, and 1963 have already appeared. The information is derived from an analysis of published accounts.

DISCOUNTED CASH FLOW

The student with particular interests in accountancy should make himself familiar with this new technique for measuring the worthwhileness of investment. The return on a firm's capital expenditure should be sufficient to repay the initial outlay and also to pay an adequate rate of interest on the balance outstanding at any time. The worthwhileness of the investment can therefore be expressed by the magnitude of the average effective rate of interest on the outstanding balances over the life of the investment. This is what is measured by the discounted cash flow. This technique recognizes that a stream of income over time is worth less now than the sum of its annual instalments and, accordingly, makes a realistic allowance for this.

STUDENT WORK

1. Explain how some comparable measure of the efficiency of labour may be obtained.
2. What is meant by the Average Hourly Cost of Labour in a factory? How is its value calculated? Suppose the examination of records shows that in the case of a particular factory its value is increasing, what possibilities are indicated?

3. The following table shows the expenses and sales of a firm over a period of years. Complete the table by calculating for each year the separate expenses as a percentage of the sales for that year.

Year	1932		1933		1934		1935	
Sales	£250,000		£260,000		£275,000		£300,000	
		% of		% of		% of		% of
Expense	1932	sales	1933	sales	1934	sales	1935	sales
	£		£		£		£	
Raw materials	97,000		10,000		102,000		105,000	
Wages	82,000		76,000		83,000		102,000	
Salaries	20,000		19,000		22,000		28,000	
Fuel and light	18,000		18,500		19,000		19,500	
Maintenance of plant	12,000		13,000		17,000		20,000	
Maintenance of tools	3,500		3,600		4,000		4,000	
Maintenance of buildings	1,500		1,000		1,000		800	
Stationery, etc.	850		900		1,050		1,300	
Rent and rates	2,500		2,500		2,500		2,500	
Advertising	1,500		1,500		1,500		1,600	
Carriage	1,500		1,600		1,700		1,800	
Packing materials	1,200		1,300		1,400		1,500	
Insurance	1,500		1,400		1,650		1,750	
Total								
% of Total to Sales								

What conclusions do you draw from your results?

4. Calculate the rate of turnover of stock in each of the following cases:

			Article A	Article B	Article C
			£	£	£
Year's turnover			15,000	82,000	27,000
Value of stock Jan. 1st			500	6,000	500
,,	,,	Feb. 1st	1,800	8,000	2,000
,,	,,	Mar. 1st	1,600	7,500	1,500
,,	,,	April 1st	1,200	7,200	1,700
,,	,,	May 1st	1,300	7,000	1,600
,,	,,	June 1st	1,500	10,000	1,200
,,	,,	July 1st	1,400	8,000	1,000
,,	,,	Aug. 1st	1,450	7,000	800
,,	,,	Sept. 1st	1,600	6,000	900
,,	,,	Oct. 1st	1,800	5,000	1,000
,,	,,	Nov. 1st	1,800	5,000	3,000
,,	,,	Dec. 1st	2,000	10,000	3,000

Appendix 1

Sampling

In Chapter 2 it was pointed out that a statistical investigation might be carried out by the method of sampling. In such a case only a proportion of the available subject matter is studied and the results applied to the whole field of inquiry. It was also pointed out in that chapter that the theoretical basis of sampling is the 'Law of Statistical Regularity', which was defined as follows: 'A small group chosen at random from a large group will have much the same characteristics as the large group.'

It is obviously much easier and much less expensive to examine a sample than to deal with the whole of the possible items. But before the results obtained from sampling can be applied to the whole field of the inquiry it is essential that the sample shall be a random sample and that it should be sufficiently representative. A random sample is one on which every item in the whole group has an equally good chance of selection. Such a sample will then contain examples of all the types which occur in the whole group. The actual proportion of items examined should also be a sufficiently large proportion of the whole.

Sampling methods are finding ever-increasing uses in all kinds of social investigations, agricultural science, industrial experiments, and even in accounting. Very many examples could be given, but we will mention only two. In Chapter 14 we referred to the fact that some of the information published in the preliminary reports of the 1951 Census of Population had been obtained from an analysis of a small sample of completed forms. This was done in this way. A copy was made of one schedule in every hundred relating to private households, with an addition of one person in a hundred for the non-private population. From this 1 per cent random sample, a quick snapshot of the chief features to be expected from the main tables was obtained. Part of the information collected in the 1961 census was obtained from a sample of

one in ten of the returns. In 1950, and again in 1951, certain government departments carried out a sample investigation into the capital
expenditure of private industry. For this purpose a list of industrial
establishments employing over ten persons was used as the basis of the
sample. This list was arranged into eighteen industry groups which, in
the main, coincided with Standard Industrial Classification headings.
Within each industry group there was a further grouping or stratification by size of establishment as measured by the numbers employed.
From this stratification, according to industry and size, a sample was
taken. But unlike the population sample just described, the sample
fraction was not constant and the sample design was broadly as follows.
For all establishments employing 2,000 or more persons, the sampling
fraction was 100 per cent, i.e. all were included. For those employing
between 1,000 and 1,999, the fraction was $\frac{1}{2}$; for size group 750 to 999,
the fraction was $\frac{1}{5}$, and so on, down to the smallest group 11–19 employees where the fraction was as small as $\frac{1}{200}$.

There were some 55,000 establishments listed and, of these, 4,300 or
nearly 8 per cent were included in the sample. The use of a varying
sampling fraction is always desirable when the characteristics which are
being assessed show a wide variation. In this particular inquiry some
establishments had no capital expenditure, others, hundreds of thousands of pounds' worth. And, in any case, a carefully worked out stratified
sample yields the most reliable results with the minimum total sample
size. The randomness of this kind of sample can be assured quite easily.
By way of an illustration, let us take the case of the stratum which has
been given a 1 in 10 sampling fraction. If a digit is selected at random
from the digits 0 to 9, this digit can be used to indicate the starting
point of the sample and every tenth card thereafter will be selected.

Once the sample results have been obtained they must be applied to
the whole field of the inquiry. In the case of the population sample, the
sample results were multiplied by 100 to give the results for the total
population. For the capital expenditure inquiry the totals for each
stratum were obtained and these were multiplied by the reciprocal of the
sampling fraction. The question immediately arises regarding the
accuracy and reliability of the results obtained. The limits within which
the results of sampling may be applied to the whole field of the inquiry
have been worked out by mathematicians. We are proposing to deal
here with only the simplest case of random sampling and for this pur-

pose we must refer once more to the Normal Frequency Curve (see Fig. 31).

In passing, we should mention that a Normal Frequency Curve (sometimes called a Gaussian Curve) is uniquely determined by its arithmetic mean and standard deviation. Fig. 31 shows that in a normal distribution only a very small part of the distribution lies outside the

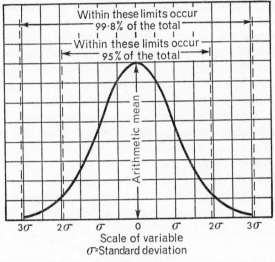

Fig. 31

limits of three times the standard deviations away from the mean. This point is also noted in the Appendix on Quality Control. The diagram also shows that limits drawn at a distance from the mean equal to twice the standard deviation will enclose about 95 per cent of the area of the curve.

These facts can be applied to calculate the possible range of variations in the total which has been obtained by grossing up from a sample. There are only two chances in a thousand that the true answer will differ from the computed answer by as much as three times the standard deviation. There is one chance in twenty that this computed answer will differ from the true one by as much as twice the standard deviation, and one chance in two that the difference will be as great as two-thirds of the standard deviation.

The next step in this brief exposition is to associate the standard deviation with the number of items in the sample and the sample results. To do this we will use a simple example. Suppose there are 1,000 small cards in a pack, 750 of which bear a consonant and 250 a vowel. If the cards are shuffled and 60 drawn at random, the experiment being repeated many times with all the cards replaced and reshuffled each time, the number of cards on which a consonant appears will vary around 45. If the results are tabulated and the average number of consonant cards worked out together with the standard deviation of the frequency distribution, it will be found that the average is 45 and the standard deviation about 3·35. The frequency distribution will also be found to obey the law illustrated in the diagram. The chances of drawing a consonant card are, of course, three in four; those of drawing a vowel, one in four. If the chances are stated in general terms, p and q (where $p + q = 1$) with a sample size of n items, then the standard deviation of the frequency distribution obtained by taking many samples will be $\sqrt{pqn}$ with a mean of pn for one characteristic and qn for the other.

However we wish to proceed from the sample to the whole field. Observed results differ from the expected true results by chance factors due to random sampling. The extent of this possible difference is dependent upon what is known as the 'standard error'. In the case we are considering the standard error is given by the expression $N \times \sqrt{\dfrac{pq}{n}}$ where N represents the whole field. Following the principles shown in Fig. 31 we can say that there will be only two chances in 1,000 of the true value differing from the computed value by as much as three times the standard error. There will be one chance in 20 of the difference being as much as twice the standard error, and a fifty-fifty chance of its being 0·67 times, or two-thirds, the standard error. Let us apply this to our pack of cards example. If we know that there are 1,000 cards in the pack, some bearing a consonant and the rest a vowel, and a random sample of 100 shows 75 consonant cards and 25 vowel cards, what can be concluded about the whole pack?

Applying the expression for the standard error $N \times \sqrt{\dfrac{pq}{n}}$ we find that this is $1{,}000 \sqrt{\dfrac{\frac{1}{4} \times \frac{3}{4}}{100}} = 1{,}000 \sqrt{\dfrac{3}{1{,}600}} = 43\cdot25$

We can therefore say that there is an even chance of the number of consonant cards being as much as, or as small as, $750 \pm 0\cdot67$ times the standard error, or $750 \pm (0\cdot67 \times 43\cdot25)$ or 750 ± 29.

We can also say that there is one chance in twenty of this number being different from 750 by as much as twice the standard error, or, in other words, there is a 95 per cent chance of it falling between 750 ± 86. And, finally, there are only two chances in 1,000 of the number falling outside the range 750 ± three times the standard error, or 750 ± 130.

The student should now be able to appreciate how these principles can be applied to a practical example, as for instance, the one per cent sample of population census forms. In quoting the results of this sample, the Registrar-General quotes the equivalent of Np or Nq, and in the general introduction discusses the size of the standard error as a percentage of N. In the case of stratified samples the formulae have to be applied to each stratum taken separately.

It will, of course, be realized that sampling has now become a large and important branch of statistics and that the foregoing only touches the fringe of the subject. But in mitigation we must plead that this book serves as an introduction to the study of statistics, and nothing more.

Appendix 2

Quality Control

A COMPARATIVELY recent development in the application of statistical processes to industrial operations is to be found in the principles of quality control. In brief, *quality control aims at maintaining a careful survey of industrial processes in order to locate any faulty operation as soon as it occurs.* Much of modern industry is carried on by methods of mass production. This involves making, separately, the standard parts of an article and then assembling them. The number of separate parts which go to make up a modern bomber, for example, is enormous. If all the parts were exactly alike, they would be an exact fit and the assembled articles would be completely alike in character and quality. Such exactness cannot be reached. Raw materials may vary in quality, the conditions under which the productive processes are conducted will vary from time to time on account of differences in temperature, humidity, etc. The machine tools used may be in various states of wear, and, of course, the operators, being human, cannot work with perfect precision. Nor is the degree of precision attained constant for one individual; it will vary even more still as between operators. The result of all these variants is that some components differ in size and shape so much that they will not fit the final assembly; others may be too low in quality to give a satisfactory performance.

An obvious solution to all this is to test each part carefully and reject those which are not of the required standard. But in many industrial processes testing all the components would be a colossal task. More, it would be quite unnecessary, for in spite of all the factors which appear to hinder, a very high degree of precision is usually obtained and rejects are generally few in number. A second alternative is inspection by sample. If one article in a sample falls outside the prescribed tolerances, should the whole sample be rejected? This would be illogical, if at the same time there is a possibility of accepting a batch in which some articles are outside the limits, but none of them happened to come in the sample. Quality control accepts the fact that a 100 per cent inspection is in general impracticable. It further accepts the fact that a certain proportion of the components produced may be defective *but its essential feature is that it provides a method of ensuring that this proportion shall not be exceeded*. Considered in this way it becomes a necessary part of any planned system of industrial production. There is no doubt that it has now found a permanent place in the training and mental equipment of the production engineer.

THEORETICAL BACKGROUND

The mathematical and statistical theory on which quality control is based is outside the scope of this textbook. The following principles must therefore be taken for granted but read in conjunction with Appendix 1.

Let us suppose that a machine is set to turn out steel rods 20 inches in length, and that production is ideally stable. By this we mean that while it is impossible for every rod to be exactly 20 inches, no individual deviation is significant and the average length of a large number of rods taken at random is exactly 20 inches. In other words, the production process is operating ideally. Let us now take a number of rods, measure them as accurately as possible, and from the results obtain the standard deviation from the mean. If now we take a large number of samples, each containing n rods, it can be shown that so long as production is stable:

(*a*) 99·8 per cent of the rods will fall within a distance of 3·09 × Std. Dev.[1] on each side of the average, and

(*b*) 99·8 per cent of the mean of a large number of samples, each of size n, will fall in the range

$$\text{Average} \pm \frac{3 \cdot 09 \times \text{Std. Dev.}}{\sqrt{n}}$$

(*c*) 95 per cent of the means of a large number of samples, each of size n, will fall in the range

$$\text{Average} \pm \frac{1 \cdot 96 \times \text{Std. Dev.}}{\sqrt{n}}$$

[1] In Appendix 1, 3·09 is stated roundly as 3, and 1·96 as 2.

These facts can provide us with our first attempt at quality control. Let us suppose that the variations in length of the rods in question which occur under satisfactory conditions are such as give a standard deviation of 0·005 in. We could now take batches of, say 9, at regular intervals, and so long as production continues to be stable it would be found:

(1) Practically all (99·8 per cent) of the averages of the batches of 9 would fall within a band

$$20 \pm \frac{3 \cdot 09 \times 0 \cdot 005}{\sqrt{9}} = 20 \pm 0 \cdot 00515$$

(2) At least 95 per cent of the averages of the batches of 9 would fall within a band

$$20 \pm \frac{1 \cdot 96 \times 0 \cdot 005}{\sqrt{9}} = 20 \pm 0 \cdot 00327$$

If the results of a test taken on another occasion provide results which are within the limits prescribed in (1) and (2) above, can it be concluded that production is still ideally stable? Generally speaking, yes, but note that we are using the average of nine readings. Each of these nine readings could, but is not likely to, differ appreciably from the average – although the average itself lies between the prescribed limits. The maintenance of an additional record – the spread or range of each sample – i.e. difference between greatest and least length will provide this. If under ideally stable production, the ranges of successive batches have been found to give an average range of w, then no future range should be outside the limits $\bar{\omega}$ to $D\bar{\omega}$, where D is a fixed number depending only on the size of the batches. The value of D calculated on theoretical grounds is given below for each size of a batch from 2 to 10.

Size of batch	2	3	4	5	6	7	8	9	10
Corresponding value of D	3·52	2·58	2·26	2·08	1·97	1·90	1·84	1·79	1·75

From the foregoing, we can arrive at a satisfactory method of quality control. We can decide whether a production process continues to remain ideally stable once it has been so established.

SCHEME OF OPERATION

The following steps incorporate a simple outline of a reasonably straightforward method of quality control.

1. Obtain the average value of the particular measurements with which the process is concerned. This, of course, should be the measurement which the process produces when working under ideally stable conditions. In practice, it is found by measurement of every part produced during an extended trial when production is ideal.

2. Calculate the standard deviation of the particular measurement under ideally stable conditions.

3. Draw on a chart a line parallel to the horizontal axis at a distance equal to the average from that axis. Having decided on the size of the trial batches, on each side of this line, draw parallel lines distant $\dfrac{3 \times \text{Std. Deviation}}{\sqrt{n}}$ from it (n is the number in each trial batch).

4. Plot the average of each batch on the foregoing chart. If any point falls outside this range, there is an immediate indication that something may have gone wrong with the production process.

5. A severer test is to draw two lines parallel to the horizontal axis at distances $\dfrac{2 \times \text{Std. Dev.}}{\sqrt{n}}$ from the average value. Not less than 95 per cent of the averages plotted from each batch should fall within this narrower field.

6. Determine the average value of the range of a large number of samples. On another chart, let this average range be represented by the horizontal axis.

7. From the values of D given in paragraph (2) calculate the value of $D \times$ the average range and draw a line parallel to the axis but $D \times$ average range away from it. The range of each succeeding batch is found and plotted on a third chart, and if any value falls outside the $D \times$ average range limit, this should be regarded as evidence that a change in the production process may be taking place.

PROCEDURE WHEN MANUFACTURING TOLERANCES ARE GIVEN

In the case we have been considering, a manufacturing tolerance may be stated. For example, rods which are within the limits 20 $\pm$ 0·002 inches may be acceptable. In this case satisfactory production will demand that no more than a small percentage shall fall outside these limits. As a check that the tolerances are not being exceeded, the

I

average sample range must not be more than a certain fraction of the tolerance range – in this case, 0·004. This fraction, which we will denote by L, will depend on the number of readings in the sample batch – i.e. n. The relation of n to L is given by the following:

n	2	3	4	5	6	7	8	9	10
L	0·18	0·27	0·33	0·37	0·41	0·44	0·46	0·48	0·50

If our batch is of 9 items, we should proceed by drawing a line parallel to the x axis at a distance of 0·48 × 0·004 units from it, choosing of course a suitable scale.

If any average ranges fall outside this limit, it should be regarded as an indication that a deviation from the ideally stable production process may be taking place.

The foregoing description should only be regarded as an attempt to outline the purposes and methods of quality control. The types of charts which are appropriate to each given case must be considered on their own merits. The subject is a wide one and has in no sense yet reached a state of finality. Certain it is, however, that quality control has found a lasting place in every scientifically planned factory. For actual examples of quality control processes and charts, the interested reader is referred to a pamphlet, *A First Guide to Quality Control for Engineers*, written by Dr Sealey, formerly of the Ministry of Supply and now published by Her Majesty's Stationery Office.

The Coefficient of Rank Correlation and the Equation of the Regression Line

THE information in Chapter 12, 'Correlation', can be usefully supplemented by a brief discussion on rank correlation and the algebraic equation of the regression line.

RANK CORRELATION

If, in place of the actual marks in Table 28, an order or ranking in English and French only had been given it would still be possible to calculate the degree of correlation between them. The method used was devised by Spearman and the coefficient of rank correlation (sometimes denoted by V_r) is calculated from the formula

$$V_r = 1 - \left(\frac{6\Sigma d^2}{n(n^2 - 1)} \right)$$

where Σd^2 represents the sum of the squares of the numerical differences between corresponding pairs of ranks, and n is the number of pairs.

The first six entries in a table for calculating the rank coefficient for the English and French marks would be as follows:

Table 28A. *Calculation of rank coefficient of correlation*

Rank (or order) in English	Rank (or order) in French	d	d^2
1	1	0	0
2	4	2	4
3	3	0	0
4	2	2	4
5	7	2	4
6	9	3	9

If the reader will complete the table he will find that the sum of the d^2 column is 135. As there are twenty pairs, the rank coefficient of correlation is:

$$1 - \left(\frac{6 \times 135}{20(400 - 1)}\right) = 1 - \frac{810}{20 \times 399} = 1 - \frac{810}{7980} = 0.90$$

This is the value obtained for the coefficient of correlation (Table 29).

THE ALGEBRAIC EQUATION OF THE REGRESSION LINE

The method of plotting the Scatter Diagram is explained in Chapter 12 (see page 115). In this section it is stated that the line which most nearly indicates the trend of the points in this diagram is known as the Regression Line. If an algebraic relationship can be established between the ordinates and abscissae of this line, then for any value of y, the corresponding theoretical value of x can be calculated. Thus, the algebraic equation which best represents the regression line is of considerable value. The line for which the algebraic sum of the squares of the vertical distances between all the points and the line, is a minimum, is regarded as the line which best fits the readings. The process of obtaining the equation to this line is an example of 'least squares' calculation.

We will use the figures in Table 29 to establish the equation of the regression line. Let this equation be represented by $y = a + bx$. In this case we shall be calculating the regression of y upon x and we have to determine the value of the unknowns a and b.

The value of b, which is in fact the gradient of the regression line and hence the reciprocal of the ratio of variation, is obtained from the relationship $b =$ the sum of the products of the deviations from their respective means divided by the sum of the squares of x values from the mean of x. In symbolic notation,

$$b = \frac{\Sigma(x - \bar{x})(y - \bar{y})}{\Sigma(x - \bar{x})^2}$$

Referring to Table 29 we see that the sum of the products of the deviations is 2,389 and the sum of the squares of the x deviations is 1,994, b is therefore $\frac{2389}{1994}$ or 1.198.

In order to solve the equation $y = a + bx$ we require another relationship. This is given by the knowledge that when x has its average value, the best estimate of the corresponding value of y is also its average value. Thus, an x value of 46 corresponds with a y value of 54.

Using these two relationships the equation becomes

$$54 = a + 1.198 \times 46 \quad \text{or} \quad 54 = a + 55.13.$$

a is therefore -1.13 and the equation of the regression line is $y = -1.13 + 1.198x$.

This equation can be tested by taking examples of y values from Table 29, calculating the corresponding x values, and comparing these with known values of x from Table 29. Thus when $y = 70$ (the English mark of 70), the calculated value of x is given by $70 = -1.13 + 1.198x$

$$\therefore \ 1.198x = 71.13 \quad \text{or} \quad x = \left(\frac{71.13}{1.198}\right) \quad \text{or} \quad 59$$

to the nearest whole number. From the table we see that the French marks, of the student obtaining 70 marks in English, were 58. This is a fairly close correspondence, but as we can see from the scatter diagram some points are near the line, others are at some distance from it. The 77 English mark associated with the 55 French mark is an example of the latter. In this case the French mark given by the equation is 65. When the value of the coefficient of correlation is high the correspondence between the predicted and actual values will be good. There is little point in obtaining the equation to the regression line and using it to calculate the values of one variable from given values of the other if r is less than 0.5.

We can, of course, find the equation to the regression line of x upon y in which case the general equation is given by the relationship $x = a + by$ and b will be given by the equation

$$b = \frac{\Sigma(x - \bar{x})(y - \bar{y})}{\Sigma(y - \bar{y})^2}$$

The equation to a time series which can be represented by a trend line can also be calculated by the least squares method. In this case, the time periods are numbered successively and these numbers are regarded as abscissae. It must be remembered, however, that the foregoing calculations are only applicable if the relation between the two variables is a linear one, i.e. capable of being represented by a straight line. If the relationship is non-linear, the calculation becomes more complicated.

The scatter diagram will generally indicate whether the relationship is linear or not.

Finally, if instead of using deviations from the mean, the actual figures themselves are used, the two unknowns a and b may be obtained from the following equations:

$$na + b\Sigma x = \Sigma y \qquad \text{I.}$$

$$a\Sigma x + b\Sigma x^2 = \Sigma xy \qquad \text{2.}$$

where n is the number of pairs, Σb the sum of the abscissae, Σy the sum of the ordinates, Σx^2 the sum of the squares of the abscissae, and Σxy the sum of the products of the corresponding x and y readings.

Appendix 4

The Calculation of Rates of Growth

TRENDS in economic statistics are often expressed as rates of change, usually increases, per annum. The calculation of these rates of change is a simple algebraic problem. The method is illustrated below. It will be obvious that this type of problem is identical with that which arises from compound interest calculations.

The *O.E.C.D. Bulletin* for May 1963 quotes the following indices of industrial production for 1950 and 1963 (1953 = 100)

	1950	1963
United Kingdom	95	135
United States	82	136
Sweden	95	153
West Germany	72	207
Japan	28	142

What average annual rates of growth do these figures represent?

The formula,[1] $A = P \cdot R^n$., applies to compound interest (or similar growth) questions. In compound interest, A is the amount, P the principal, R $1 + \dfrac{\text{rate of interest}}{100}$, and n is the time.

Taking logarithms, the equation becomes $\log R = \dfrac{\log A - \log P}{n}$

Applying this formula to the figures for the United Kingdom we have

$$\log R = \frac{\log 135 - \log 95}{13} = \frac{2 \cdot 1303 - 1 \cdot 9777}{13}$$

$$= \frac{0 \cdot 1526}{13} = 0 \cdot 01174$$

---

[1] The graphical representation of 'A' and 'n' provides an example of what is sometimes called an exponential curve.

Therefore R which equals antilog $0.01174 = 1.028$

$$\therefore \ r = 2.8 \text{ per cent}$$

The reader may wish to satisfy himself that the average growth rates for the remaining four countries are: 4.0; 3.7; 8.5, and 15.0 per cent, respectively.

If the figures show a decline, R will be less than 100 and r a minus quantity. Employment in the textile industries of England and Wales fell from $994,000$ in 1954 to $790,000$ in 1964 – what is the average annual rate of decline?

Here, $\qquad A = 790,000, \ P = 994,000,$ and n is 10

$$\log R = \frac{\log 790 - \log 994}{10} = \frac{2.8976 - 2.9974}{10}$$

$$= \frac{\bar{1}.9002}{10} = \frac{\overline{10}\ 9.9002}{10} = \bar{1}.99002$$

$$R = 0.9957 \quad \text{and} \quad r = -4.3 \text{ per cent}$$

Finally, a quick method of estimating the time taken for any variable to double itself at a given rate of growth. Divide 70 by the rate of growth. Thus, if production grows at 5 per cent per annum it will double itself in fourteen years. Conversely, if a variable doubles itself in ten years, the average annual rate of growth will be 7 per cent. The student may be interested to find a theoretical justification for this rule.

General Exercises

1. Construct in blank a table designed to show the percentages of men and of women unemployed in the years 1931 and 1935, in three administrative areas, for four main groups of industries, with totals and sub-totals and appropriate headings.

2. Assuming that you are to take a traffic census of all vehicular traffic on the Great West Road, construct in blank a table designed to show the density of traffic passing, distinguishing between the different types of vehicles, their direction and also the hour of the day from 6 a.m. to 9 p.m.

3. Obtain month by month and plot on a suitable scale the weekly traffic receipts for the British railway system over a period of six months, and on the same graph show the corresponding figures for the previous year.

4. The following is a record of marks gained by a group of candidates at an examination:

```
76  25  35  72  81  96   0  23  17  38  63  57  12  71  82  63  54
 3  61  82  71  60  15   2  93  18  43  44  45  70  70  19  23  25
90  89  53  52  50  58  27  18  83  62  63  70  40  42  44  48  50
20  30  33  37  58  72  23  19  28  32  31  58  70  81  62  64  53
52  53  47  63  75  73  81  46  37  35  38  59  62  63  65  71  38
```

(a) Tabulate the results in the form of a frequency distribution grouping by intervals of 5 marks.

(b) Plot result of (a) in the form of (1) a histogram, and (2) a frequency polygon.

(c) Prepare a cumulative frequency table for the above and plot the cumulative frequency curve.

5. Using the results obtained in Question 4, find the arithmetic mean, the median, and the mode.

6. What is meant by 'dispersion' in the case of a frequency distribution? Calculate the standard deviation and also the quartile deviation for the frequency distribution obtained in Question 4.

7. In a mental test of 290 persons the following results were obtained:

Percentage of ability	10–19	20–29	30–39	40–49	50–59	60–69
No. of persons	4	21	82	116	63	4

Find the mean, median, mode, and quartiles.

8. In an efficiency test of the 290 persons, the productiveness they displayed, measured as a percentage of standard productiveness in the industry concerned, was as follows:

Productiveness, %	50–59	60–69	70–79	80–89	90–99	100–109
No. of persons	14	38	44	54	44	46
Productiveness, %	110–119	120–129	130–139	140–149	150–159	160–169
No. of persons	17	8	7	6	6	6

Find the mean, median, mode, and quartiles.

9. For the frequency distribution in Question 7, find the standard deviation and the coefficient of dispersion.

10. For the frequency distribution of Question 8, find the standard deviation and also the coefficient of dispersion. Compare the two coefficients obtained in Question 9 and Question 10.

11. Write a careful explanation of the meaning of the terms: mean, median, and mode, and indicate the purpose for which each is found useful.

12. Explain carefully what you understand by 'standard deviation' and why this measure of dispersion is often used.

13. Find the average age, and the median age of the married men included below:

Age	Under 20	20–25	25–30	30–35	35–40	40–45	45–50
No. of men (in 000's)	1	34	99	132	139	138	130

Age	50–55	55–60	60–65	65–70	70–75	75–80	Over 80
No. of men (in 000's)	104	78	53	33	15	6	2

14. From the following table obtain and plot the general trend of the mean daily temperature for the period under consideration. Plot also the original figures:

Date	Mean temp. in degrees Fahr.	Date	Mean temp. in degrees Fahr.	Date	Mean temp. in degrees Fahr.
Mar. 1	20	Mar. 9	28	Mar. 17	43
2	25	10	34	18	48
3	22	11	39	19	47
4	35	12	40	20	39
5	26	13	30	21	35
6	22	14	32	22	42
7	18	15	26	23	49
8	20	16	34	24	50

15. From the following indices of business activity as calculated by the *Economist*, calculate a twelve-months' moving average. Plot the indices and the moving average on one graph.

	Period	Index		Period	Index		Period	Index
1933	July	89	1934	July	94½	1935	July	99½
	Aug.	90½		Aug.	96½		Aug.	99½
	Sept.	92½		Sept.	96½		Sept.	100
	Oct.	91		Oct.	96		Oct.	101
	Nov.	92½		Nov.	96		Nov.	102
	Dec.	93½		Dec.	97		Dec.	104½
1934	Jan.	96	1935	Jan.	97	1936	Jan.	101½
	Feb.	95		Feb.	97		Feb.	102½
	Mar.	95		Mar.	96		Mar.	102½
	April	95		April	97		April	104½
	May	94		May	99		May	104
	June	95		June	100		June	106
							July	107

16. What is meant by 'weighting' in the construction of index numbers? Illustrate by reference to the Ministry of Labour cost-of-living figure.

17. Using the weights assigned for the calculation of the Ministry of Labour cost-of-living figure, ascertain the food index for 1 August 1936, from the following figures. The percentage shows the increase at 1 August over July 1914.

Article	% Increase	Article	% Increase
Beef	13½	Sugar	12
Mutton	23½	Milk	71
Bacon	26	Butter	4
Fish	103	Cheese	2
Flour	26	Margarine	−17
Bread	42	Eggs	37
Tea	38	Potatoes	59

18. In a certain month the indices for food, rent, clothing, fuel and light, and other items were: 29 per cent, 59 per cent, 90 per cent, 80 per cent, and 70 per cent respectively. Using the weights assigned for each group, calculate the final cost-of-living figure.

19. The following table shows the value of a life annuity for every £100 paid:

Age in years	40	50	60	70
Annuity in £'s	6·2	7·2	9·1	12·8

Ascertain, by graphic interpolation, the annuity corresponding to ages 35, 45, and 65.

20. A machine depreciates at the rate of 12½ per cent per annum, its purchase price was £1,600. Draw up a table showing its value at the end of 4, 8, 12, and 16 years, plot a curve to show these results and obtain the value at the end of 5, 10, and 15 years.

21. What do you understand by 'correlation'? Explain briefly how its value may be measured and discuss the points that arise when co-efficients of correlations are used in statistical argument.

22. Give a general description of the variation in unemployment over the last twelve years.

23. Using the method and weights set down in the chapter on Index Numbers, calculate the *Economist* Index of Business Activity for July 1936 from the following individual indices:

Employment	105½	Consumption of cotton	120
Coal consumption	105	Imports of raw materials	122
Electricity consumption	109½	Exports of British manu-	
Merchandise on railways	103	factures	107
Commercial motors in use	105½	Shipping movements	101½
Postal receipts	103½	Provincial metropolitan	
Building activity	109½	clearings	104
Consumption of iron and		Town clearings	97
steel	123		

24. Give an account of the information which is conveyed to you by the following figures:

	Firm A	Firm B
Number of wage earners	625	680
Average wage (A.M.)	55s. 9d.	50s. 6d.
Median wage	54s. 6d.	51s. 6d.
Modal wage	53s.	49s. 6d.
Quartiles	44s.–59s.	41s.–54s. 6d.
Standard deviation	11s.	12s. 6d.

25. Obtain the coefficient of correlation for the following two series, if:

1. Standard Deviation of first $= 10\cdot3$
2. Standard Deviation of second $= 6\cdot11$
3. Mean Product of Deviations $= -50\cdot38$

   What do you gather from the result?

26. What do you understand by the following terms: (a) crude and corrected death rates, and (b) infant mortality rates?

27. Discuss fully the statement that 'industry is tending to move south'. Use as much statistical evidence as you can in your answer.

28. Explain why it is unsatisfactory to compare the figures for one month's imports and exports with the corresponding figures for the previous month.

29. From the following figures of overcrowding and infant mortality, calculate the coefficient of correlation between the two.

District	Percentage of population overcrowded	Infant mortality
1	23·4	156
2	33·2	151
3	13·5	109
4	12·3	124
5	12·2	142
6	14·6	125
7	12·1	128
8	14·2	146
9	7·1	78
10	25·6	115
11	20·0	127
12	13·6	123
13	3·9	104

District	Percentage of population overcrowded	Infant mortality
14	20·6	157
15	20·7	108
16	36·6	170
17	25·8	144
18	8·8	102
19	6·3	122
20	12·9	103

30. In a statistical investigation carried out by the method of sampling, 640 houses out of 16,000 were visited. It was found that 192 houses out of the 640 conformed to a certain standard. If the sample is taken as a representative one, how many houses out of the 16,000 would you expect to conform to the standard? If there were actually 4,930 would you consider the sample to be fairly representative? (See Appendix 1.)

31. In a certain batch of articles made under the same conditions, a random sample of 500 articles is examined. Of these, 30 are found to be defective. If the whole batch contains 10,000 articles, how many sound articles can reasonably be expected in the whole batch? (See Appendix 1.)

32. The Minister of Labour a few years before the war appointed a Committee to examine the basis on which the Cost-of-Living Figure was calculated and to make any necessary recommendations regarding its calculation. Why was this step necessary?

33. Distinguish carefully between seasonal and cyclical variations in business activity.

34. Discuss the social significance of the change which has taken place in the birth rate in Great Britain during the last twenty-five years.

35. From the following table calculate the mean wage and the median wage. (Note that the intervals are unequal.)

Wage earned	No. of wage earners	Wage earned	No. of wage earners
17s. 6d.–20s.	15	46s. 48s.	483
20s.–22s.	18	48s.–50s.	325
22s.–25s.	38	50s.–52s.	176
25s.–27s. 6d.	57	52s.–55s.	112
27s. 6d.–30s.	62	55s.–60s.	97
30s.–32s. 6d.	83	60s.–65s.	63

Wage earned	No. of wage earners	Wage earned	No. of wage earners
32s. 6d.–35s.	97	65s.–70s.	50
35s.–37s. 6d.	112	70s.–75s.	28
37s. 6d.–40s.	114	75s.–80s.	17
40s.–42s.	187	80s.–90s.	12
42s.–44s.	195	90s.–100s.	8
44s.–46s.	571	Over 100s.	2

36 and 37. From the following statistics, calculate:

(a) The crude death rate for the town.

(b) The death rate in each age group.

(c) The corrected death rate.

(d) The infant mortality rate.

The population of the town in June of the year in question was 96,500.

The number of deaths during the year, 1,150. The number of live births was 2,205. The number of deaths of children under 1 year, 135.

Age group	0–4	5–14	15–24	25–34	35–44	45–54	55–64	65 or over
Population in each	19,020	18,700	16,335	14,725	13,540	7,200	3,560	3,420
Deaths in each	305	235	163	140	108	84	70	45
% of population of Great Britain in each group	12·1	17·7	15·8	15·1	14·0	11·6	7·7	6·0

38. Time study of certain operations reveals the following times:

Workman A	$2\frac{2}{5}$	$2\frac{1}{5}$	$2\frac{3}{5}$	$2\frac{1}{2}$	$2\frac{1}{5}$	$2\frac{1}{5}$	$2\frac{2}{5}$	$2\frac{3}{5}$	$2\frac{2}{5}$	$2\frac{1}{5}$ secs.
„ B	$3\frac{1}{5}$	$3\frac{1}{5}$	3	$2\frac{2}{5}$	3	$3\frac{1}{5}$	$3\frac{2}{5}$	$3\frac{1}{5}$	$3\frac{1}{5}$	$3\frac{1}{5}$ „
„ C	$2\frac{2}{5}$	$2\frac{2}{5}$	$2\frac{1}{5}$	$2\frac{2}{5}$	$2\frac{2}{5}$	$2\frac{1}{5}$	$2\frac{3}{5}$	$2\frac{2}{5}$	$2\frac{2}{5}$	$2\frac{2}{5}$ „
„ D	$2\frac{3}{5}$	$2\frac{1}{5}$	$2\frac{1}{5}$	$2\frac{1}{5}$	3	3	$2\frac{3}{5}$	$2\frac{4}{5}$	$2\frac{4}{5}$	3 „
„ E	$2\frac{1}{5}$	2	$2\frac{1}{5}$	2	$2\frac{2}{5}$	2	2	2	$2\frac{1}{5}$	$2\frac{1}{5}$ „

Calculate:

(a) The average time taken by each person to the nearest one-tenth of a second.

(b) The average time taken by workmen generally.

39. The weekly value of the sales of a certain firm throughout the year are as follows:

£55, £112, £115, £100, £136, £157, £168, £153, £158, £167, £182, £185, £251, £65, £68, £137, £157, £178, £185, £188, £197, £95, £194, £210, £205, £220, £236, £284, £290, £176,

£283, £255, £250, £240, £238, £236, £220, £250, £210, £200, £188, £190, £150, £162, £155, £150, £167, £176, £220, £250, £276, £110.

Arrange the above as a frequency distribution with an interval of £10. Find the arithmetic mean.

40. Calculate the standard deviation for the distribution obtained in Question 39.

41. Explain how the hourly rate of wages may be obtained, for a period of a month, in a given factory. Is it possible to obtain any idea as to the relative efficiency of labour in normal working times and in periods when much overtime is being worked?

42. The following figures represent the percentage of unemployment among insured workers each month from the month of January 1930 to June 1936:

12·4	21·5	22·4	23·1	18·6	17·6	16·3
12·9	21·7	22·0	22·8	18·1	17·5	15·4
13·7	21·5	20·8	21·9	17·2	16·4	14·4
14·2	20·9	21·4	21·3	16·6	15·6	13·8
15·0	20·8	22·1	20·4	16·2	15·5	13·0
15·4	21·2	22·2	19·4	16·4	15·4	13·1
16·7	22·0	22·8	19·5	16·7	15·3	
17·1	22·0	23·0	19·1	16·5	14·9	
17·6	22·6	22·8	18·4	16·1	15·0	
18·7	21·9	21·9	18·1	16·3	14·6	
19·1	21·4	22·2	17·9	16·3	14·6	
20·2	20·9	21·7	17·5	16·6	14·2	

Without adding the separate values together, obtain the figure which represents the average unemployment over the period.

43. Calculate the standard deviation for the statistics given in Question 42.

44. The following percentages were obtained by twenty pupils in mathematics and book-keeping, observations being taken over a period.

Book-keeping	Mathematics	Book-keeping	Mathematics
77	53	54	76
70	71	69	64
83	64	47	58
85	80	72	76
83	58	68	47
74	70	62	51
83	73	48	41
77	70	80	86
59	81	51	43
59	58	68	74

Calculate the average mark obtained in each subject and also the standard deviation for both sets of figures.

45. Calculate the degree of correlation existing between the two sets of marks given in Question 44.

46. Calculate the final percentages allocated to the following pupils. The percentages in each subject and the weight assigned to each subject are as follows:

	English	History	Geog.	Maths.	Short-hand	Typ-ing	Book-keeping	Science	French
1.	80	82	69	67	91	85	78	44	68
2.	44	57	77	53	44	75	77	62	29
Weight	4	1	2	4	4	4	3	2	3

47. Represent the following figures by 'Pie' diagrams:

Distribution of vegetation

	Woods and plantations %	Rough grazing %	Permanent pasture %	Arable %	Other land %
England	5	11	41	30	13
Wales	4	32	42	13	9
Scotland	4	52	8	17	19

48. The values of imports at some British ports in the year 1922 are given in the following table. Complete the blank columns and obtain the absolute and relative errors for both columns (c) and (e).

(a) Port	(b) Imports in million £'s	(c) Value of nearest million	(d) Error	(e) Decimals omitted	(f) Error
Hull	63·2	63	—0·2	63	—0·2
Manchester	51·8				
Glasgow	25·2				
Southampton	29·2				
Newcastle	16·3				
Bristol	32·5				
Grimsby	15·0				
Cardiff	9·0				
Total	242·2				

49. Calculate the arithmetic average, the median, and the mode for the following distribution:

Height of males (in inches)	Frequency	Height of males (in inches)	Frequency
58	3	67	187
59	5	68	296
60	8	69	357
61	12	70	207
62	15	71	76
63	28	72	37
64	55	73	5
65	87	74	1
66	123		

50. A man travels 50 miles at a speed of 20 miles per hour and then returns at a speed of 30 miles per hour. What is his average speed for the whole journey?

51. Supposing you had to compare the relative prosperity of two towns A and B, what statistics would you try to obtain and how would you use them?

52. Criticize the following statements:

   (a) Out of 24 boys examined, 7 or 29·167 per cent were found to be suffering from malnutrition.

   (b) An examination of the Ministry of Labour cost-of-living figures shows that the cost of living rose by 169 per cent between July 1914 and the end of 1920; by the end of 1928 it had risen by 68 per cent, and by December 1933, by 43 per cent.

53. Census of Industrial Production in U.K., 1907 and 1924.

	1907	1924
Net output (million £'s)	712	1,719
Persons employed (000's)	7,087	7,821

From the above figures, calculate to the nearest significant figures the net output per head in 1907 and 1924, and the percentage increase in the net output per head from 1907 to 1924.

54. Calculate the probable error in the totals of columns (d) and (f) of Example 48.

55. Explain what is meant by an 'array'.

56. The tolerances allowed on the diameter of 3-inch rods are +0·005. Explain how you would draw up a suitable control chart.

57. Metal rods are being produced 12 inches in length. The variations which occur under satisfactory stable conditions give a standard deviation of 0·004 inches.

Show (a) that the chance of a rod exceeding 12·0124 inches is 1 in 2,000; (b) the chance of a rod being less than 11·992 inches is 1 in 20.

58. Outline a method of procedure for drawing up a control chart to be used with the machining of shell cases to a diameter of 4·5 inches.

59. What advantages would an employer gain if he were able to forecast his sales for the next year with a fair degree of accuracy?

60. What do you understand by cyclical variations in business activity?

61. Give an account of the chief figures or indices which indicate the progress of the trade cycle.

62. As manager of a radio firm, describe briefly how you would estimate your sales for the next year.

63. What do you know of the Statistics of Trade Act?

64. What information would you expect to find in (a) Trade and Navigation Accounts; (b) U.N. Statistical Bulletin?

65. Write notes on: Terms of trade; Sampling as applied to the 1951 census of population.

66. Calculate the 'All Items' index from the following sub-indices for January 1959 – Food, 109·8; Drink, 105·9; Tobacco, 107·8; Housing, 125·8; Fuel and light, 116·6; Durable household goods, 100·1; Clothing and footwear, 102·2; Transportation, 113·4; Miscellaneous goods, 113·6; Services, 114·8.

67. Give some examples of the recent tendency to employ sampling methods in place of a full scale inquiry.

68. What do you understand by Accountancy Ratios; Input–Output Analyses?

69. What proportion of the gross national product is derived from –

(a) agriculture, forestry, and fishing;
(b) mining and quarrying;
(c) manufacturing industries;
(d) building and contracting?

70. What proportion of the working population is engaged in each of the four groups listed in Question 69? Account for the differences in the proportions found to occur in Questions 69 and 70.

71. Complete the calculation of the rank coefficient of correlation Table 28A, Appendix 3.

72. Calculate the rank coefficient of correlation between overcrowding and infant mortality from the figures given in Exercise 29.

73. Using the figures in Exercise 29 and taking the degree of overcrowding as the y variable, obtain the equation for the regression of y upon x.

74. Obtain the equation giving y (the retail food price index) in terms of x (wholesale food price index) which best fits the following data:

	1928	1929	1930	1931	1932	1933	1934	1935	1936	1937
x	89	86	74	65	65	63	66	67	72	79
y	92	$91\frac{1}{2}$	84	75	$73\frac{1}{2}$	72	$70\frac{1}{2}$	75	$77\frac{1}{2}$	84

75. Write a note on the sampling procedure adopted in the 1961 census of population.

76. Describe an inquiry aimed at estimating the volume of road goods transport.

77. What are the sources of information on the employment of qualified scientists in industry?

78. What average annual rate of growth would be required for production to double itself in twenty-five years?

79. Employment in coal mining fell from 786,000 in 1954 to 590,000 in 1964. What average annual rate of decrease does this represent?

Supplementary General Exercises

THE following exercises have been taken from Statistics papers in the G.C.E. Ordinary Level Examinations 1961–63. They are reproduced by permission of the Senate of the University of London.

1. The following figures give the total annual expenditure (in million pounds) on cinema admissions for the period 1949–59 inclusive:

   105, 107, 110, 112, 111, 112, 108, 106, 95, 85, 71.

   Calculate the median, the mean, and the variance of this group of numbers.

2. The following marks were obtained by two candidates A and B in four subjects.

	Mathematics	Physics	English	French
A	76	70	50	68
B	64	66	66	74

   For the purpose of awarding a science scholarship the following weights were attached to the subjects: Mathematics 3; Physics 4; English 2; French 1. Calculate the weighted mean score of each candidate.

3. Explain the terms:
   (a) perfect correlation and
   (b) inverse (or negative) correlation.

   The following table gives the total annual expenditure (in million pounds) on Fuel and Light (FL) and on Entertainments (E) for the period 1949–59 inclusive

FL	432	451	467	462	466	486	497	516	507	547	542
E	198	195	195	192	189	189	190	185	171	160	150

   Calculate the coefficient of rank correlation between these items and comment on your result.

4. Distinguish between:

    (a) crude death rate and standardized death rate;
    (b) a random sample and a sample showing bias;
    (c) numerical and descriptive data.

5. The mean of two numbers x and y is $1\frac{3}{4}$ and the variance of the two numbers is $\frac{1}{4}$. Find x and y.

    A third number is taken so that the mean of x, y, and z is 2. Find the variance of x, y, and z.

6. The following table gives the steel production in four districts in 1953 and 1954.

District	1953 '000 tons	1954 '000 tons	Change %
Sheffield	2,412·6	2,520	+4
Lincolnshire	1,859·8	1,970	
N.E. Coast	3,447·4		+7
Scotland		2,230	−4

    (a) Calculate the items omitted.
    (b) Construct a pie diagram of radius 2 inches to illustrate the steel production in these four districts in 1954.

7. The following numbers give the average weekly amount of electricity generated (in million kilowatt hours) by nuclear power stations for the first nine months of 1958.

$$5\cdot6 \quad 5\cdot9 \quad 6\cdot8 \quad 11\cdot4 \quad 9\cdot6 \quad 10\cdot7 \quad 3\cdot9 \quad 2\cdot5 \quad 3\cdot0$$

Calculate the mean and standard deviation.

8. What is the connexion between: (i) median and percentile, (ii) histogram and frequency distribution, (iii) correlation and a scatter diagram?

9. The mean of the numbers x, y, and z is 6 and the mean of the numbers x, y, z, a, b, c, and d is 9. What is the mean of the numbers a, b, c, and d?

10. The following table gives the monthly totals (in thousands) of workers involved in industrial stoppages during the period May 1957 to August 1958.

May	31	Sept.	42	Jan.	61	May	95
June	44	Oct.	38	Feb.	55	June	38
July	129	Nov.	48	Mar.	49	July	35
Aug.	45	Dec.	22	Apr.	27	Aug.	25

(a) Draw a graph to illustrate these data

(b) Smooth the series by calculating the four-monthly moving average and superimpose the graph of these averages.

11. The following table gives X the number of radio sets (in thousands) and Y, the number of television sets (in thousands) sold in the home market for each of nine months from September, 1958 to May, 1959.

X	137	148	130	100	93	83	87	119	129
Y	269	353	345	239	192	168	152	177	166

Plot this data and draw the line of regression of X on Y. From your graph, find a suitable equation for this line.

12. The following table gives the distribution of the marks of 942 candidates in an examination.

90–100	80–89	70–79	60–69	50–59	40–49	30–39	20–29	10–19	0–9
2	10	51	125	179	227	181	108	45	14

Working from an assumed mean of $44\frac{1}{2}$, calculate the mean and the standard deviation of this distribution.

Answers to Numerical Examples

Chapter 3 *Accuracy and Approximation*

3. (*a*) Absolute Error   52; Relative Error 0·3%
   (*b*)   „   „   548;   „   „   3·5%
4. (*a*) Probable Error   86·5
   (*b*)   „   „   600

Chapter 7 *Statistical Averages*

1. A.M., 29s.; Median, 28s. 1d.; Modes, 25s. 10d., 35s. 8d.
2. (*b*) A.M., 91½; Median, 91½; Mode, 90.
   (*c*) 1¼d.
   (*d*) Averages: A, 88; B, 89; C, 89; D, 96; E, 91; F, 93; G, 91; H, 95.
   Final average: 91½.
3. A.M., 154; Median, 127; Mode, 83 approx.
4. A.M., 45·7%; Median, 46·8%; Mode, 49·7% approx.; L.Q. 36·3%;
   U.Q., 54·9%.
5. A.M., 4·7%; Median, 4¼%.
6. A.M., 104 lb.; Median, 102 lb.; Mode, 101 lb. approx.
9. A.M., 13s. 1d.; Median, 12s. 6d.; Mode, 11s. 6d.; L.Q., 10s. 1d.;
   U.Q., 15s. 7d.
11. (*b*) 9·47.

Chapter 8 *Dispersion or Variability*

1. Standard Deviation, 6s. 5d.; Quartile Deviation, 5s. 2d.
2. Quartiles, 71, 213; Quartile Deviation, 71; Standard Deviation, 115.
3.

	Firm A	Firm B
Total wages	£1,688	£1,325
Average wage, A.M.	39s. 8½d.	42s.

	Firm A	Firm B
Average wage, Median	40s. 5d.	42s.
Average wage, Modal	42s.	42s. 9d.
Standard deviation	6s. 4d.	8s.
Quartiles	35s. 3½d., 44s. 2½d.	36s. 1d., 47s. 10d.

4. Mean Deviation, 11·05; Quartile Deviation, 9·15; Standard Deviation, 12·21.

5. Standard Deviation, 0·167 francs; Coefficient of Dispersion, 0·0022.

6. Courtauld's, Standard Deviation, 4·95d.; Coefficient of Dispersion, 0·007.

   U.S. Co., Ltd., Standard Deviation, 3·84d.; Coefficient of Dispersion, 0·01.

Chapter 9 *Skewness*

3. Median Coefficient, 0·167; Quartile Coefficient, 0·65.

Chapter 11 *Correlation*

1. Coefficient of Correlation = −0·55.
2. Coefficient of Correlation = 0·78.
3. Coefficient of Correlation = −0·56.
4. Coefficient of Correlation = 0·65.
6. Ratio of Variation (obtained graphically).

Chapter 12 *Index Numbers*

4. Cost-of-living figure = 52.
5. Index of Business Activity = 108.
6.

	1924	1931	1932	1933
Unemployment Insurance	18·3	38·7	46·8	44·8
Health Insurance	11·8	14·7	14·3	14·3
Pensions	9·1	27·5	29·9	31·0
Education	33·0	39·9	39·4	38·7
Housing	6·3	15·2	16·2	16·2
Poor Relief	16·0	16·2	15·7	16·8
Miscellaneous	5·5	7·4	7·6	8·1
	100·0	159·6	169·9	169·9

Chapter 14 *Vital Statistics*

1. (a) 13·42 per 1,000.
   (b) 24·91, 14·28, 8·48, 8·94, 9·87, 10·76, 11·61, 14·6.
   (c) 12·63.
   (d) 69·6.

Chapter 17 *Statistics of Prices*

1. Food Index = 31%.
2. Cost-of-living figure = 47.

Chapter 21 *The Application of Statistical Methods to Business Problems*
4.

Article A	Article B	Article C
10	11·5	20

GENERAL EXERCISES

5. A.M., 50; Median, 53; Mode, indeterminate, original figures give a mode of 70.
6. Quartile Deviation, 16·5.
7. A.M., 42·5%; Median, 43%; Mode, 44%; Quartiles, 36%, 49·5%.
8. A.M., 92·5%; Median, 89%; Mode, 85%; Quartiles, 75%, 105%.
9. Standard Deviation, 9·6%; Coefficient of Dispersion, 0·23.
10. Standard Deviation, 24·5%; Coefficient of Dispersion, 0·26.
13. A.M., 43·8 years; Median, 42·8 years.
17. 29·5%.
18. 47%.
23. 107.
25. −0·80.
29. +0·68.
30. 4,800 ± 194 even chance; 4,800 ± 580 95 per cent chance.
31. 9,400 ± 71 even chance; 9,400 ± 213 95 per cent chance.
35. A.M., 45s. 5d.; Median, 45s. 9d.
36 and 37. (a) 11·92 per 1,000.
        (b) 16·03, 12·57, 9·97, 9·51, 7·98, 11·67, 19·66, 13·16.
        (c) 11·91.
        (d) 61·2.
38. (a) A   B   C   D   E

$2\frac{9}{20}$ $3\frac{1}{5}$ $2\frac{4}{5}$ $2\frac{2}{5}$ $2\frac{1}{10}$ seconds.

    (b) $2\frac{4}{5}$ seconds.
39. £185.
40. Standard Deviation, £56 10s. 0d. (approx.).
42. 18·3.
43. 3·07.
44. Book-keeping, A.M., 68·5; Standard Deviation, 11·9.
    Mathematics, A.M., 64·5; Standard Deviation, 12·8.
45. +0·45.
46. (1) 70·3%; 52·3%.

48. (c) Absolute error, 0·2 millions; Relative error, 0·083%.
   (e) Absolute error, 2·2 millions; Relative error, 0·9%.
49. A.M., $67\frac{9}{10}$ in. Median, $67\frac{8}{10}$ in.; Mode, 69 in.
50. 24 m.p.h.
53. Output per head £100·5, £219·8; Percentage Increase 119.
54. 7·08; 36.
66. 110·4.
71. 0·90.
72. 0·63
73. $y = 0·263x - 14·1$.
74. $y = 0·825x + 19·5$.
78. 2·8 per cent.
79. 2·9 per cent.

SUPPLEMENTARY GENERAL EXERCISES

1. Median £107 million; A.M. £102 million; Variance £157·3 million
2. A 67·6; B 66·2.
3. −0·891.
5. $x = 1\frac{1}{4}$; $y = 2\frac{1}{4}$; variance $\frac{7}{24}$.
6. 6 per cent; 3,689; 2,322·9.
7. A.M. 6·6 million. Standard Deviation. 3·12 million.
9. A.M. $11\frac{1}{4}$.
11. $Y = 20 + 1·8X$.
12. A.M. 45; Standard Deviation 16·6.

Index

Abscissa, 47
Absolute scale, 45
Abstract of Regional Statistics, 137
Accountancy ratios, 236, 237
Accounts relating to Trade and Navigation of U.K., 132, 169, 173, 190
Accuracy, 7, 15 et seq.
— spurious, 8
Advisory Council on Scientific Policy, 204
Annual Abstract of Statistics, 132, 136, 160, 174, 193
Apparent excess of imports over exports, 174
Approximations, 17 et seq.
Arithmetic mean, 66 et seq., 245, 246
— in index numbers, 124, 125
Array, 36
Arraying, 53
Assumed mean, 69–71, 87, 88
Average deviation, 85
Averages, 66 et seq., 231, 232
Axes of reference, 47

Balance of Payments, 176, 177
Bank clearings, 125–7, 130
Bank of England, 130
Bank of England Quarterly Bulletin, 136
Bar chart, 32–4
— diagram, 35
Base, for index numbers, 122
Basic Road Statistics, 139
Biased errors, 8, 20
Birth rates, 147, 150
Board of Trade, 130, 168, 174, 180, 181, 193, 199 et seq.
Board of Trade Journal, 137, 139, 174, 179 et seq., 199
— Index of Production, 130, 193
— of Wholesale Prices, 181
Bowley Index, 165
Bray, Prof., Sewell, 237
Britain's Shops, 221
British Institute of Management, 236
Brussels tariff nomenclature, 169
Budgets—working class, 183
Business Monitor series, 137
Business statistics, 228 et seq.

Census of Distribution, 220 et seq.
— of Population, 2, 129, 141 et seq.
—— Preliminary Report, 143
—— One per cent sample, 143, 239
Census of Production, 129, 131, 197 et seq.
Central Statistical Office, 130, 194, 195, 206
Chain base, 123
Charts, 31 et seq.
Circle diagram, 32
Civil employment, total in, 155
Classification, 22–4
— of Occupations, 154
Class interval, 56
— statistical, 25
Coefficient of correlation, 108 et seq.
— of dispersion, 86
— of skewness, 94
Collection of data, 6 et seq.
Common characteristic, 23
Complex tabulation, 25
Computers, use of, 140
Consumer Price Index, 211
Continuous series, 44
Correlation, 41, 106 et seq.
Corrected death rate, 151
Cost-of-living Advisory Committee, 187
Cost-of-living Figure, 100–4, 183–6
—— trends in, 100–4, 189
Criminal Statistics, 139
Crude death rate, 151, 152
Cumulative frequency curve, 64 et seq.
— distribution, 64 et seq.
Cyclical variation, 98, 104.

Data, collection of, 6 et seq.
Death rate, 147
Decile, 73
Degree of accuracy, 7, 15 et seq.
Demographical statistics, 141
Depreciation, 208, 209, 212
Development areas, 159
Deviation, average (or mean), 85, 89
— quartile, 83, 89
— standard, 86–9, 241, 245–7
Deviations, mean product of, 108, 109

Diagrammatic representation, 31 et seq.
Digest of Statistics Monthly, 132, 139, 157 and many other places
Digest of Scottish Statistics, 136
Digest of Statistics of Northern Ireland, 137
Digest of Welsh Statistics, 137
Direct correlation, 107, 108
Discrete series, 44
Discounted Cash Flow, 237
Dispersion, measures of, 82 et seq.
Distribution of national income by size of incomes, 213–15

Earnings, weekly in industry, 163
Economist, The, 125, 126, 127
— Index of Business Activity, 33
—— of Wholesale Prices, 180
Economic Commission for Europe (E.C.E.), 135, 140
Economic Report, 136
Economic Review, 136
Economic Survey, 136
Economic Survey for Europe, 140
Economic Trends, 136
Economic trends, appreciation of, 131
Efficiency of labour, 233, 234
Employment statistics, 154-158
Error, absolute, 15
— biased, 17
— cumulative, 17
— estimation of, 19, 20.
— standard, 242, 243
— unbiased, 17
Exchange of employment books, 156, 157
Exports, 168 et seq.
Export list, 168
— price indices, 190
— volume indices, 172, 173

Financial Statistics, 139
Financial Times Index of Stock and Share Price, 191
First Guide to Quality Control, 248
First moment, 95
Fixed base, 123
Fluctuations, cyclical, 97
— seasonal, 97, 98
— secular, or long-term, 97
— special, 97, 98
Frequency distribution, 26, 38, 53 et seq.
— curve, 39, 57–64
— polygon, 38, 57
— tables, 26, 53 et seq.

Galton, Francis, 114
Gaussian curve, 241
Geometric mean (average), 78
—— in index numbers, 125, 126
Graphs, 38, 47–9
— in business, 230, 231
— rules for plotting, 46
Gross domestic product, 207
— national product, 207 et seq.
— output, 202
Groups, statistical, 26

Histogram, 38
Historigram, 38, 98
H.M. Forces, numbers in, 155
Hourly cost of labour, 232
Hours worked, 163
Housing Return for Great Britain, 138, 145

Import Duties Advisory Council, 203
Import List, 168
Imports, trends in, 171, 172
Import price indices, 190
— volume indices, 173
Income from foreign investments, 175
—— shipping, 175
Index of Production, 130, 193 et seq.
— of Retail Prices, 187, 188
— of Retail Sales, 224
— of Stocks (retail), 225
Infant mortality rate, 151
Input–Output Analysis, 216
International Labour Office, 134
International Monetary Fund, 135
International statistics, 134
Interim index of production, 194
—— of retail prices, 186
Interpolation, 43
Inverse correlation, 42, 108
Invisible earnings, 174

Journals, statistical, 136 et seq.
Journal, Board of Trade, 137, 139, 169, 174, etc.

'L' return, 12, 13, 157
Labour turnover, 160
Lag, 112, 113
Laspèyrés formula, 187, 189
Law of Statistical Regularity, 9
Lead, 112, 113
League of Nations publications, 134
Line chart, 37 et seq.
Location of mode, 75, 76
Logarithmic scale, 45, 46

'London and Cambridge Economic Service', 165
Long-term variations, 97
Lorenz curve, 213, 215

Manpower statistics, 154 et seq.
Marriage rates, 150
Mean, arithmetic, 66 et seq, 245 et seq.
— deviation, 85, 89
— geometric, 78
Median, 71 et seq., 86
— of Agriculture, 7, 129
Ministry of Aviation, 131
— of Labour, 12, 129, 154 et seq.
— of Power, 134
— of Public Works and Buildings, 131
— of Supply, 131
— of Transport, 225
Ministry of Labour Gazette, 134, 157, 160, 161, 162
Mode, 75–7
Moments, 95
Monthly Bulletin of Statistics (U.N.), 134
Monthly Digest of Statistics, 132, 139, 157 and elsewhere
Moving average, 100–5

National Coal Board, 165
National income, 205 et seq.
— Income and Expenditure, 206 et seq.
— White Papers and Blue Books, 205, 206, et seq.
National Plan, 5, 136
Net Output, 202, 203
—— per person, 202, 203
Normal frequency curve, 62, 241
Norm, 75

Occupation tables, 154
Ogive, 64
Ordinate, 47
Organization for European Co-operation and Development (O.E.C.D.), 135, 140
Output per manshift, 165
Overseas Trade Accounts of the U.K., 169
Overseas trade, statistics, 168 et seq.
—— trends in, 171, 172
—— general nature of, 170

Pearson, Prof. Karl, 107
Percentage bar chart, 34
Percentile, 73
Personal consumption, 211

Picturegram, 31–3
Pie diagram, 34
Plan, The National, 5, 136
Population, 141 et seq.
— census, 2, 141 et seq.
— Preliminary Report, 143
Price relative, 121
Prices, statistics of, 179 et seq.
Price variation clause, 182
Price indices of industrial output, 182
—— of imports and exports, 190
—— of materials used in industry, 181
—— of manufactured goods, 183
Probable error, 19
—— in coefficient of correlation, 110
—— in sampling formulae, 242, 243
Probability curve, 63
Production, census of, 130
— Board of trade index of, 193
— Interim index of, 194
— Index of, 195 et seq.
— Statistics, 193 et seq.
Productivity, 165, 202
— Anglo-American Council of, 165
Progressive average, 102
Published statistics, 136 et seq.
Purchases records, 229, 232

Quadrant, 47, 48
Quality control, 244 et seq.
Quantity Theory of Money, 179
Quartile, 73
— deviation, 83, 84
Questionnaires, 11
— requiring skilled treatment, 12

Railway Traffic Receipts, 130
Random sample, 9, 10, 239 et seq.
Range, 83
Rank correlation, coefficient of, 117, 249
Rate of change, 45, 253
— of growth, 253
— of stock turnover, 235
Ratio of variation, 114
— scale, 45
Records of expenses, 229
— of purchases, 229, 232
— of sales, 229, 232
Regional changes in population, 149
Registrar-General, 132, 141, 143, 147
Regression equation, 115, 250–2
— line, 116, 250–2
Relative, 110
Retail price indices, 183 et seq.

Retail sales, index of, 224
— stocks, index of, 225
— trade, statistics of, 223–4
Rules for graphical representation, 46
    47
— for tabulation, 27, 28

Sample, stratified, 240
Sampling, 9, 10, 239 et seq.
— fraction, 240
Sauerbeck's Index, 180, 181
Scatter diagram, 115, 250
Scientific and Technological Man-
    power, 145, 146, 166
Seasonal variation, 98, 100, 103, 196,
    231
Second moment, 95
Secular variation, 98, 100
Series, statistical, 24
— time, analysis of, 96 et seq.
Short-cut methods for mean, 69
————— for standard deviation, 87
Simple tabulation, 24
Skewness, 92 et seq.
Smoothing, 58, 59, 62
Social Insurance Budgets, 33
Sources of Statistical Information,
    129 et seq.
Special variations, 98, 99
Standard deviation, 86 et seq., 245
    et seq.
— error, 242, 243
— Industrial Classification, 131, 157,
    158, 161, 195
— International Trade Classification,
    169
Statist Index of Wholesale Prices,
    181
Statistical Bulletin of B.I.S.F., 134,
    137
Statistical Digest, Ministry of Power,
    134, 137
Statistics of Incomes, Prices, Employ-
    ment and Production, 138, 157
Statistics, scope and definition, 2, 3
— of Trade Act, 12, 131, 198
— of Prices, 179 et seq.
———— Overseas Trade, 168 et seq.
———— Research and Development, 203
Statistics Relating to the War Effort
    of U.K., 32
Sterling liabilities, 177
Stock appreciation, 207, 209, 210, 211
Subject, 110
Survival rate, 150
Survey of Road Transport, 225

Tabulation, 22 et seq.
— complex, 25
— rules for, 27, 28
— simple, 24
— treble, 26
Terms of trade, 191
Third moment, 95
Time lost through industrial disputes,
    161
Time series, 24
———— analysis of, 96 et seq.
Tolerances, 247
Trade and Navigation Accounts, 132,
    169, 173
Trade, overseas, 168 et seq.
———— trends in, 171
———— volume indices, 172
Transport Statistics, 225, 226
Trend, 97, 100–3, 112
— detection and estimation of, 100
— of cost of living, 101, 185
— of wholesale prices, 182
— of unemployment, 159
Types, 66

Unbiased error, 8, 20
Unemployment, duration of, 160
— statistics, 158 et seq.
— by regions, 160
— trends in, 159
Unfilled vacancies, 161, 162
United Nations Statistical Office, 135,
    140
Units, 7

Variable, 24, 47
— dependent, 47
— independent, 47
Variable margin, 237
Variability, 82 et seq.
Variance, 86
Verdon Smith Committee, 199, 220
Vital Statistics, 141 et seq.

Wage drift, 166
Wages records, 229, 232
Wage rates, index of, 165
Weighted arithmetic mean, 67–71,
    122 and elsewhere
Weighting in index numbers, 122
Wholesale prices, 179
— price indices, 179–83
———— Board of Trade, 181
———— The Economist, 180
———— Statist, 180
Working population, 155